NEW
PLANE GEOMETRY

BY

A. M. WELCHONS AND W. R. KRICKENBERGER

The Arsenal Technical High School
Indianapolis, Indiana

GINN AND COMPANY

BOSTON · NEW YORK · CHICAGO · ATLANTA · DALLAS
PALO ALTO · TORONTO

Foreword

This *New Plane Geometry* is based on the authors' *Plane Geometry, Revised Edition.* Those features of the older text which proved to be desirable and best fitted to the needs of the teacher and pupil have been retained. Changes have been made, however, in the subject matter, proofs, and exercises wherever it was felt that such alterations would improve the usefulness of the text.

SPECIAL FEATURES OF THE TEXT

1. Creation of Interest · Interest is one of the greatest motivating forces in the study of any subject. It is essential for the successful study of geometry. Attention is called to some of the ways in which the text assists the teacher in securing and holding the pupil's interest. The illustrations show applications of geometry to art, nature, industry, and engineering. In the problem material there is an application of geometry to various trades. At many points in the book the usefulness of geometry as an aid to everyday reasoning is explained, and the pupil is encouraged to strive for clear thinking in his daily life. Brief references to the history of geometry also add interest.

2. Gradual Approach to Formal Proof · After the motivating Introduction and the preliminary work of Chapter I, the pupil is first led to see the need of basing a conclusion on proof rather than on observation and measurement. The use of axioms and the form of a proof are then illustrated by solutions of algebraic equations. Next there is practice in the use of postulates and definitions. Then, finally, the pupil studies the arrangement and character of a formal demonstration.

3. Standard Requirements Met · The most important propositions and corollaries are marked with two stars; the subsidiary propositions and corollaries are marked with one star; and the less important propositions and corollaries, including the theorems in optional subject matter, are unmarked. This system of marking is the result of a study of the relative importance of the propositions, in which the authors took into consideration the Report of the Joint Commission of the Mathematical Association of America and the National Council of Teachers of Mathematics on "The Place of Mathematics in Secondary Education," the recommendations of the College Entrance Examination Board, the Syllabus of the University of the State of New York, and the studies of Lankford* and Pickett.†

4. Unusual Flexibility · By organizing the text in seventeen chapters the authors have provided for a high degree of flexibility and adaptability to various types of classes and curricula.

The treatment of constructions is an example of this flexibility. Some teachers prefer to postpone constructions until the pupils have acquired considerable skill in proofs. These teachers will wish to follow the sequence of the text. Other teachers prefer to apply the theorems to constructions much earlier. These teachers can use the footnotes as a guide to the desired sequence (see pp. 89, 132).

Any or all of the last four chapters may be omitted without destroying any sequence. Footnotes in the preceding chapters designate appropriate times of presenting these latter chapters.

The abundance of exercises in the text also increases its adaptability.

5. Provision for Individual Differences · To provide for individual differences, three levels of work are provided. Exercises marked *A* are for all pupils, those marked *B* offer additional work for pupils having more ambition and interest, and those marked *C* are a challenge to the exceptional pupils.

A minimum course consists of the proofs of the propositions and corollaries marked with two stars, an informal treatment of the propositions and corollaries marked with one star, and some of the *A* exercises.

*Lankford, F. G., Jr., "A Study of Elements and Proofs of Plane Geometry." Abstracts of Dissertations, University of Virginia, 1938.

†Pickett, Hale, "An Analysis of Proofs and Solutions of Exercises Used in Plane Geometry Texts." Contributions to Education, No. 747, Teachers College, Columbia University, 1938.

A medium course consists of the proofs of all starred propositions and corollaries, exercises in A groups, and some exercises in B groups.

A maximum course includes the proofs of additional propositions and corollaries and some exercises in the A, B, and C groups. Some of the optional work can be assigned. No class can be expected to do all the exercises in this text during one school year, but some exceptional pupils may be able to do so.

6. Selection of Method of Proof · The logical method of discovering a proof of a theorem or original exercise involves a combination of the analytic and synthetic methods. A plan for the "Selection of Method" is described on page 83 and used in theorem proofs. It is recommended as an aid to the pupil in acquiring the proper method for attacking a proof. The use of this plan also provides for a review of theorems.

7. Summary of Methods of Proof · A summary of the methods of proof is given for each chapter (excluding the last four) and a complete summary is given on pages 543–553. This complete summary may be used for reference in the Selection of Method. For example, on page 184 instead of using §§ 143, 169, 187, we can use § 501 a–i.

8. Proper Stress on Theorems, Problems, and Corollaries · A proper balance of theorems, corollaries, construction problems, and numerical applications is maintained throughout the text. An undue emphasis on any particular type of work is thus prevented.

9. Preparation for Theorems · Where desirable, the groups of A exercises include developments of theorems which appear later. Examples are Ex. 9, p. 85, and Ex. 5, p. 121. By this procedure the pupils are encouraged to discover proofs and are not thrust into new situations without proper preparation.

10. Treatment of Corollaries · The corollaries in this text are corollaries in the strictest sense and are not theorems listed as corollaries to reduce the number of theorems. They are, in most cases, based upon theorems and corollaries which immediately precede.

11. Reasons Required for Constructions · Reasons are required for all constructions, thus preventing errors that might otherwise result. For example, such statements as "Construct $CD \perp AB$ and bisecting $\angle BAC$" are usually eliminated when reasons are required for the constructions.

12. Training in Solution of Original Exercises · Various means are used to teach pupils how to solve original exercises successfully. These are as follows:

a. By the algebraic proofs in Chapter II.

b. By training in the selection of method for a proof.

c. By the gradation of exercises. For example, see one-step exercises on pages 73 and 75, and two-step exercises on page 79.

d. By the use of examples. See pages 72 and 128.

e. By the use of exercises after propositions.

f. By explicit directions for (1) proving corollaries (page 71); (2) proving theorems (pages 82, 176, 360); (3) indirect proofs (page 106); (4) constructions (pages 162, 330); (5) proving locus theorems (page 311).

13. Applications · The text is well supplied with interesting applications, which can be comprehended by most pupils without any extensive study of other subjects.

14. Map Making, Artillery Fire, and Aeronautics · These subjects are treated in Chapter XVII. Many pupils will find these topics of special interest.

15. Reasoning Applied to Life Situations · The sections on the application of the reasoning of geometry to life situations are optional. Many teachers will wish to use at least some of this material.

16. Word Lists · To improve spelling and give reviews of word meaning, many word lists are included.

17. Tests · The text includes 41 chapter tests and 8 comprehensive tests. These tests may be used to test the pupil's mastery of subject matter but they serve better as reviews and self-measuring tests.

A. M. WELCHONS
W. R. KRICKENBERGER

Contents

Pattern Making Is One of the Many Trades in Which a Knowledge of Geometry Is of Great Practical Value

NEW PLANE GEOMETRY

Introduction

Why We Study Geometry. One of the principal reasons for studying geometry is that it teaches you how to think clearly. Of all subjects taught in high school, geometry can give the best training in correct methods of thinking. The habits of logical thinking acquired in the study of geometry will be beneficial to you regardless of the occupation you will later pursue. Because of your training in geometry you will be able to converse more intelligently and read with better understanding; and you will be better prepared to evaluate the logic in the reasoning of others. The habits of thought acquired in the study of geometry are so important that many colleges and universities require a year of geometry for entrance.

The study of geometry will have a practical value for many of you. If you expect to become an artist, a designer, a machinist, a carpenter, a tinsmith, or a stonecutter, or to engage in a related occupation, the facts learned in geometry will be of great value to you. If you expect to be a physician or a dentist, the habits of thinking acquired in geometry study will help you to make better decisions.

If you are planning on becoming a lawyer, geometry study will be useful to you. Before a lawyer makes an argument to a jury, he must study the evidence presented during the trial and choose the facts which have the greatest bearing on the case; he must search the court records for past decisions on similar cases; and then he must arrange his argument in a logical order, proving each statement by giving an acceptable reason. It is said that Abraham Lincoln borrowed a geometry text and learned the proofs of most of the plane geometry theorems so that he could make better arguments in court.

1

Another reason for studying geometry is its cultural value. It is said that a pupil once asked Euclid (a teacher in Alexandria about 300 B.C.), "What shall I profit by learning these things?" Then Euclid called his servant and said, "Give him threepence since he must make gain out of what he learns." In 1910 Charles Evans Hughes said, "When the time comes that knowledge will not be sought for its own sake and men will not press forward simply in a desire of achievement, without hope of gain, to extend the limits of human knowledge and information, then, indeed, will the race enter upon its decadence." Napoleon once said, "The advance and perfecting of mathematics are closely related to the prosperity of the nation."

There are many other reasons for studying geometry. Geometry study will help you in the use of English and in public speaking. As you study the many interesting properties of geometric figures, you should have a greater interest in art and architecture, which make abundant use of geometric designs. When you wander through the woods and fields, you will observe how nature uses geometric figures and proportions. You will see that the spider knows how to make parallel lines and that the honeybee uses regular hexagonal prisms for storing its honey. If you will collect snowflakes on a dark cloth, you will find all of them different but all possessing a system of six in a beautiful geometric arrangement.

The Growth of Geometry. Geometry had its beginning either in Egypt or in Babylonia and consisted in methods of measuring simple geometric figures. The building of the Pyramids in Egypt (between 4000 B.C. and 3000 B.C.) is evidence that the Egyptians had a knowledge of many geometric principles at that time. (The great Pyramid of Cheops is shown in the picture on page 6.)

Babylonian diviners (wise men who attempted to foresee coming events) are known to have used parallel lines, triangles, and quadrilaterals in their mystic processes. The Egyptians must have had some knowledge of surveying when they irrigated the land during the rule of Amenemhat III (about 1850 B.C.).

A Spider's Web, Some Dogwood Blossoms, and a Magnified Snowflake Are Combined Effectively in This Design. What Geometric Figures Do You Recognize in It?

These Egyptian Ceiling Patterns from a Tomb at Thebes Date from about 1400 B.C.

Both the Egyptians and the Babylonians made use of geometric figures in decoration. Pottery made in Babylonia as early as 3000 B.C. is decorated with geometric designs. In early Egypt, the walls of important buildings consisted of woven mats fastened to poles. Geometric patterns which were developed in the process of weaving such mats were later used in the decoration of the ceilings of tombs.

The earliest documents of early Egyptian geometry which we have were written on papyrus paper about 1550 B.C. by Aāhmesu, commonly called Ahmes. This manuscript was copied from another manuscript, now lost, which was written about 2300 B.C. Ahmes's work consists of arithmetic and geometric problems, dealing with the volumes of barns, the areas of rectilinear figures, and the area of the circle. The rule for finding the area of a circle as given by Ahmes is, in substance, given by the formula $A = 3.1605\, r^2$. Herodotus, the Greek historian, tells us that about 1400 B.C. Rameses II divided Egypt into rectangular plots of ground and assigned them to his subjects. This indicates that the early Egyptians knew something of surveying.

From Egypt, and perhaps Babylonia, this geometry of measurement was carried into Greece and Asia Minor. Thales of Miletus (640–546 B.C.) accumulated much wealth as a merchant and spent his later years in travel and study. While studying in Egypt he became interested in geometry. Upon his return to Greece he taught geometry to his friends, who made many contributions to the subject.

The greatest pupil of Thales was Pythagoras, who was born about 580 B.C., probably on the island of Samos, near Asia Minor. He was one of the most remarkable men of antiquity and gave to us many of the proofs of theorems found in our geometries of today. He is said to have been the founder of the *Pythagoreans*, a society of about 300 members interested in mathematics and philosophy. The members of the society were divided into two groups, the mathematicians and the listeners. Before one could become a member of the mathematicians, he first had to be a good listener. Pythagoras is said to have been the first one to prove that the square on the hypotenuse of a right triangle is equal to the sum of the squares on the other two sides.

During the two hundred years following the death of Pythagoras, the Greeks, who were interested in geometry more for its own sake than for its practical value, discovered and proved a large number of new propositions. Among these notable scholars who contributed to this new science appear the names of Antiphon, Hippias, Plato (429–348 B.C.), Eudoxus (408–355 B.C.), Aristotle (384–322 B.C.), and Hippocrates. From 600 B.C. to 300 B.C. the study of geometry consisted in research, discovery, and proof. During this time there were few textbooks and the propositions were not arranged in logical order.

Greece reached its pinnacle as a world power during the reign of Alexander the Great (336 B.C.–323 B.C.). After his death the empire was divided and Ptolemy became the ruler of Egypt. Under Ptolemy's rule, Alexandria became the center of learning of the world. One of the teachers of mathematics at the University of Alexandria was Euclid. It was while teaching at Alexandria that Euclid wrote the first great textbook of geometry (about 300 B.C.). This geometry text of

Wide World

Visitors at One of the Great Pyramids of Egypt

Euclid was called "Elements." It contained the first systematic, orderly, and logical arrangement of geometry and was divided into thirteen chapters, called *books*. The "Elements" contained most of our present plane geometry and some solid geometry. The substance of Books I and II is probably the work of Pythagoras; that of Book III, of Hippocrates; and that of Book V, of Eudoxus, who also contributed much to the science of solid geometry.

The greatest contributor to solid geometry was Archimedes (287–212 B.C.), the famous mathematician and physicist of Syracuse. At the time of his death, the plane and solid geometry, as given in our high-school texts, was almost completed.

Since the death of Archimedes, geometry has been enriched by many prominent mathematicians. Among these are Apollonius (260–200 B.C.), Hipparchus (about 140 B.C.), Heron, Descartes (1596–1650 A.D.), Gauss (1777–1855 A.D.), Saccheri (1667–1733 A.D.), Lobachevsky (1793–1856 A.D.), Bolyai (1802–1860 A.D.), and Riemann (1826–1866 A.D.).

SYMBOLS AND ABBREVIATIONS

The following symbols and abbreviations are used in this text. Each should be learned when it first occurs in the subject matter.

SYMBOLS

$\angle$	angle	$\perp$	(is) perpendicular to; perpendicular
$\rightarrow$	approaches as a limit; tends to		
$\frown$	arc	$\stackrel{\circ}{=}$	is equal in degrees to
$\odot$	circle	$\sim$	(is) similar to; similar
$=$	(is) equal to; equals; equal	$\square$	parallelogram
$\neq$	is not equal to	§	article
$>$	is greater than	$\therefore$	therefore
$<$	is less than	$\triangle$	triangle
$\cong$	(is) congruent to; congruent	$x', x'', \cdots$	x-prime, x-second, $\cdots$
$\parallel$	(is) parallel to; parallel	$x_1, x_2, \cdots$	x-sub-one, x-sub-two, $\cdots$

The plural of any symbol representing a noun is formed by adding the letter s. Thus ⊚ means *circles*.

ABBREVIATIONS

adj.	= adjacent		**Iden.**	= identity
alt.	= alternate		**int.**	= interior
Ax.	= axiom		**isos.**	= isosceles
comp.	= complementary		**opp.**	= opposite
Const.	= construction		**Post.**	= postulate
Cor.	= corollary		**Prop.**	= proposition
corr.	= corresponding		**quad.**	= quadrilateral
cos.	= cosine		**rect.**	= rectangle
Def.	= definition		**rt.**	= right
Ex.	= exercise		**sin**	= sine
ext.	= exterior		**st.**	= straight
Fig.	= figure		**supp.**	= supplementary
Hyp.	= hypothesis		**tan**	= tangent

S.A.S. = If two triangles have two sides and the included angle of one equal respectively to two sides and the included angle of the other, the triangles are congruent.

A.S.A. = If two triangles have two angles and the included side of one equal respectively to two angles and the included side of the other, the triangles are congruent.

S.S.S. = If two triangles have the three sides of one equal respectively to the three sides of the other, the triangles are congruent.

How Many Different Kinds of Angles Can You Find in This Picture?
Chapter I Will Help You to Answer This Question

Lines and Angles

1. What Plane Geometry Is. In your study of arithmetic and algebra you learned many facts about squares, rectangles, triangles, and circles. In geometry you will learn many more interesting facts relating to these and other plane figures. You will also learn how to prove these facts. In proving these facts you will use a type of reasoning which you can apply to your daily life.

2. Solids and Surfaces. The figure pictured just below represents a *physical solid.* Any physical solid has size, shape, color, and weight. Blocks, books, bricks, and crystals are some familiar examples of physical solids. In geometry, the weight, texture, and color of objects are not considered; only the size and shape are studied.

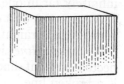

The figure *ABCDE* represents a *geometric solid.* This geometric solid has the same size and shape as the physical solid above, but it has no color, weight, or any other physical quality. When we think only of the size and shape of a physical solid, we think of a geometric solid.

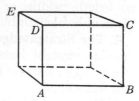

The six surfaces of the solid *ABCDE* are smooth and flat. They are called *plane surfaces* or simply *planes.* A *plane surface* is such that if a straight line is applied anywhere to it, the line throughout will touch the surface. The surfaces of blackboards, windowpanes, and table tops are plane surfaces. Other examples of plane surfaces will occur to you as you look about the room.

3. Points and Lines. We all know what points and lines are but we cannot define them. A point is represented on paper by a dot and is named by placing a capital letter near it. A geometric point cannot be seen, since it has no length, width, or thickness.

There are three kinds of lines,—the *straight line*, the *broken line*, and the *curve line*. A straight line is represented by a straight mark and is named by any two points on it, or by placing a small letter l near it. The line shown here is read "line AB" or "line l." Unless otherwise stated, the word "line" means "straight line." A straight line extends infinitely far in both directions and has no ends. Parts of lines are called *line segments* and are named by naming their end points. Thus AB is a line segment of the line l.

A *ray* is the part of a line extending infinitely far in one direction from a point. The ray m extends infinitely far in one direction from A.

A *curve line* or a *curve* is a line no part of which is straight, such as line CD.

A *broken line* is composed of connected straight line segments. $ABCDE$ is a broken line.

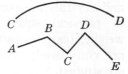

Although we represent points and lines by marks on paper and blackboard, we must remember that a geometric point has no length, width, or thickness, and that a geometric line segment has length but neither width nor thickness.

4. The Straightedge. The *straightedge* is an instrument for drawing straight lines. The ordinary ruler is more than a straightedge, because it can be used to measure the lengths of line segments.

5. How to Add and Subtract Line Segments. Two line segments can be added by placing them end to end on the same line. In the figure the segment EF is the sum of the segments AB and CD.

One line segment can be subtracted from a longer line segment by placing the smaller segment upon the larger with one end of the smaller falling upon one end of the larger. In the figure, *FD* is the remainder when *AB* is subtracted from *CD*.

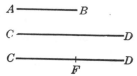

EXERCISES [A]

1. Draw two line segments, *AB* and *CD*, which intersect (cross each other) in *E*. How large is the point *E*?

2. Place a point *P* on paper. Draw a line *RS* through *P*. How many other lines can you draw through *P*? How many lines can be drawn through any other point?

3. Place two points, *A* and *B*, on paper. With the ruler draw a line through them. Try to draw another line through them. What is your conclusion about the number of lines that can be drawn through two given points?

4. Draw line segments *AB* and *CD* which intersect (cut each other) in point *E*. Do you think that *AB* and *CD* can intersect in another point if they are extended?

5. When men set fence posts, why do they first set the end posts?

6. Draw a curve line through two points, *A* and *B*. Can you draw another curve line through these points? How many curve lines can be drawn through two points? How many straight lines can be drawn through two points?

7. If segment *AB* is placed on segment *CD* with point *A* falling on point *C*, where will point *B* fall if *AB* = *CD*? if *AB* < *CD*? if *AB* > *CD*?*

8. What kind of line is formed when a piece of paper is folded?

9. How many end points has a line segment? a ray? a line?

10. How many line segments does a triangle contain? a square?

*If you do not know the meaning of the symbols used in this exercise, refer to page 7.

11. Name line m in the diagram in two other ways.

12. Complete: Line ABC is a _ _?_ _ line.

13. Name line AB by using one letter.

14. Name all ten of the line segments in the diagram.

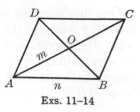

Exs. 11–14

6. Distance between Two Points. In geometry the distance between two points is the length of the line segment joining them.

7. Equal Line Segments. Two line segments are equal if they can be placed, one on the other, so that the ends of one will fall exactly on the ends of the other. Since all definitions are reversible, we know that two equal line segments can be made to *coincide* (fit together exactly).

If we wish to test the equality of two line segments such as AB and CD, we can cut the paper, separating the two segments, and try to make one segment fit exactly on the other. A better method of testing the equality of the two segments is to use compasses. Open the compasses so that one of the end points can be placed on A and the other on B. Without changing the distance between the points, place the points of the compasses on the segment CD. If one of the points of the compasses falls on C and the other falls on D, the two line segments are equal.

8. Measurement Is Approximate. No one can measure the length of an object and be sure that the measurement is correct. Yet the object can be measured to any degree of accuracy desired.

The degree of accuracy in any measurement depends upon the person making the measurement and upon the delicacy of the measuring instrument. With an ordinary yardstick a measurement can be made to the nearest eighth of an inch. A machinist, using a micrometer caliper (commonly referred to as a

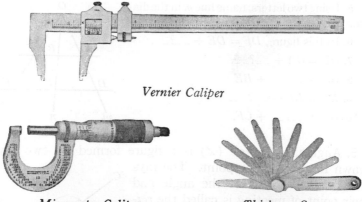

Vernier Caliper

Micrometer Caliper   *Thickness Gauge*

"mike") can measure objects to the nearest thousandth of an inch. The auto mechanic uses thickness gauges to measure the gaps in spark plugs. Measurements made to the thousandth of an inch are precise but they are not exact. It is not correct to say that two line segments are equal because they have the same measurement, since any measurement is only approximate.

EXERCISES [A]

1. Using a ruler, find the length and width of this page to the nearest inch; to the nearest eighth of an inch. Can you find the length to the nearest sixteenth of an inch?

2. Find the length of the second line of print in Ex. 1. Express the length to the nearest eighth of an inch.

3. Using the compasses, determine which line segments in the figure at the right are equal. Which is the shortest segment? the longest?

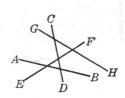

4. Using a ruler, measure each of the four sides of the polygon *ABCD*. Which sides are equal according to your measurements?

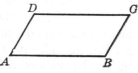

5. Using two letters, name line m in the diagram in three ways; name line n in three ways.

6. In this figure, $DF = DE + $ __?__.

7. $OD = OA + $ __?__.

8. $OE = $ __?__ $ + BE$.

9. $DE = DF - $ __?__.

10. $OF = $ __?__ $ + CF$.

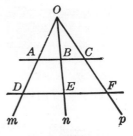

9. Angles. An *angle* ($\angle$) is a figure formed by two rays drawn from the same point. The rays are called the *sides* of the angle and their point of meeting is called the *vertex* of the angle. Thus AB and BC are the sides of $\angle ABC$ and B is the vertex.

There are three common ways of naming an angle: (1) by a capital letter at its vertex, as $\angle B$; (2) by a small letter within the angle, as $\angle x$; and (3) by three capital letters, the middle letter being the vertex letter and the other two being the names of points on the sides of the angle, as $\angle ABC$. In naming an angle by three letters, you should always remember that the vertex letter is the middle letter. When confusion might arise, always name an angle by three letters. The *size* of an angle depends only upon the amount of opening between its sides. Thus $\angle x$ is greater than $\angle y$, even though the sides of $\angle y$ are longer than those of $\angle x$.

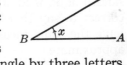

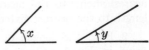

Two angles are equal if they can be made to coincide. Since a definition is reversible, two angles which are equal can be made to coincide. Thus if the sides of $\angle MOP$ can be made to fall on the sides of $\angle TRS$, the angles are equal; and if $\angle MOP$ equals $\angle TRS$, the sides of $\angle MOP$ can be made to fall on the sides of $\angle TRS$.

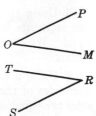

10. Generating an Angle. Suppose that the ray *OB* lies upon the ray *OA*. Now let the ray *OB* rotate counterclockwise about *O*. As it rotates, it generates ∠ *AOB*. Can you see that the size of an angle depends upon the amount of rotation of one of its sides?

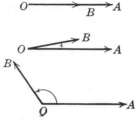

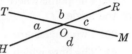

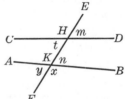

EXERCISES [A]

1. Does the size of an angle depend upon the length of its sides? upon the amount of opening between its sides? Can a 30° angle have sides equal to the sides of a 40° angle?

2. Read each of these angles by naming one letter; by naming three letters.

3. Make an angle equal to ∠ *TOH* by folding a piece of paper. Compare the angle you made with ∠ *MOR*.

4. Draw an angle *ABC*. Draw an angle approximately twice as large as ∠ *ABC* and label it ∠ *DEF*.

5. In the figure read by naming three letters: ∠ *m*; ∠ *n*; ∠ *x*; ∠ *y*; ∠ *t*.

6. Draw a square. Draw a line from each vertex to the opposite vertex. How many such lines can you draw? Why? How many angles are in the completed figure?

7. Draw a five-pointed star (pentagram). How many angles are formed inside the figure? Which of these angles seem to be equal?

8. Draw a line segment *AB*. Then draw another line segment *CD* meeting *AB* at *C* so that ∠ *ACD* = ∠ *BCD*.

Complete:

9. ∠ *ADC* = ∠ *ADO* + __?__.

10. ∠ *DCB* = ∠ *DCO* + __?__.

11. ∠ *ABO* + __?__ = ∠ *ABC*.

12. ∠ *BAO* = ∠ *BAD* − __?__.

13. ∠ *AOC* = ∠ *DOC* + __?__.

14. *BD* = __?__ + __?__.

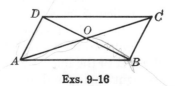

Exs. 9–16

15. Using the compasses, determine which line segment in the figure at the foot of page 15 is equal to segment *DO*; to *AD*; to *AO*; to *AB*.

16. Which angle in the same figure do you think is equal to ∠ *AOD*? to ∠ *AOB*?

17. Draw two angles which have a common vertex but no common side.

18. Draw two angles which have a common vertex and a common side between them.

Complete the following sentences:

19. The point where the sides of an angle meet is called the _ _?_ _ of the angle.

20. Two angles are _ _?_ _ if they can be made to coincide.

21. The lines which form an angle are called the _ _?_ _ of the angle.

11. Adjacent Angles. Two angles which have a common vertex and a common side between them are *adjacent angles* (adj. ∡). In the figure, ∡ *AOB* and *BOC* are adjacent angles. Are ∡ *AOB* and *AOC* adjacent? Why?

12. Perpendiculars and Right Angles. Two lines are *perpendicular* (⊥) to each other if one of them forms two equal adjacent angles with the other. Thus *CD* in the figure below is perpendicular to *AB* (*CD* ⊥ *AB*) and *AB* ⊥ *CD*.

The equal adjacent angles which are formed by a line and its perpendicular are called *right angles* (rt. ∡). Thus ∠ *x* and ∠ *y* are right angles.

The *foot* of the perpendicular to a line is the point where the perpendicular meets the line. *D* is the foot of *CD*, the per-

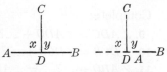

pendicular to the line *AB*. It is also the foot of the perpendicular *AB* to the line *CD*. The angles at the corners of this page are right angles, and the side edge is perpendicular to the edges adjacent to it.

13. Distance from a Point to a Line. The distance from a point to a line is the length of the perpendicular *from* the point *to* the line. Thus the distance from P to AB is the length of PR.

14. Angles Classified as to Size. A *straight angle* (st. ∠) is an angle whose sides extend in opposite directions from the vertex, forming a straight line. In the figure, ∠ x, or ∠ BOA, is a straight angle. Since two adjacent right angles (§ 12) form a straight angle, *a right angle is half of a straight angle.*

An *acute angle* is an angle less than a right angle, and an *obtuse angle* is an angle greater than a right angle but less than a straight angle. In the figure, ∠ MNP is an acute angle and ∠ PNR is an obtuse angle.

An *oblique angle* is an angle that is either acute or obtuse. The sides of an oblique angle are *oblique lines*. Two lines that meet are either oblique or perpendicular to each other.

EXERCISES [A]

1. Sketch and label an acute ∠ ABC; a rt. ∠ EFH; an obtuse ∠ PQR.

2. A right angle is what part of a straight angle?

3. Name four articles in your home which contain right angles.

4. In this figure, $CD \perp AB$.

a. What kind of angle is ∠ ADC? ∠ DCB?

b. Name two pairs of adjacent angles.

c. What is the foot of the perpendicular CD?

d. To what line is AB perpendicular?

e. What angle has the same size as ∠ ADC?

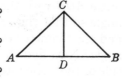

5. What kind of angle is formed by the hands of a clock at 2 o'clock? at 3 o'clock? at 6 o'clock? at 7 o'clock?

6. Name four angles of this figure that seem to be right angles. Name two obtuse angles; two acute angles.

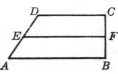

7. In this figure which angle is adjacent to ∠ WSR? to ∠ SWT?

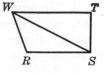

8. Is ∠ RWT adjacent to ∠ SWT? Why?

9. With a ruler draw two right angles. Do you think they are equal?

10. Draw a quadrilateral (a figure with four sides) which contains two right angles, one acute angle, and one obtuse angle.

11. Which of the two angles, *ABF* and *EBC*, is the larger?

12. If ∠ *DBE* is added to ∠ *EBF*, what angle is the result?

13. If ∠ *CBF* is subtracted from ∠ *CBD*, what angle is the remainder?

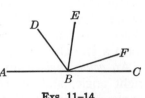

14. ∠ *ABD* + ∠ *DBE* = ∠ __?__.

Exs. 11–14

15. Measurement of Angles. A common unit for measuring angles is the *degree* (°), which is one ninetieth of a right angle. A right angle contains 90° and a straight angle contains 180°. For greater accuracy in measurement the degree is divided into 60 equal parts, each of which is called a *minute*. Mariners and engineers divide the minute into 60 equal parts called *seconds*. Thus 60 seconds (60″) = 1 minute (1′) and 60′ = 1°.

16. How to Use the Protractor. The *protractor* is an instrument used in measuring angles. A simple protractor which is graduated in degrees is shown on page 19. To measure an angle *AOB* with the protractor, place the protractor upon the angle so that the arrow point is on *O*, the vertex of the angle, and the diameter of the semicircle lies on *OA*, one side of the angle. Next find the scale reading of the point where the other side of the angle intersects the semicircle. In the diagram, this reading is 32°. This reading gives the number of degrees in the angle. If the sides of the angle are too short to cut the circle, they should be extended.

To draw an angle of any given size, say 47°, draw a line segment to be used as a side of the angle. Then select a point on this segment for the vertex of the angle. Place the protractor so that the arrow point of the protractor falls on this point and the diameter of the protractor semicircle falls on the line segment. Make a dot on the paper (or blackboard) opposite the 47° division mark. Then draw a line from this point to the point chosen for the vertex.

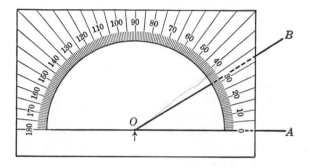

EXERCISES [A]

1. Draw an angle of 36° and label it ∠ x.

2. From any point P draw two rays forming an angle of 47°. On each ray locate a point 2 inches from P. Letter these points M and N. Draw MN. Measure ∡ PMN and PNM.

3. Draw two nonadjacent angles of 21° and 59° respectively.

4. Draw any triangle ABC (△ ABC). Measure each of its angles. What is the sum of its angles?

5. Draw a quadrilateral ABCD and measure each of its four angles. What is the sum of its angles?

6. Draw a line segment, AB, 3 inches long. Place a point C on the line halfway between A and B. Draw a perpendicular to AB at C. Locate a point D on this perpendicular so that CD is 3 inches in length. Draw AD and BD. Measure ∠ CAD and ∠ CBD. Which angle is the larger?

Add:

7. 18° 45′ and 32° 30′.

8. 7° 18′ 32″ and 15° 16′ 43″.

9. 19° 27′ 42″ and 42° 46′ 15″.

Subtract:

10. 7° 23′ from 25° 42′.

11. 31° 16′ 40″ from 45° 20′ 15″.

12. 18° 32′ 25″ from 90°.

17. Vertical Angles. Two nonadjacent angles which are formed by two intersecting straight lines are called *vertical angles*. In the figure, $\angle x$ and $\angle y$ form one pair of vertical angles and $\angle m$ and $\angle n$ form another pair of vertical angles.

18. Complementary Angles. Two angles are *complementary* (comp.) when their sum is a right angle (90°). In the figure, $\angle a$ and $\angle b$ are complementary angles, $\angle a$ being the complement of $\angle b$, and $\angle b$ being the complement of $\angle a$.

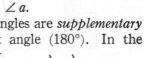

19. Supplementary Angles. Two angles are *supplementary* (supp.) when their sum is a straight angle (180°). In the figure, $\angle h$ and $\angle k$ are supplementary, $\angle h$ being the supplement of $\angle k$, and $\angle k$ being the supplement of $\angle h$.

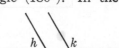

EXERCISES [A]

In the following exercises use arithmetic or algebra:

1. Find the complement of an angle of 30°; of 40°; of 19.2°; of 32° 18′; of x°; of $(2x - 18)$°; of $(3x + 7)$°.

2. Find the supplement of an angle of 60°; of 45°; of 37°; of 118°; of 30° 45′; of x°; of x° + 40°; of $(3a + 45)$°.

3. One of two complementary angles is twice the other. Find the angles.

4. Find the angle which is four times as large as its complement.

5. Find the angle which exceeds twice its complement by 8°.

6. In the figure, $\angle a = 140$°. How large is $\angle c$? $\angle d$? $\angle b$? Are two adjacent angles equal? Are two vertical angles equal?

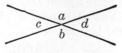

7. Find the angle whose supplement is three times as large as its complement.

8. Find the number of degrees in each of the four angles of the adjoining figure.

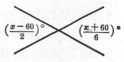

20. Congruent Figures. Any two geometric figures are said to be *congruent* (≅) if they can be made to coincide (fit exactly on each other). Since a definition is reversible, if two figures are congruent, they can be made to coincide. The word "con-gruent" means more than the

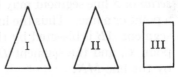

word "equal." Figures I, II, and III are all equal in area, but only Figs. I and II are congruent.

If two figures coincide, each side of one coincides with the corresponding side of the other and each angle of one coincides with the corresponding angle of the other.
Thus, if triangle *ABC*
coincides with triangle
DEF, then *AB*, *BC*,

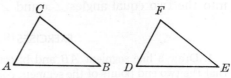

and *AC* coincide respectively with *DE*, *EF*, and *DF*; and ∠ *A*, *B*, and *C* coincide respectively with ∠ *D*, *E*, and *F*.

EXERCISES [A]

1. If two line segments are equal, are they necessarily congruent? If two line segments are congruent, are they necessarily equal? If two angles are equal, are they necessarily congruent? Are two line segments congruent if their end points can be made to coincide?

2. If two squares are equal in area, are they necessarily congruent? If two triangles are equal in area, are they necessarily congruent?

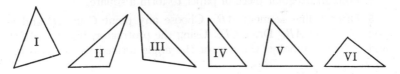

3. Determine which of these triangles are congruent by tracing each on thin paper and applying the tracing to each of the remaining triangles.

4. The sum of two angles is 80° and their difference is 20°. How large is each?

21. Bisectors. A line segment is *bisected* when it is separated into two equal parts. The *bisector* of a line segment may be a point or a line. Thus the line segment *AB* is bisected by the point *C*, and the segment *DE* by the line *MN*.

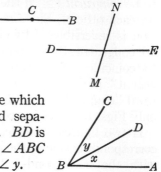

The *bisector of an angle* is the line which meets the vertex of the angle and separates the angle into two equal angles. *BD* is the bisector of ∠ *ABC*. It separates ∠ *ABC* into the two equal angles ∠ *x* and ∠ *y*.

EXERCISES [A]

1. Draw a line segment *AB* and bisect it by folding the paper so that the two end points of the segment coincide. At how many points may a line segment be bisected?

2. Are handkerchiefs ever bisected when they are ironed? Explain.

3. How can you bisect a string without using a ruler? How can you divide a string into four equal parts without using a ruler?

4. How many bisectors may an angle have?

5. Cut a piece of paper so that its shape is irregular. Fold the paper to form a straight line. Fold the paper to erect a perpendicular to this straight line.

6. Starting with an irregular piece of paper, fold the paper to form a right angle. Bisect the right angle, forming an angle of 45°.

7. Fold an irregular piece of paper to form a square.

8. Draw a line segment *AB*. Choose any point *C* in *AB* and a point *D* not in *AB*. Draw *CD*. Using the protractor, bisect ∠ *ACD* and ∠ *BCD*. What is the size of the angle formed by the two bisectors?

9. Study the result of Ex. 8 and state a fact concerning the bisectors of two supplementary adjacent angles.

10. One of two complementary angles is seven-eighths as large as the other. How many degrees are in each angle?

11. Find two angles whose sum is 40° and whose difference is 8°.

22. Circle. A *circle* (⊙) is a plane closed curve all points of which are equidistant from a point within called the *center*. A *radius* (plural, *radii*) of a circle is the line joining the center to any point on the circle, such as *OA*. An *arc of a circle* is any part of the circle, such as arc *AB* ($\widehat{AB}$). A circle is drawn by using a pair of compasses.

EXERCISES [A]

1. Draw a circle whose center is *O*. Draw a line through *O*. At how many points does the line intersect the circle? What is the greatest number of points at which a line may intersect a circle? the least number?

2. Draw any circle *O*. Choose any two points, *A* and *B*, on the circle. Draw *AB*. Does *AB* pass through the center? If *AB* should pass through the center, what would be its name?

3. Can you draw a line touching a circle in one point?

4. Draw two circles (*a*) which do not intersect; (*b*) which intersect in two points; (*c*) which touch at one point. Can two circles intersect in three points?

5. Draw a circle whose center is *O*. Draw a line through *O*, intersecting the circle in points *A* and *B*. What is the name of the line segment *AO*? of *BO*? of *AB*? How many diameters of the circle can be drawn?

6. Draw two unequal circles which intersect in *A* and *B*. Label the centers *O* and *O'*. Draw *AB* and *OO'* intersecting in *C*. Draw *AO*, *BO*, *AO'*, and *BO'*. Does *OB* = *OA*? Does *O'B* = *O'A*? Does *OC* = *O'C*? Does *AC* = *CB*?

A Fabric Design

Fleischer for Blockhouse

23. How to Make Some Important Constructions. You have been drawing lines with the ruler and measuring angles with the protractor. You will now learn how to construct some figures, using only a pair of compasses and a *straightedge* (an unmarked ruler). The straightedge is used for drawing straight lines and the compasses for drawing circles and measuring line segments.

From now on, unless otherwise stated, all constructions are to be made with the straightedge and compasses.

a. How to construct a line segment equal to a given line segment.

Let *AB* be the given line segment. Suppose you are required to construct another line segment equal to *AB*.

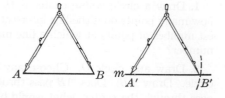

Draw a line *m* and choose any point *A'* on it. Adjust the compasses so that the end points coincide with the points *A* and *B* of the given line. Without changing the opening between the legs of the compasses, set one of the points on *A'* and draw an arc which intersects *m* at point *B'*. Then *A'B' = AB*.

b. How to bisect a line segment.

Let *AB* be the given line segment. With *A* and *B* as centers and with equal radii, draw arcs intersecting at *C* and *D*. Draw line *CD*, intersecting *AB* in *E*. Then *CD* bisects *AB*. That is, *AE = EB*. *CD* is also perpendicular to *AB*. Therefore *CD* is the perpendicular bisector of *AB*, and *E* is the *midpoint* of *AB*.

c. How to construct an angle equal to a given angle.

Let ∠ *AOB* be the given angle. Draw a line *MN*. With *O* as a center, draw an arc intersecting *OA* in *C* and *OB* in *D*. With *M* as a center and the same radius, draw an arc *PQ*. With *P* as a center and a radius equal to the line segment *CD*, draw an arc intersecting arc *PQ* in *R*. Draw *MR*. Then ∠ *PMR = ∠ AOB*.

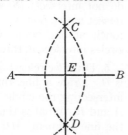

d. How to bisect an angle.

Using the figures below, let $\angle AOB$ be the given angle. With O as a center, draw an arc intersecting OA in C and OB in D. With C and D as centers and with equal radii, draw arcs intersecting in E. Draw OE. Then OE bisects $\angle AOB$.

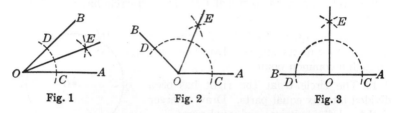

Fig. 1   Fig. 2   Fig. 3

Bisecting the straight $\angle AOB$ divides the angle into two right angles. Therefore the line which bisects a straight angle is perpendicular to the line forming the sides of the angle. In Fig. 3, $EO \perp BA$ at O.

e. How to construct a perpendicular through a given point to a given line

The given point is P and the given line is AB.

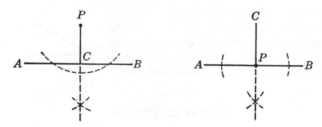

In one case the point P is without the line and in the other case the point P is on the line. Does PC bisect a line segment? Does it bisect an angle?

EXERCISES [A]

1. Divide a given line segment EF into two equal segments.

2. Divide a given line segment BD into four equal segments.

3. Bisect a given angle FGH.

4. Divide a given angle MON into four equal angles.

5. Draw a line *MN* and construct a perpendicular to it from an external point *J*. Draw a line *RS* and construct a perpendicular to it at a point *K* on the line.

6. Draw an acute ∠ *HKL*. Construct ∠ *ABC* equal to ∠ *HKL*.

7. Construct a right angle. Construct a 45° angle.

8. Bisect a given line segment *CD*. Draw a circle having *CD* as a diameter.

9. Draw a square *CDEF* and construct the bisectors of its angles. Do they pass through a common point?

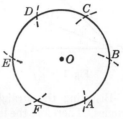

10. The circle *O* at the right has been divided into six equal parts. Draw a larger circle and divide it into six equal parts.

11. Divide a circle into four equal arcs.

12. Divide a circle into eight equal parts.

13. Can you divide a circle into twelve equal arcs?

14. Draw a triangle. Construct the perpendicular bisectors of its sides.

15. Draw a triangle having the shape of triangle *ABC* but having its sides about three times as long. From *C* construct a line perpendicular to *AB*. From *B* construct a line perpendicular to *AC* produced (extended).

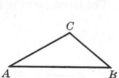

REVIEW QUESTIONS

1. Upon what does the size of an angle depend?

2. What is the difference between a line and a line segment?

3. How many straight lines can be drawn through one point? through two points? through three points?

4. How many points can lie on one line? How many points are common to two intersecting lines? to three intersecting lines?

5. What do you know about the sides of a right angle?

6. What is the name of an angle which is equal to its supplement? which is less than its supplement? which is greater than its supplement?

7. What is the name of two angles which have a common vertex and a common side between them?

8. What is the name of a pair of angles whose sum is a right angle? whose sum is a straight angle?

9. What instruments are used in geometry for the construction of figures?

10. When two lines meet to form an angle, what do you call their neeting point?

11. What word means "to divide into two equal parts"?

12. What is true of the radii of the same circle?

13. How many dimensions has a line? a plane surface? a solid?

14. How many end points has a line? a line segment? a circle?

15. Define congruent figures.

16. What is the name of an angle if it is less than a right angle?

17. Which is greater, an obtuse angle or a right angle? an obtuse angle or a straight angle?

18. Is a perpendicular always a vertical line?

19. If line a is perpendicular to line b, is line b perpendicular to line a?

Complete:

20. If $\angle x = 47°$ and $\angle y = 43°$, then $\angle x$ and $\angle y$ are _ _?_ _.

21. $\angle a$ and $\angle c$ are _ _?_ _ angles.

22. $\angle d$ and $\angle c$ are supplementary _ _?_ _ angles.

WORD LIST

At this time you should be able to spell and use correctly in sentences each of the following words:

acute	compasses	length	protractor
adjacent	complementary	midpoint	radius
angle	congruent	oblique	ray
arc	construction	obtuse	segment
bisect	curve	perpendicular	straight
center	geometry	plane	supplementary
circle	intersection	point	vertex

TEST I

True-False Statements (*Eight Minutes*)

Copy the numbers of these statements on your paper. Then if a statement is *always* true, write T after its number. If a statement is *not always* true, write F after its number. Do not guess.

F 1. A straight line has a definite length.

T 2. The size of an angle does not depend upon the lengths of its sides.

T 3. The bisector of an angle divides the angle into two equal parts.

T 4. A straight angle is a straight line.

F 5. Two lines can intersect in two points.

T 6. A protractor is used to measure angles.

F 7. A straightedge is used to measure line segments.

F 8. If ∠ *x* = 41° and ∠ *y* = 139°, then ∠ *x* is complementary to ∠ *y*.

T 9. The sides of an oblique angle are oblique to each other.

+ 10. The sides of a right angle are perpendicular to each other.

F 11. The supplement of an angle of 63° 18′ contains 36° 42′.

T 12. In the figure, *CD* is constructed perpendicular to *AB*.

T 13. At 4 o'clock the hands of a clock form an obtuse angle.

T 14. Two angles which have a common vertex and a common side are adjacent angles.

T 15. A degree contains 60 minutes.

T 16. Two adjacent angles are either complementary or supplementary.

T 17. A diameter of a circle joins any two points of a circle.

F 18. "Intersect" means "to divide into equal parts."

T 19. A line has one dimension.

F 20. A machinist can measure the diameter of a cylinder exactly.

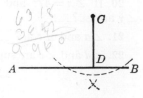

CHAPTER II

Reasoning and Proof

The kinds of reasoning used by man in making conclusions can be in general separated into three types, known as intuitive, inductive, and deductive reasoning. In our thought processes there is usually a certain amount of blending or overlapping of these three types.

Reasoning by intuition is an attempt to explain things as they appear to us without scientific observation, experimentation, or an ordered chain of reasoning based on known facts. Frequently intuitive reasoning is affected by the emotions and prejudice. We can never be sure of the truth of conclusions that are based on intuition.

24. Discovering Facts by Measurement. The ancients learned their first geometry from observation and measurement. We shall now see if we can discover and prove some facts of geometry. In the exercises which follow, use the compasses or ruler for measuring line segments and the protractor for measuring angles.

EXERCISES
A

1. Find the number of degrees in $\angle AOB$; $\angle BOC$; $\angle COD$; $\angle DOE$; $\angle EOA$. What is the sum of all the angles about point O? about any point?

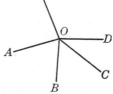

2. Draw several triangles. Find the sum of the angles of each triangle. What is the sum of the angles of any triangle? Have you proved your answer?

3. Draw a triangle having two equal sides. Measure each of its angles. Have you discovered any fact concerning two angles of a triangle having two equal sides? If not, draw another

triangle having two equal sides and measure its angles. If you think you have discovered a principle, test your conclusion by measuring the angles of other triangles each having two equal sides.

4. Draw two lines, *AB* and *MN*, intersecting at *O*. Measure ∠ *AON* and ∠ *BOM*. What is the name of this pair of angles? How do they compare as to size? If any two straight lines intersect, do you think the vertical angles are equal? Test your answer by measuring other pairs of vertical angles. If you find that vertical angles are equal in ninety cases, is this positive proof that vertical angles are equal in all cases?

5. On paper place any three points which are not in the same straight line and letter them *A*, *B*, and *C* respectively. Draw *AB*, *BC*, and *CA*. Measure the three line segments and find the sum of the length of the two shorter segments. Is this sum greater than the length of the longest segment? Complete: "The sum of two sides of a triangle is __?__ than the third __?__." If you should find the above statement true for one thousand triangles, should you know conclusively that it is true for all triangles?

6. The two parallel lines *m* and *n* are intersected by the line *t*. Do you think any four of the eight angles are equal? Test your answer by measurement.

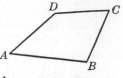

B

7. Draw a triangle *ABC*. Draw a line segment from *D*, the midpoint of *AC*, to *E*, the midpoint of *BC*. Compare the length of *DE* with the length of *AB*. State your conclusion. Test your conclusion by drawing other triangles.

8. *ABCD* is a quadrilateral. Find the sum of its angles. Draw another quadrilateral and find the sum of its angles. What fact have you discovered? Test your conclusion by measuring the angles of a third quadrilateral.

9. Draw a triangle. Bisect each of its angles. What statement can you make concerning the bisectors of the angles of a triangle?

10. Draw a number of quadrilaterals and bisect their angles. Do the bisectors pass through a common point?

11. Draw any triangle *ABC*. Bisect its sides. Let *D* be the midpoint of *AB*, *E* be the midpoint of *BC*, and *F* be the midpoint of *AC*. Draw *AE*, *CD*, and *BF*. Draw as many conclusions as you can from the figure, testing them by measurement.

12. Draw triangle *ABC*. Construct the perpendicular bisectors of *AB* and *AC*. Label their intersection *O*. Does *OA* = *OB* = *OC*?

13. Draw any line segment and construct its perpendicular bisector. Select any point on the perpendicular bisector and compare its distances to the end points of the line segment. Select another point on the perpendicular bisector and compare its distances to the end points of the segment. If you have made a discovery, test its correctness by repeating the experiment.

14. Draw any triangle *ABC* having *AC* = *BC*. Bisect *BC*. Let *O* be the midpoint of *BC*. With *O* as the center and a radius equal to *OB*, draw a circle, intersecting *AB* in *D*. Draw *CD*. See how many facts you can discover. Verify your conclusions by making other triangles.

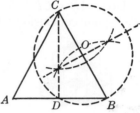

25. Inductive Reasoning. In the exercises above you were asked to make conclusions based upon observation and measurement. Thus in Ex. 3 on page 29 you were asked to draw a triangle having two equal sides and to make a conclusion concerning two of its angles. When you had drawn the triangle and measured its angles, you no doubt discovered that two of the angles were equal. Then you repeated the experiment several times and concluded that any triangle with two equal sides has two equal angles. The reasoning which you used in arriving at this conclusion is known as *inductive reasoning*. Whenever we arrive at a general truth or statement by investigating a number of particular cases, we are using inductive reasoning.

Inductive reasoning has made a large contribution to civilization. Geometry was first studied by induction, and each year new facts of geometry are discovered inductively. Induction has been used to discover laws and principles in the arts and sciences, such as chemistry, physics, astronomy, architecture, and medicine. Through its use we have acquired knowledge of the weather, crops, and the behavior of human beings.

Inductive reasoning does not always prove the conclusion obtained by it, for it has two sources of error:

First, it depends upon measurement and observation, neither of which can be said to be absolutely accurate.

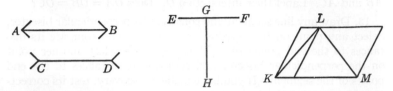

Does *AB = CD*? Test by measurement. Does *EF = GH*? Test your conclusion. Does *KL = LM*?

 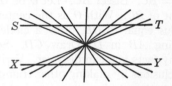

Are there six or seven blocks in the left figure above? Are *XY* and *ST* straight lines?

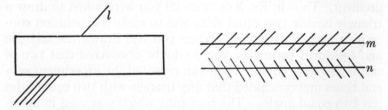

Which of the four lines below the rectangle is the continuation of *l*? Are the line segments *m* and *n* the same distance apart at both ends?

Second, inductive reasoning usually arrives at the conclusion before all possible cases have been studied. Any exception to a conclusion obtained through inductive reasoning proves that the conclusion is false. For example, the pupils in a certain class concluded that all rainbows appear in the east. Later they knew that their conclusion was false, for one of the pupils saw a rainbow in the west.

EXERCISES [A]

1. A farmer in Ohio experimented on the use of lime as a fertilizer for corn. In each hill of one row he placed a small amount of lime. In the next row he used no lime. The fertilized row gave the better yield. The next year he repeated the experiment and obtained the same result. Should he conclude that lime benefits his corn crop?

2. In a Western city some people say that if it rains on Easter Sunday, it will rain on each of the next seven Sundays. How do you think this conclusion was made? Do you believe that it is valid?

3. Ten boys went camping and six of them became ill. To determine the cause of their illness, they checked five of the possible causes as follows:

Boys	Ill	Chicken	Oranges	Sand-wiches	Drinking Water	Pool
Frank Wilson	Yes	Yes	Yes	Yes	Yes	Yes
Eugene Webb	No	No	Yes	Yes	Yes	Yes
Ores Jones	Yes	Yes	Yes	No	Yes	Yes
Blair Wilson	Yes	Yes	No	Yes	Yes	Yes
Edson Frank	Yes	Yes	Yes	Yes	Yes	No
Bill Flick	No	No	No	No	Yes	No
John Eiler	Yes	Yes	Yes	Yes	Yes	Yes
Joe Gregg	No	No	Yes	Yes	Yes	Yes
Forrest Black	No	No	No	Yes	Yes	Yes
Glen Morris	Yes	Yes	Yes	No	Yes	Yes

Tell what you think was the cause of the illness and give the reason for your answer.

4. Explain how each of the following proverbs is the result of inductive reasoning:

 a. All is not gold that glitters.

 b. A bird in the hand is worth two in the bush.

 c. A rainbow at night is the sailor's delight.

26. Deductive Reasoning.
Inductive reasoning selects a common property of many specific cases and concludes that this property fits all cases. It proceeds from the particular to the general. Deductive reasoning works the other way. In de-

ductive reasoning we always start with a general statement which has been accepted as true and apply this statement to specific cases   Deductive reasoning proceeds from the general to the specific.

Each of us uses some form of deductive reasoning daily. We constantly make conclusions which depend upon some general principles of conduct. The conclusions reached by deductive reasoning are true only when the general statements upon which they are based are true.

27. How to Reason Deductively. Suppose that every student in your high school has at least one study period. Richard Johnston is a student in your school. What do you know about Richard immediately?

The main steps of your reasoning process probably are:

Step 1. If a person is a student in your school, he has at least one study period.

Step 2. Richard Johnston is a student in your school.

Step 3. Therefore he has at least one study period.

How do you know that Step 3 is true? You did not actually see Richard during his study period. He did not tell you that he had a study period. Yet, because you knew that Steps 1 and 2 were true, you knew that Step 3 was true.

The example above is a very simple and easy case of deductive reasoning. In it there is not much chance of reaching the wrong conclusion. Often, however, when the reasoning is not so simple, we are apt to *jump* at conclusions and err in our reasoning. You will now be given six examples of deductive reasoning. Study these examples and see if you can tell which illustrate good reasoning and which illustrate faulty reasoning.

Example 1. (1) If a person is a student in your school, he has at least one study period.

(2) Arthur York is a student.

(3) Therefore he has at least one study period.

Example 2. (1) If a person is a student in your school, he has at least one study period.

(2) Mary Thomas is in your school.

(3) Therefore she has at least one study period.

Example 3. (1) Every student who intends to graduate from high school must take one year of mathematics.

(2) Joan is a student and intends to graduate from high school.

(3) Therefore she must take one year of mathematics.

Example 4. (1) If the sum of two angles is a straight angle, the angles are supplementary.

(2) $\angle x + \angle y = 1$ st. $\angle$.

(3) Therefore $\angle$ x and y are supplementary.

Example 5. (1) If a line meets the vertex of an angle and separates the angle into two equal parts, it is the bisector of the angle.

(2) BD meets the vertex of $\angle ABC$.

(3) Therefore BD bisects $\angle ABC$.

Example 6. (1) If two angles are nonadjacent and are formed by intersecting straight lines, they are vertical angles.

(2) $\angle$ x and y, which are nonadjacent, are formed by intersecting straight lines.

(3) Therefore $\angle x$ and $\angle y$ are complementary.

Do you agree that 1, 2, 5, and 6 are examples of incorrect reasoning? In Examples 1, 2, and 5, step (2) failed to fulfill completely the requirements laid down in step (1). In Example 1 we do not know whether Arthur York attends your school or not. In Example 2 Mary Thomas may be a teacher or some other school employee. In Example 5 we do not know whether BD separates $\angle ABC$ into equal parts. But in Examples 3 and 4 step (2) fulfills the conditions of step (1). The first two requirements of good deductive reasoning are:

1. *A general statement,* and

2. *A specific statement which satisfies all the conditions of the general statement.*

In Example 6 statement (2) fills all the requirements of statement (1), but the conclusion is incorrect. The conclusion called for in statement (1) is that the angles be vertical angles. It said nothing about complementary angles. Thus a third requirement of good deductive reasoning is:

3. *The conclusion must be the one called for in the general statement.*

Read Example 4 on the preceding page again. Notice that statements (2) and (3) taken together are actually only a specific example of the general statement (1). Therefore we can express them in the "If . . . then" form of sentence used in statement (1), as follows: If the sum of $\measuredangle x$ and y is a straight angle, the angles are supplementary.

We shall use this type of reasoning throughout geometry. It is the basis of formal proof.

EXERCISES [A]

See if you can draw valid conclusions from the following:

1. (1) John's dog barks whenever a stranger enters the yard.
(2) John's dog is barking.

2. (1) When the outside temperature is below 60° F., Mr. Jones always keeps a fire in his shop.
(2) The outside temperature today is 20° F.

3. (1) Mr. Allen always buys candy when he goes to Black's store.
(2) Mr. Allen bought candy today.

4. (1) Vertical angles are equal.
(2) Angles A and B are vertical angles.

28. Proof by Demonstration. As has been stated before, a proof by induction, which is based upon observation and measurement, is subject to error. For this reason we shall, in the main, study geometry by the demonstration method, which is deductive. By this method we shall first agree upon some fundamental statements as a foundation upon which to argue. Then, using these fundamental statements, we shall prove a large number of other statements. A geometry worked out in this manner is known as *demonstrative geometry*. The fundamental statements upon which the reasoning is based consist of definitions, axioms, and postulates.

29. Importance of Definitions. If we are to reason accurately in geometry, we must thoroughly understand the meaning of all words and terms that we use. A definition of a term is a statement of the meaning of that term. A good definition first places a term to be defined in the smallest class to which it belongs and second gives the definite characteristic that distinguishes it from all other members of that class.

On page 17 a *straight angle* was defined as *an angle whose sides extend in opposite directions from the vertex, forming a straight line.* First the definition places a straight angle in the subclass *angles* of the larger class *geometric figures.* Then the definition gives the characteristic that distinguishes a straight angle from all other angles. This is illustrated by the diagram at the right.

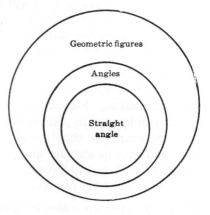

It is very important that you understand and be able to define at any time all the terms that you have studied. No one is able to talk or reason about any subject successfully unless he knows the exact definitions of the terms he uses.

30. Definitions Are Reversible. A correct definition is reversible and in geometry we have occasion to use both forms of a definition. The definition of perpendicular lines may be stated in the following two forms:

1. Two lines are perpendicular to each other if one of them forms two equal adjacent angles with the other.

2. Two lines form two equal adjacent angles if the lines are perpendicular.

While all definitions are reversible, not all the statements of geometry are reversible. For example, the statement *two straight angles are equal* is true, but it is obvious that the statement *if two angles are equal, they are straight angles* is not true

EXERCISES [A]

1. Define complementary angles. State the definition reversed.

2. Define supplementary angles. State the definition reversed.

3. Define equal angles. State the definition reversed.

4. Define "touchdown" as used in football.

5. Explain why this is not a definition: "A horse has four legs."

6. John came into his geometry classroom while the class bell was ringing. The teacher said, "I will have to mark you tardy, John." John said, "I wasn't tardy; I was in the room before the bell finished ringing." The teacher said, "Yes, but you were not in your seat." Can you tell why John and his teacher disagreed?

31. Axioms. An *axiom* is a general statement which we accept as true without proof. An axiom applies to all branches of mathematics. Following are listed nine axioms, seven of which you learned in your study of algebra. Study each axiom and the examples that follow it very carefully. Make sure that you understand the meaning of the axiom and can state it correctly. You will have occasion to quote each axiom many times in your study of geometry.

Ax. 1. *If equals are added to equals, the sums are equal.*

Example 1.
$$2 \text{ feet} = 24 \text{ inches}$$
$$\underline{3 \text{ feet} = 36 \text{ inches}}$$
$$5 \text{ feet} = 60 \text{ inches}$$

Example 2. If $x = 5$
and $y = 2$
then $x + y = 7$

Ax. 2. *If equals are subtracted from equals, the remainders are equal.*

Example 1. If $2x + 3y = 12$
and $\underline{x + 3y = 9}$
then $x = 3$

Example 2. If $\angle a + \angle b = \angle c$
and $\underline{\angle b = \angle d}$
then $\angle a = \angle c - \angle d$

Ax. 3. *If equals are multiplied by equals, the products are equal.*

Example 1. If $2x = 7$,
then $6x = 21.$

Example 2. If $\frac{1}{5}\overline{AB} = 6$,
then $\overline{AB} = 30$.

Ax. 4. *If equals are divided by equals, the quotients are equal.* (Division by zero is not permissible.)

Example 1. If $6x = 30$,
then $x = 5$.

Example 2. If $\angle AOB = 90°$,
then $\frac{1}{3}\angle AOB = 30°$.

Ax. 5. *A quantity may be substituted for its equal.*

Example. If $x + y = 6$ and $y = 2$, then $x + 2 = 6$.

Ax. 6. *Quantities which are equal to the same quantity or to equal quantities are equal to each other.*

Example 1.	If $x = m$		**Example 2.**	If $x = m,$
and	$y = m,$			$y = n,$
then	$x = y.$	and		$m = n,$
		then		$x = y.$

Ax. 7. *Like powers or like roots of equals are equal.*

Example 1.	If $a = 8,$		**Example 3.**	If $m = 3,$
then	$a^2 = 64.$		then	$m^3 = 27.$
Example 2.	If $a^2 = 64,$		**Example 4.**	If $x^3 = 8,$
then	$a = 8.$		then	$x = 2.$

Ax. 8. *The whole is equal to the sum of its parts and is greater than any one of them.*

    Example 1. $\angle ABC = \angle ABD + \angle DBC.$
    Example 2. $\angle ABC > \angle ABD.$

Ax. 9. *Of two quantities of the same kind, the first is greater than, equal to, or less than the second.*

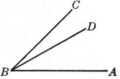

    Example. Thus, James weighs more than Henry, the same as Henry, or less than Henry.

Ax. 10. A quantity is equal to itself.

EXERCISES [A]

Answer each question by stating an axiom:

1. If $k = 5$, why does $3k = 15$?   2. If $7x = 14$, why does $x = 2$?

3. If $m = 3$, why does $m^2 = 9$?

4. If $x = 20$ and $y = 2$, why does $x + y = 22$?

5. If $x = 20$ and $y = 2$, why does $x - y = 18$?

6. If $a = 6$ and $b = 4$, why does $ab = 24$?

7. If $\frac{x}{6} = 3$, why does $x = 18$?   8. If $ax = 4a$, why does $x = 4$?

State the axiom which is the reason for each of the statements in Exs. 9–32.

9. If $x + y = m$ and $y = a$, then $x + a = m.$

10. If $x + y = 90$ and $a + b = 90$, then $x + y = a + b.$

11. If $x = 7$ and $y = 4$, then $xy = 28.$ 12. If $c = 6$, then $c^3 = 216.$

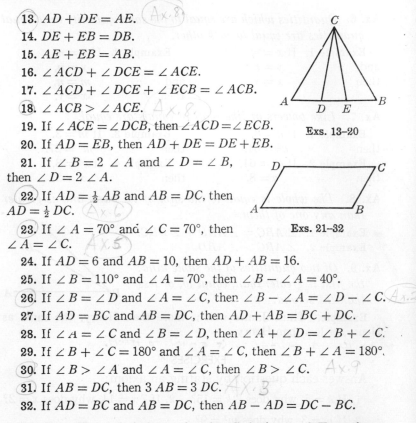

13. $AD + DE = AE.$ (Ax. 8)

14. $DE + EB = DB.$

15. $AE + EB = AB.$

16. $\angle ACD + \angle DCE = \angle ACE.$

17. $\angle ACD + \angle DCE + \angle ECB = \angle ACB.$

18. $\angle ACB > \angle ACE.$ (Ax. 8)

19. If $\angle ACE = \angle DCB$, then $\angle ACD = \angle ECB.$

20. If $AD = EB$, then $AD + DE = DE + EB.$

Exs. 13–20

21. If $\angle B = 2 \angle A$ and $\angle D = \angle B$, then $\angle D = 2 \angle A.$

22. If $AD = \frac{1}{2} AB$ and $AB = DC$, then $AD = \frac{1}{2} DC.$ (Ax. 6)

Exs. 21–32

23. If $\angle A = 70°$ and $\angle C = 70°$, then $\angle A = \angle C.$ (Ax. 5)

24. If $AD = 6$ and $AB = 10$, then $AD + AB = 16.$

25. If $\angle B = 110°$ and $\angle A = 70°$, then $\angle B - \angle A = 40°.$

26. If $\angle B = \angle D$ and $\angle A = \angle C$, then $\angle B - \angle A = \angle D - \angle C.$ (Ax. 2)

27. If $AD = BC$ and $AB = DC$, then $AD + AB = BC + DC.$

28. If $\angle A = \angle C$ and $\angle B = \angle D$, then $\angle A + \angle D = \angle B + \angle C.$

29. If $\angle B + \angle C = 180°$ and $\angle A = \angle C$, then $\angle B + \angle A = 180°.$

30. If $\angle B > \angle A$ and $\angle A = \angle C$, then $\angle B > \angle C.$ (Ax. 9)

31. If $AB = DC$, then $3 AB = 3 DC.$ (Ax. 3)

32. If $AD = BC$ and $AB = DC$, then $AB - AD = DC - BC.$

32. The Use of Axioms in the Solutions of Equations.

Many times in your study of geometry you will have occasion to work with equations. The following exercises are intended to give you a review of the methods of solving equations.

EXERCISES [A]

Example 1. Solve $2 c + 14 = 8$ and state the axioms used.

Solution.

1. $2 c + 14 = 8.$	1. Given.	
2. $\quad\quad 2 c = -6.$	2. Ax. 2.	[Students should always give
3. $\quad\quad\quad c = -3.$	3. Ax. 4.	axioms in full.]

Following the solution of Example 1, solve:

1. $3x - 1 = 8.$

2. $7x + 2 = 23.$

3. $5x + 4 = -26.$

4. $\frac{1}{2}m + 4 = 6.$

5. $7c - 10 = 2c.$

6. $8m - 4 = 3m.$

7. $6c - 9 = 15.$

8. $4x = 12 - 2x.$

9. $3p = 30 - 5p.$

10. $2x = 14 + 9x.$

11. $6y + 4 = 20.$

12. $a = \frac{2}{5}a + 6.$

Example 2. Solve $2(x - 3) - (x + 2) = 2.$

Solution.

1. $2(x - 3) - (x + 2) = 2.$	1. Given.
2. $2x - 6 - x - 2 = 2.$	2. Ax. 5.
3. $x - 8 = 2.$	3. Ax. 5.
4. $x = 10.$	4. Ax. 1.

Example 3. Solve $\frac{4x}{5} - 1 = \frac{x}{2}.$

Solution.

1. $\frac{4x}{5} - 1 = \frac{x}{2}.$	1. Given.
2. $10\left(\frac{4x}{5}\right) - 10(1) = 10\left(\frac{x}{2}\right).$	2. Ax. 3.
3. $8x - 10 = 5x.$	3. Ax. 5.
4. $3x - 10 = 0.$	4. Ax. 2.
5. $3x = 10.$	5. Ax. 1.
6. $x = 3\frac{1}{3}.$	6. Ax. 4.

Solve the following equations, stating the axiom used in each step as in Examples 2 and 3:

13. $\frac{m}{4} - \frac{m}{5} = 4.$

14. $\frac{2x}{3} - \frac{x}{4} = 1.$

15. $\frac{5c}{6} + 4 = \frac{c - 6}{3}.$

16. $\frac{y + 6}{4} = 4\frac{1}{2}.$

17. $\frac{2}{3}(x + 5) = \frac{12x}{5} - \frac{44}{5}.$

18. $\frac{b - 4}{9} - \frac{b}{3} = \frac{b + 2}{6}.$

Example 4. Solve the system $\begin{cases} 2x - 7y = 8, \\ 9x - 4y = -19. \end{cases}$

Solution.

1. $2x - 7y = 8$.	1. Given.
2. $9x - 4y = -19$.	2. Given.
3. Multiplying (1) by 9, $18x - 63y = 72$.	3. Ax. 3.
4. Multiplying (2) by 2, $\underline{18x - 8y = -38.}$	4. Ax. 3.
5. $-55y = 110.$	5. Ax. 2.
6. $y = -2.$	6. Ax. 4.
7. Substituting -2 for y in (1), $2x + 14 = 8$.	7. Ax. 5.
8. $2x = -6.$	8. Ax. 2.
9. $x = -3.$	9. Ax. 4.

Solve the following sets of equations:

19. $3x + y = 11,$
$4x - y = 3.$

20. $2x + 3y = 0,$
$5x + 7y = 2.$

21. $6x - 3y = -12,$
$5x + 2y = -8.$

22. $4x + y = 6\frac{1}{2},$
$8x = 15 - 6y.$

Example 5. Two angles are complementary and one of them exceeds twice the other by 18°. How many degrees are there in each angle?

Solution. Let $x =$ the number of degrees in the smaller angle.
Then $2x + 18 =$ the number of degrees in the larger angle.
$$x + 2x + 18 = 90.$$
$$x + 2x = 90 - 18.$$
$$3x = 72.$$
$$x = 24, \text{ the number of degrees in the smaller angle.}$$
$$2x + 18 = 66, \text{ the number of degrees in the larger angle.}$$

23. One of two complementary angles is 5 times as large as the other. How large is each angle?

24. One of two supplementary angles is 8 times as large as the other. How many degrees are there in each angle?

25. The difference between two complementary angles is 18°. How large is each angle?

26. Find the angle which is 10° smaller than its complement.

27. Find the angle which is $\frac{1}{4}$ as large as its supplement

28. Find the size of two supplementary angles whose ratio is 2 : 7.

SUGGESTION. Let $2x =$ the number of degrees in the smaller.
     Then $7x =$ the number of degrees in the larger.

29. Two complementary angles have the ratio 4 : 5. How large are they?

30. If two supplementary angles have the ratio 3 : 5, how many degrees are there in each angle?

31. Two complementary angles contain $a°$ and $(a - 6)°$. How many degrees are there in each angle?

32. How many degrees are there in the angle formed by the bisectors of two complementary adjacent angles?

33. Two lines intersect so that one pair of vertical angles are complementary. How many degrees are there in each of the four angles?

34. Two lines intersect so that one pair of vertical angles are supplementary. How many degrees are there in each of the four angles?

33. Postulates. A *postulate* (Post.) is a geometric statement which is accepted as true without proof. Postulates are statements concerning points, lines, and other geometric figures. At this time let us agree that all the following postulates are true. Other postulates will be stated when needed.

In studying these postulates, read each postulate several times and illustrate it with a figure each time. If any postulate is not clear to you, ask your teacher to explain it. The more familiar you are with the wording of the postulates, the better you will be able to use them in the exercises that follow the postulates. You need not memorize them at this time.

Post. 1. *One straight line, and only one, can be drawn through two points.*

Post. 2. *Two straight lines cannot intersect in more than one point.*

Post. 3. *A straight line segment can be extended indefinitely in two directions.*

Post. 4. *A straight line segment is the shortest line segment that can be drawn between two points.*

Post. 5. *One circle, and only one, can be drawn with any given point as a center and any given line segment as a radius.*

Post. 6. *Any geometric figure can be moved without changing its size or shape.*

Post. 7. *A straight line segment has one midpoint, and only one.*

Post. 8. *An angle can be bisected by one line, and only one.*

Post. 9. *All right angles are equal and all straight angles are equal.*

Post. 10. *At any point in a straight line one perpendicular, and only one, can be drawn to the line.*

Post. 11. *The perpendicular is the shortest line segment that can be drawn from a given point to a given line.*

Post. 12. *The sum of all the angles about a point is two straight angles.*

Post. 13. *The sum of all the angles about a point on one side of a straight line is a straight angle.*

Post. 14. *If two adjacent angles have their exterior sides in a straight line, they are supplementary.*

Post. 15. *If two adjacent angles are supplementary, their exterior sides lie in a straight line.*

Post. 16. *All radii of a circle or of equal circles are equal.*

Post. 17. *A straight line cannot intersect a circle in more than two points.*

Example. *Given* triangle *ABC* with *AD* ⊥ *BC* and bisecting *BC*. Why does *BD = DC* and why does ∠*ADC* = ∠*BDA*?

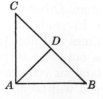

Answers. *BD = DC* because a line segment is separated into two equal parts when it is bisected (§ 21). ∠*ADC* = ∠*BDA* because two lines that are perpendicular form two equal adjacent angles (§ 12). Notice that these definitions are given in the reverse order.

EXERCISES [A]

Answer each of the following questions by stating a definition, an axiom, or a postulate:

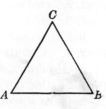

1. If *AC = BC* and *AB = BC,* why does *AC = AB?*

2. If ∠*A* = ∠*C* and ∠*B* = ∠*C,* why does ∠*A* = ∠*B?*

3. If $8x = 32$, why does $x = 4$?

4. If $\frac{1}{4}m = 3$, why does $m = 12$?

5. $\angle x$ and $\angle y$ are vertical angles. Why?

6. $\angle m$ and $\angle n$ are vertical angles. Why?

7. If $\angle x = \angle y$ and $\angle m = \angle y$, why does $\angle m = \angle x$?

8. If $\angle m + \angle h = 180°$ and $\angle y = \angle m$, why does $\angle y + \angle h = 180°$?

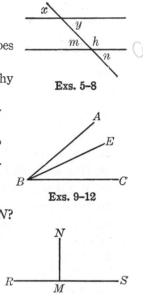

Exs. 5-8

9. If $\angle CBE = 25°$ and $\angle EBA = 15°$, why does $\angle CBE + \angle EBA = 40°$?

10. Why does $\angle ABC = \angle ABE + \angle EBC$?

11. If $\angle ABE = \angle EBC$, why does BE bisect $\angle CBA$?

12. $\angle CBA$ has only one bisector. Why?

Exs. 9-12

13. If $NM \perp RS$, why is $\angle RMN = \angle SMN$?

14. If $NM \perp RS$, why are $\angle RMN$ and NMS right angles?

15. On your paper place two points A and B about two inches apart. Draw straight line AB. Why can you not draw another straight line through A and B?

Exs. 13-14

Figure ABC is a triangle having CE bisecting AB and with line segments AD and BD drawn as shown.

16. Why does $AE + EB = AB$?

17. If $AB = 2$ inches, $AD + DB > 2$ inches. Why?

18. $\angle EAD + \angle DAC = \angle EAC$. Why?

19. AD can be extended to BC. Why?

20. If $\angle EBD + \angle DBC = \angle EBC$, why does $\angle EBD = \angle EBC - \angle DBC$?

21. Why does $AE = EB$?

22. If lines c and d can be moved to coincide with lines e and f respectively, why will point A coincide with point B?

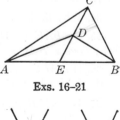

Exs. 16-21

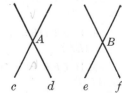

In the figure at the right below, *ABCD* is a straight line segment.

23. Why are ∠ *ABE* and *EBC* supplementary?

24. If *AB* = *CD*, why does *AB* + *BC* = *BC* + *CD*?

25. Why does *AB* + *BC* = *AC*? Why does *BC* + *CD* = *BD*?

26. If *AB* + *BC* = *BC* + *CD*, *AB* + *BC* = *AC*, and *BC* + *CD* = *BD*, why does *AC* = *BD*?

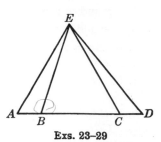

Exs. 23–29

27. Why is *AE* < *AB* + *BE*?

28. Why are ∠ *BCE* and *DCE* supplementary?

29. If ∠ *A* = ∠ *BCE* and ∠ *BCE* = 60°, why does ∠ *A* = 60°?

30. *OC* is a radius. Why?

31. If *OC* = 2 inches, why does *OB* = 2 inches?

32. If *OA* ⊥ *m* and *OD* is not ⊥ *m*, then *OA* < *OD*. Why?

33. Draw any line and label it *AB*. From *C*, any point in *AB*, draw *CD* ⊥ *AB*. Why does ∠ *ACD* = ∠ *BCD*? Why can you not draw another perpendicular to *AB* at *C*?

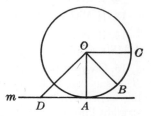

Exs. 30–32

In the figure, *AC* = *BC* and *CD* = *CE*.

34. Why does *AD* = *BE*?

35. If ∠*BAE*=∠*ABD* and ∠*EAD*=∠*DBE*, why does ∠ *BAC* = ∠ *ABC*?

36. If ∠*ABC*=∠*BAC*, ∠*ABD*=½ ∠*ABC*, and ∠*BAE*=½∠*BAC*, why is ∠*BAE*=∠*ABD*?

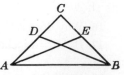

Exs. 34–39

37. If ∠ *CAB* = ∠ *CBA* and ∠ *EAB* = ∠ *DBA*, why does ∠ *CAE* = ∠ *CBD*?

38. If ∠ *CDB* = ∠ *CEA* and ∠ *CDA* = ∠ *CEB*, why does ∠ *ADB* = ∠ *AEB*?

39. If *CEB* is a straight line, why is ∠ *CEA* supplementary to ∠ *AEB*?

34. Proving Statements by Axioms, Postulates, and Definitions. In the preceding exercises conclusions were made and you were asked to tell the reasons for them. You will now learn how to draw your own conclusions and give a reason for each.

Example. See if you can complete the following proof:

Given figure $ABCDE$ with $AB \perp BD$ and $BC \perp BE$.

Prove that $\angle ABC = \angle DBE$.

Proof:

STATEMENTS	REASONS
1. $AB \perp$ __?__.	1. Why?
2. $EB \perp$ __?__.	2. Why?
3. $\angle ABD$ is a __?__ $\angle$.	3. Why?
4. $\angle CBE$ is a __?__ $\angle$.	4. Why?
5. $\angle ABD = \angle CBE$.	5. Why?
6. $\angle ABD = \angle ABC + \angle$ __?__.	6. Why?
7. $\angle CBE = \angle CBD + \angle$ __?__.	7. Why?
8. $\therefore \angle ABC + \angle CBD = \angle CBD + \angle$ __?__.	8. Why?
9. $\therefore \angle ABC = \angle DBE$.	9. Why?

Statement 1 is "$AB \perp BD$." Reason 1 is "Given." This word is used for the reason of a statement which repeats a given condition.

Statement 2 is "$EB \perp BC$" and its reason is "Given."

Statement 3 is "$\angle ABD$ is a rt. $\angle$." It follows from Statement 1, and its reason is "The equal adjacent angles which are formed by a line and its perpendicular are called right angles."

Statement 4 is "$\angle CBE$ is a rt. $\angle$." It follows from Statement 2, and its reason is the same as Reason 3.

Statement 5 is derived from Statements 3 and 4, and the reason for it is "All right angles are equal."

Statement 6 is "$\angle ABD = \angle ABC + \angle CBD$." Its reason is "The whole is equal to the sum of its parts."

Statement 7 is "$\angle CBE = \angle CBD + \angle DBE$." Its reason is the same as Reason 6.

Statement 8 is "$\angle ABC + \angle CBD = \angle CBD + \angle DBE$." It is obtained by substituting in Statement 5 the values of $\angle ABD$ and $\angle CBE$ given in Statements 6 and 7. The reason for Statement 8 is "A quantity may be substituted for its equal."

The reason for Statement 9 is Ax. 2.

EXERCISES [A]

1. Complete the following proof by supplying the reasons:

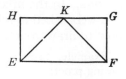

Given figure *EFGH* with *FG* ⊥ *KG*, and *EH* ⊥ *HK*.

To prove that ∠ *H* is supplementary to ∠ *G*.

Proof:

STATEMENTS	REASONS
1. *EH* ⊥ *HK*.	1. Why?
2. *FG* ⊥ *KG*.	2. Why?
3. ∠ *H* is a rt. ∠.	3. Why?
4. ∠ *G* is a rt. ∠.	4. Why?
5. ∠ *H* + ∠ *G* = 2 rt. ∡.	5. Why?
6. ∴ ∠ *H* + ∠ *G* = 1 st. ∠.	6. Why?
7. ∠ *H* is supp. to ∠ *G*.	7. Why?

2. Complete the following:

Given triangles *ABC* and *ABD* having ∠ *CAB* = ∠ *CBA* and ∠ *DAB* = ∠ *DBA*.

To prove that ∠ *CAD* = ∠ *CBD*.

Proof:

STATEMENTS	REASONS
1. ∠ *CAB* = __?__.	1. Why?
2. __?__ = ∠ *DBA*.	2. Why?
3. ∠ *CAB* − __?__ = __?__ − ∠ *DBA*.	3. Why?
4. ∠ *CAD* = ∠ *CBD*.	4. Why?

3. In the figure at the right, ∠ *m* = ∠ *n* and *AB* is a straight line. We are to prove that ∠ *x* = ∠ *y*. Complete the following proof by giving the reason for each statement:

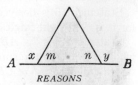

Proof:

STATEMENTS	REASONS
1. ∠ *x* + ∠ *m* = 1 st. ∠, or 180°.	1. Why?
2. ∠ *n* + ∠ *y* = 1 st. ∠, or 180°.	2. Why?
3. ∴ ∠ *x* + ∠ *m* = ∠ *n* + ∠ *y*.	3. Why?
4. But ∠ *m* = ∠ *n*.	4. Why?
5. ∴ ∠ *x* = ∠ *y*.	5. Why?

4. *Given AB and CD,* two lines intersecting at *O,* forming vertical angles *x* and *y.*

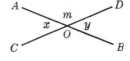

To prove that $\angle x = \angle y.$

Complete the following proof:

Proof:

STATEMENTS	REASONS
1. $\angle x + \angle m = 1$ st. $\angle$, or 2 rt. $\angle\!\!\!\angle$.	1. Why?
2. $\angle y + \angle m = $ __?__, or __?__ rt. $\angle\!\!\!\angle$.	2. Why?
3. $\therefore \angle x + \angle m = \angle y + \angle$ __?__.	3. Why?
4. $\therefore \angle x = \angle y.$	4. Why?

5. Draw line segment *ABCD* with $AB = CD.$ Prove that $AC = BD.$

Proof:

STATEMENTS	REASONS
1. $AB = CD.$	1. Why?
2. $AB + BC = BC + CD.$	2. Why?
3. $AB + BC = AC$ and $BC + CD = BD.$	3. Why?
4. $\therefore AC = BD.$	4. Why?

35. Making Proofs. In the preceding exercises, skeleton proofs were given and you were asked to complete the proofs. Now you will be asked to make proofs in full without any specific helps. Study the two examples below and then see if you can write the proofs to the exercises that follow.

Example 1. *Given* $\frac{2}{3} x = 6.$
Prove that $x = 9.$

Proof:

STATEMENTS	REASONS
1. $\frac{2}{3} x = 6.$	1. Given.
2. $2 x = 18.$	2. If equals are multiplied by equals, the products are equal.
3. $x = 9.$	3. If equals are divided by equals, the quotients are equal.

Notice that each of the statements in the proof above either is a repetition of what is given or is derived from a preceding statement.

Example 2. *Given* straight lines *AB*, *CD*, and *EF* with ∠ *x* = ∠ *y* and ∠ *z* = ∠ *y*. *Prove* that *EF* ⊥ *CD*.

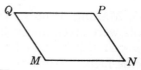

Proof:

STATEMENTS	REASONS
1. ∠ *x* = ∠ *y*.	1. Given.
2. ∠ *z* = ∠ *y*.	2. Given.
3. ∠ *x* = ∠ *z*.	3. Quantities equal to the same quantity are equal to each other.
4. *EF* ⊥ *CD*.	4. If two lines form equal adjacent angles, they are perpendicular.

EXERCISES [A]

1. *Given* $3x + 4 = 10$. *Prove* that $x = 2$.

2. *Given* $5a = 3a + 6$. *Prove* that $a = 3$.

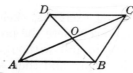

3. *Given* figure *ABCD* with *AC* and *BD* bisecting each other at *O*. *Prove* that $AO + OB = DO + OC$.

4. *Given* *MNPQ* with ∠ *M* + ∠ *N* = 180° and ∠ *N* + ∠ *P* = 180°. *Prove* that ∠ *M* = ∠ *P*.

36. Propositions. A *theorem* is a statement to be proved.

A *problem* is a geometric construction to be made or a computation to be performed.

A *proposition* (Prop.) is either a theorem or a construction problem.

An *exercise* in geometry may be a theorem, a problem, or a question.

37. Hypothesis and Conclusion. Every theorem can be expressed by a complex sentence which has one clause beginning with "if" and a second clause beginning with "then." The *if clause* contains the condition which *is given* or assumed to be true for the sake of argument, and the *then clause* states what is to be proved. The *if clause* is called the *hypothesis* and the *then clause* is called the *conclusion*.

Example 1. If equals are added to equals, then the sums are equal.

The hypothesis is "If equals are added to equals," and the conclusion is "then the sums are equal." The word "then" is usually omitted in a theorem.

Example 2. If I live in Ohio, I live in the United States.

The hypothesis is "If I live in Ohio," and the conclusion is "I live in the United States."

Some theorems are expressed by sentences which do not contain *if clauses*. In such cases the complete subject is the hypothesis.

Example 3. All right angles are equal.

The hypothesis is "All right angles," and the conclusion is that the angles "are equal." This example may be written, "If angles are right angles, then they are equal."

EXERCISES [A]

Tell which is the hypothesis and which is the conclusion in each of the following:

1. If air is heated, it will expand.

2. The boy who eats slowly will have little sickness.

3. Radio reception is best if the weather is clear.

4. If two straight lines intersect, the vertical angles are equal.

5. If two parallel lines are cut by a transversal, the corresponding angles are equal.

6. The diagonals of a rectangle are equal.

7. The acute angles of a right triangle are complementary.

8. If two sides of a triangle are unequal, the angles opposite these sides are unequal.

9. If the opposite sides of a quadrilateral are equal, the quadrilateral is a parallelogram.

10. If two lines are perpendicular to a third line, they are parallel.

11. Any two consecutive angles of a parallelogram are supplementary.

12. The opposite sides of a rectangle are equal.

13. If Elmer Smith lives in Chicago, he lives in Illinois.

14. Propositions I, II, III, and IV on pages 67, 74, 84, and 88.

38. Parts of a Formal Proof. When a proof is arranged in a definite order after a certain form, it is called a *formal proof*. A proof which does not follow a model form is *informal*. Most of the proofs in this text are formal.

Each *demonstration* of a formal proof consists of the following five parts in the order given:

I. A statement of the theorem.

II. The figure.

III. A statement of what is given.

IV. A statement of what is to be proved.

V. An orderly proof.

---

39. Theorem. The *theorem* is always stated as a complete sentence. Since the theorem may be used later to prove other theorems, it should be thoroughly understood and memorized.

40. Figure. The *figure* is a lettered drawing of the points, lines, angles, and other geometric figures which are described in the theorem.

41. Given. Under this title is a description of the figure as given by the hypothesis.

42. To Prove. Under this title is the conclusion of the theorem stated in terms of the figure.

43. Proof. The proof consists of a series of statements of the argument and the corresponding series of reasons. The statements consist of all the items listed under the word "given" and one or more applications of definitions, axioms, postulates, and theorems previously proved. For each statement of the proof there must be a reason. This reason must be one of the following: given; definition; axiom; postulate; theorem previously proved; identity; or construction.

44. How to Make a Formal Proof. We shall now illustrate how a formal proof is made.

I. We first state the theorem: *Complements of the same angle are equal.*

II. We determine the hypothesis, which is "Complements of the same angle." We draw the figure to represent the hypothesis by drawing ∠ x and ∠ y, which are complements of ∠ m.

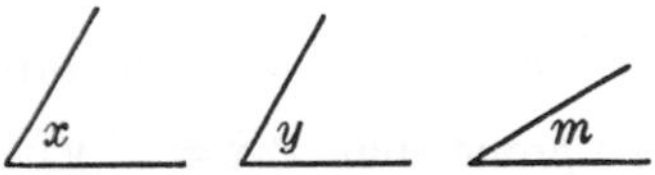

III. Under the word "Given" we describe the figure as given by the hypothesis. Thus "*Given ∡ x and y, each comp. to ∠ m.*"

IV. By referring to the conclusion, we state what relations in the figure we are to prove. Thus "*To prove that ∠ x = ∠ y.*"

V. Before attempting to give the proof of the theorem, we should first think it through. Since we are to prove two angles equal, we turn the pages we have studied to find methods of proving angles equal. Axs. 1 to 7 inclusive on pages 38 and 39 and Post. 9 on page 44 are possible methods of proving two angles equal. Since the sum of two complementary angles is a right angle and since all right angles are equal, we know that ∠ x + ∠ m = ∠ y + ∠ m. Inspection of this equation suggests the subtraction of ∠ m from each member. Performing this operation, we obtain ∠ x = ∠ y. We then write an orderly proof as follows:

Proof:

STATEMENTS	REASONS
1. ∠ x + ∠ m = 1 rt. ∠.	1. Given and def. comp. ∡.
2. ∠ y + ∠ m = 1 rt. ∠.	2. Given and def. comp. ∡.
3. ∴ ∠ x + ∠ m = ∠ y + ∠ m.	3. Post. 9 and Ax. 6. (Quantities = the same or = quantities = each other.)
4. ∴ ∠ x = ∠ y.	4. Ax. 2. (If equals are subtracted from equals, remainders are =.)

The formal demonstration of the theorem discussed in full on page 53 is given below.

45. Theorem. *Complements of the same angle are equal.*

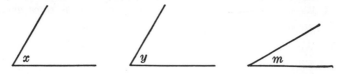

Given ∠s *x* and *y*, each comp. to ∠ *m*.

To prove that ∠ *x* = ∠ *y*.

Selection of Method: 1. Known methods of proving ∠s =: § 31, Axs. 1–7 inclusive, and § 33, Post. 9.
   2. Method to be used: Post. 9; Axs. 2 and 6.

Proof: STATEMENTS   REASONS

STATEMENTS	REASONS
1. ∠ *x* + ∠ *m* = 1 rt. ∠.	1. Given and def.
2. ∠ *y* + ∠ *m* = 1 rt. ∠.	2. Given and def.
3. ∴ ∠ *x* + ∠ *m* = ∠ *y* + ∠ *m*.	3. Post. 9 and Ax. 6. (Quantities = the same or = quantities = each other.)
4. ∴ ∠ *x* = ∠ *y*.	4. Ax. 2. (If equals are subtracted from equals, the remainders are =.)

46. Theorem. *Complements of equal angles are equal.*

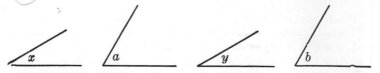

Given ∠ *x* comp. to ∠ *a*, ∠ *y* comp. to ∠ *b*, and ∠ *a* = ∠ *b*.

To prove that ∠ *x* = ∠ *y*.

(The student should select the method of proof and supply a formal proof.)

47. Theorem. *Supplements of the same angle are equal.*

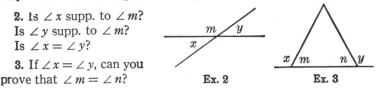

Given ∡ *x* and *y*, each supp. to ∠ *a*.

To prove that ∠ *x* = ∠ *y*.

Selection of Method: 1. Known methods of proving ∡ =: § 31, Axs. 1–7 inclusive; § 33, Post. 9; §§ 45, 46.
2. Method to be used: Post. 9; Axs. 2 and 6.

Proof: STATEMENTS	REASONS
1. ∠ *x* + ∠ *a* = 1 st. ∠.	1. Given and def.
2. ∠ *y* + ∠ *a* = 1 st. ∠.	2. Given and def.
3. ∴ ∠ *x* + ∠ *a* = ∠ *y* + ∠ *a*.	3. Post. 9; Ax. 6. (Quantities = the same or = quantities = each other.)
4. ∴ ∠ *x* = ∠ *y*.	4. Ax. 2. (If equals are subtracted from equals, the remainders are =.)

48. Theorem. *Supplements of equal angles are equal.*
(The demonstration is left to the student.)

EXERCISES [A]

1. If ∠ *x* is complementary to a 40° angle and ∠ *y* is complementary to another 40° angle, what do you know about ∡ *x* and *y*?

2. Is ∠ *x* supp. to ∠ *m*?
Is ∠ *y* supp. to ∠ *m*?
Is ∠ *x* = ∠ *y*?

3. If ∠ *x* = ∠ *y*, can you prove that ∠ *m* = ∠ *n*?

Ex. 2   Ex. 3

The proposition on the next page is written in full as a model.

In studying a theorem, first determine the hypothesis and see that the "Figure" and "Given" are correct. Then determine the conclusion and see that the "To prove" is correct.

★Proposition. Theorem

49. *If two lines intersect, the vertical angles are equal.*

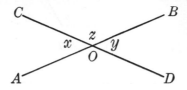

Given the lines AB and CD intersecting at O, forming the $\measuredangle$ x, z, and y.

To prove that $\angle x = \angle y$.

Selection of Method: 1. Known methods of proving $\measuredangle =$: Post. 9; §§ 31, 45, 46, 47, and 48.
2. Method to be used: § 47.

Proof:

STATEMENTS	REASONS
1. AB is a st. line.	1. Given.
2. ∴ $\angle x$ is a supplement of $\angle z$.	2. Post. 14. (If two adjacent $\measuredangle$ have their exterior sides in a st. line, they are supp.)
3. CD is a st. line.	3. Given.
4. ∴ $\angle y$ is a supplement of $\angle z$.	4. Reason 2.
5. ∴ $\angle x = \angle y$.	5. § 47. (Supplements of the same $\angle$ are =.)

NOTE. According to Eudemus, a Greek who lived before the time of Euclid, this proposition was discovered by Thales (640–546 B.C.).

EXERCISES. VERTICAL ANGLES

A

In each exercise state the reason for each conclusion:

1. If $\angle x = 60°$, how many degrees are in $\angle y$? in $\angle m$? in $\angle n$?

2. If $\angle n = 115°$, how many degrees are in $\angle m$? in $\angle x$? in $\angle y$?

Exs. 1–5

3. If $\angle y = 20° 30'$, in the figure at the foot of page 56, what is the size of each of the other angles?

4. If $\angle x = a°$, how many degrees are there in $\angle y$? $\angle m$? $\angle n$?

5. How many degrees are there in each of the four angles (*a*) if $\angle x = \angle m$? (*b*) if $\angle m = 2 \angle x$? (*c*) if $\angle m = 3 \angle x$?

6. In the adjoining figure,

Given $\angle s = \angle t.$

To prove that $\angle r = \angle u.$

Proof: STATEMENTS   REASONS

1. $\angle r = \angle s.$	1. Why?
2. $\angle u = \angle t.$	2. Why?
3. $\angle s = \angle t.$	3. Why? *Given*
4. ∴ $\angle r = \angle u.$ — Ax. 6.	4. Why?

B

7. If $\angle x = (2 a^2 - 3 a + 8)$ degrees in the figure for Exs. 1–5, find the number of degrees in each of the three remaining angles.

8. In the adjoining figure, find the number of degrees in each of the four angles.

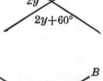

C

9. Prove that the bisector of one of two vertical angles bisects the other.

Given line EF bisecting $\angle DOB.$

Prove that EF bisects $\angle AOC.$

SUGGESTION. What two angles are equal by hypothesis?

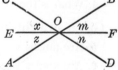

ORAL EXERCISES IN REASONING

In everyday reasoning people make use of implied assumptions. On what assumptions are the following exercises based?

1. Two or more people in the world have the same number of hairs on their heads.

2. I live under a democratic form of government and can worship where I please and in any way I please.

3. Frank Nesbit will be sixty-five years old tomorrow. He should be retired on a pension.

4. In a certain state one must be 18 years old before he can secure an automobile driver's license.

5. One paint company used this slogan: "Don't paint your house every two years. Use Luster Paint."

6. Helen will not study plane geometry next year because she does not intend to go to college.

7. We do not feed potatoes to our dog.

8. We painted our house four years ago; so we shall have to paint it again this year.

9. The teacher said to Harriet, "You cannot take five full credit subjects next semester, since you did not make the honor roll this semester."

10. Mr. Reynolds, the sales manager of the Bloomfield Department Store, always instructs his salesmen to avoid arguments with their customers

REVIEW QUESTIONS

1. How many bisectors may an angle have?

2. What is the sum of all the angles about a point on one side of a straight line?

3. What is the "if" clause of a theorem called?

4. What is the "then" clause of a theorem called?

Given straight lines AB and CD in the diagram below.

5. Are angles x and y supplementary?

6. Are angles y and w vertical?

7. Are angles x and z complementary?

8. What kind of angles are w and z?

9. Are angles m and n adjacent angles?

10. Are angles n and s vertical angles?

11. What should follow each statement in a proof?

12. How does a theorem differ from a problem?

Exs. 5–8

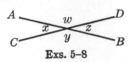

Exs. 9, 10

13. What are the two parts of a theorem?

14. Do equal circles have equal radii?

15. Are supplementary angles equal?

16. Do we prove axioms? postulates? definitions? theorems?

17. How many degrees does an angle 9 times its supplement contain?

18. What parts of a demonstration are obtained from the hypothesis? from the conclusion?

19. How many midpoints does a line segment have?

20. How many perpendiculars may be drawn to a line at a point in the line?

21. What is the sum of all the angles about a point?

22. What relation do two adjacent angles have if their exterior sides form a straight line?

23. What name is given to the shortest line segment that can be drawn from a point to a line?

24. How many circles can be drawn with a given point A as center and a given distance r as radius?

25. What do we know about the exterior sides of two supplementary adjacent angles?

SUMMARY OF PRINCIPAL METHODS OF PROOF

50. *Two angles are equal*

a. If they are right angles.
b. If they are complements of the same angle or of equal angles.
c. If they are supplements of the same angle or of equal angles.
d. If they are vertical angles.
e. By the use of axioms.
f. By superposition.

51. *Two lines are perpendicular*

a. If they form a right angle, or equal adjacent angles, with each other.
b. If one is the shortest line segment that can be drawn from a given point to the other line.

52. *Two angles are complementary*

a. If their sum is a right angle.

53. *Two angles are supplementary*

a. If their sum is a straight angle.

b. If they are adjacent angles having their exterior sides in a straight line.

WORD LIST

At this time you should be able to spell and know the meaning of each of the following words:

axiom	demonstration	intersect	quotient
bisector	exterior	postulate	theorem
complement	figure	problem	triangle
conclusion	hypothesis	proof	vertical
deductive	inductive	proposition	vertices

TEST 2

Completing Statements (*Eight Minutes*)

On your paper write one word or number, and only one, for each blank to make the following statements true:

1. If equals are added to equals, the sums are _ _ ? _ _.

2. Supplementary angles are two angles whose sum is _ _ ? _ _ degrees.

3. Only one straight line can be drawn through _ _ ? _ _ _ _ ? _ _.

4. The "if clause" of a theorem is called the _ _ ? _ _.

5. The "then clause" of a theorem is called the _ _ ? _ _.

6. ∠ *a* and ∠ *b* are supplementary _ _ ? _ _ angles.

7. ∠ *a* and ∠ *c* are _ _ ? _ _ angles.

8. ∠ *b* and ∠ *d* are _ _ ? _ _ angles.

9. *DB* is _ _ ? _ _ to *AC*.

10. *B* is the _ _ ? _ _ of the perpendicular *DB*.

11. *AC* is _ _ ? _ _ to *BD* at *B*.

12. ∠ *DBC* is a _ _ ? _ _ angle.

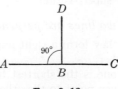

Exs. 9–12

TEST 3

Supplying Reasons (*Twenty Minutes*)

Supply the necessary axioms, postulates, definitions, or theorems as reasons for the following statements:

1. If $4x = 36$, then $x = 9$.

2. If $x + y = 72$ and $2x - y = 36$, then $3x = 108$.

3. If $6x + y = 15$ and $3x + y = 9$, then $3x = 6$.

4. If $\dfrac{a}{b} = \dfrac{c}{d}$, then $a = \dfrac{bc}{d}$. **5.** If $x = a$ and $y = a$, then $x = y$.

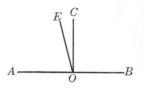

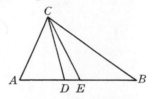

6. If $\angle AOC = \angle BOC$, then $CO \perp AB$.

8. If CE bisects AB, then DC does not bisect AB.

7. If $CO \perp AB$, then EO is not $\perp AB$.

9. If DC bisects $\angle ACB$, then CE does not bisect $\angle ACB$.

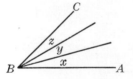

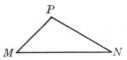

10. $\angle ABC = \angle x + \angle y + \angle z$. **11.** $MN < MP + PN$.

12. If $\angle m = \angle r + \angle t$ and $\angle r = \angle t$, then $\angle m = \angle t + \angle t$.

13. If $\frac{1}{7}x = 15$, then $x = 105$. **15.** If $x^2 = 25$, then $x = \pm 5$.

14. If $3x - 7 = 10$, then $3x = 17$. **16.** If $y = 4$, then $y^2 = 16$.

17. If $\angle y$ is the complement of $\angle x$ and of $\angle y$, then $\angle x = \angle y$.

18. If $\angle x = \angle a$, $\angle y = \angle b$, and $\angle x = \angle y$, then $\angle a = \angle b$.

19. If $\angle r + \angle m = 1$ straight angle, $\angle n + \angle s = 1$ straight angle, and $\angle m = \angle n$, then $\angle r = \angle s$.

20. If $AC = BD$, then $AB = CD$. $A\!\!-\!\!\overset{B}{\bullet}\!\!-\!\!-\!\!-\!\!-\!\!\overset{C}{\bullet}\!\!-\!\!-D$

*The George Washington Bridge over the Hudson River at New York City
Is a Fine Example of the Application of the Triangle in Engineering*

CHAPTER III

Triangles

Because of its wide application in art, architecture, and engineering, the triangle is probably the most important figure studied in plane geometry. Since the shape of a triangle cannot be altered without changing the length of a side, it is used to give rigidity in nearly all constructions.

In the picture opposite, notice how the towers of the bridge are made rigid by triangular bracing.

54. Polygon. A *polygon* is a closed broken line. The line segments AB, BC, CD, DE, and EA are the *sides* of the polygon $ABCDE$. The points A, B, C, D, and E are the vertices of the polygon, and ∢ A, B, C, D, and E are the angles of the polygon. $\angle A$ and $\angle B$ are *consecutive angles*; $\angle B$ and $\angle C$ are consecutive angles; etc. Sides 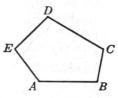 AB and BC are *adjacent* sides; and sides BC and CD are adjacent sides.

A *triangle* (△) is a polygon having three sides. Every triangle has six parts, three sides and three angles. Two sides always *include* an angle, and two angles always *include* a side. The *perimeter* of a triangle is the sum of the three sides. The *base* of a triangle is the side upon which the triangle is supposed to stand. Any side of a triangle may be taken as the base. The *vertex angle* is the angle opposite the base, and the vertex of this angle is often called the *vertex* of the triangle. Thus in the figure, AB may be considered the base, ACB the vertex angle (opposite AB), and C the vertex of the triangle ABC.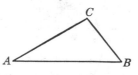

55. *a*. Triangles Classified as to Sides.

A *scalene triangle* is a triangle having *no two* sides equal.

An *isosceles triangle* is a triangle having *two* sides equal.

An *equilateral triangle* is a triangle having *all three* sides equal.

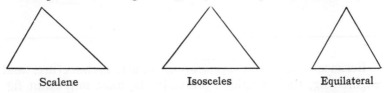

Scalene   Isosceles   Equilateral

In an isosceles triangle, the two equal sides are usually considered as including the vertex angle, and the third side is considered the base. Are all equilateral triangles isosceles? Why? Are all isosceles triangles equilateral? Why?

b. Triangles Classified as to Angles.

An *acute triangle* is a triangle having *all three* angles acute.

An *equiangular triangle* is a triangle having *all three* angles equal.

A *right triangle* is a triangle having *one* right angle.

An *obtuse triangle* is a triangle having *one* obtuse angle.

An *oblique triangle* is a triangle that does not contain a right angle.

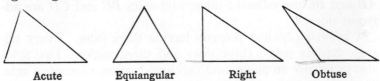

Acute   Equiangular   Right   Obtuse

ORAL EXERCISES

1. Which, if any, of the triangles shown below are scalene? isosceles? equilateral?

2. Which are right triangles? acute? oblique? equiangular?

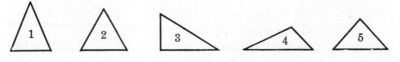

56. Included Sides and Included Angles. In △ ABC, ∠ A is included by the sides AB and AC; ∠ B is included by the sides AB and BC; and ∠ C is included by the sides AC and BC. The side AB is included by ∠ A and ∠ B; the side BC is included by ∠ B and ∠ C; and the side AC is included by ∠ A and ∠ C. The word *included* means "confined" or "enclosed."

57. Parts of a Right Triangle. In a right triangle the sides including the right angle are often called the *legs* and the side opposite the right angle is called the *hypotenuse*. In △ DEF, EF is the hypotenuse and DF and DE are the legs.

ORAL EXERCISES

1. In △ ABC, ∠ ACB, ∠ CDB, and ∠ ADC are right angles. Name the legs and the hypotenuse of △ ABC; of △ ADC; of △ DBC.

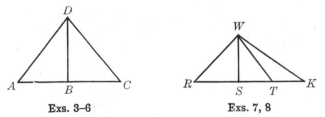

2. In △ RST, what sides include ∠ R? ∠ S? ∠ T? What angles include side RS? side ST? side RT?

3. In △ ABD what angles include side AB? side AD? side BD?

4. In △ ABD what sides include ∠ A? ∠ ABD? ∠ ADB?

Exs. 3–6   Exs. 7, 8

5. In △ BCD what side is included by ∠ DBC and ∠ BCD?

6. In △ ACD what angles include side AC? side AD?

7. In △ SWK what side is included by ∠ WSK and ∠ K?

8. In △ RTW what sides include ∠ R? ∠ RWT?

58. Congruent Figures. In § 20 we learned that geometric figures are congruent ($\cong$) if they can be made to coincide. It follows that congruent figures have the same size and shape.

EXERCISES [A]. CONGRUENT FIGURES

1. Name the pairs of figures above which seem to be congruent Test each conclusion by tracing one of the figures on thin paper and applying the tracing to the other figure.

2. Draw two triangles which have the same shape but are not congruent. Can you draw two triangles which have about the same area but not the same shape?

3. If two circles have equal radii, are they congruent?

4. Are two squares congruent if their sides have the same length?

5. If two automobile parts are made from the same mold, are they congruent?

6. Name some articles in your home that seem to be congruent.

7. In $\triangle ABC$ and DEF, $AB = DE$, $AC = DF$, and $\angle A = \angle D$. Trace each triangle on thin paper. Then cut out your tracings and place one on the other so that the point A falls on the point D and AC falls along DF. Can AB be made to fall on DE? Will C fall on F? Will B fall on E? Will the triangles coincide? Would they coincide if $\angle A$ were less than $\angle D$? Is $\angle B = \angle E$? Why? Is $CB = FE$? Why?

59. Proof by Superposition. A few theorems of geometry are proved by imagining one figure placed on another and reasoning that the figures coincide. This imaginary placing of one figure on another is called *superposition*. On the next page two triangles are proved congruent by superposition.

★★ Proposition I. Theorem*

60. *If two triangles have two sides and the included angle of one equal respectively to two sides and the included angle of the other, the triangles are congruent.* (S.A.S.)

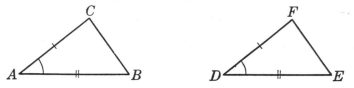

Given the △ *ABC* and *DEF* with *AC = DF, AB = DE,* and ∠ *A* = ∠ *D.*

To prove that △ *ABC* ≅ △ *DEF.*

Selection of Method: 1. Known methods of proving △ ≅: § 58.
2. Method to be used: § 58.

Proof: *STATEMENTS*   *REASONS*

STATEMENTS	REASONS
1. ∠ *A* = ∠ *D.*	1. Given.
2. Place △ *ABC* on △ *DEF* so that ∠ *A* coincides with ∠ *D,* *AC* falling along *DF* and *AB* along *DE.*	2. Post. 6 (any geometric figure can be moved without changing its size or shape); § 9 (two = △ can be made to coincide).
3. *AC = DF.*	3. Given.
4. ∴ point *C* will fall on point *F.*	4. § 7. (Two = line segments can be made to coincide.)
5. *AB = DE.*	5. Given.
6. ∴ point *B* will fall on point *E.*	6. Reason 4.
7. ∴ *BC* coincides with *EF.*	7. Post. 1. (One st. line, and only one, can be drawn through two points.)
8. ∴ △ *ABC* ≅ △ *DEF.*	8. § 58. (Geometric figures that can be made to coincide are ≅.)

*Many teachers postulate Props. I and II.

61. How to Use Proposition I. Since Prop. I has been established by proof, we can now state that any two triangles are congruent, and give Prop. I as the reason, when we can show that two sides and the included angle of one triangle are equal respectively to two sides and the included angle of the other.

Example 1. *Given* △ *ABC and* △ *DEF with* $AC = DF$, $BC = EF$, *and* ∠C = ∠F. Can Prop. I be used to prove that △ *ABC* ≅ △ *DEF*?

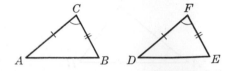

Solution. Since $AC = DF$, $BC = EF$, ∠C = ∠F, ∠C is included by AC and BC, and ∠F is included by DF and EF, Prop. I tells us that the triangles are congruent.

Example 2. *Given* △ *EDF and* △ *RST, with* $ED = RS$, $DF = TR$, *and* ∠D = ∠T. *Is* △ *DEF* ≅ △ *TRS by Prop. I?*

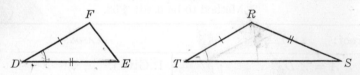

Solution. The two triangles have two sides and an angle of one equal to two sides and an angle of the other but ∠T is not included by RT and RS. Then Prop. I does not tell us that △ *DEF* ≅ △ *TRS*.

EXERCISES [A]

1. *Given* △ *ABC* and △ *DEF*, $AC = EF$, $CB = DF$, and ∠C = ∠F. Does Prop. I tell us that △ *ABC* ≅ △ *EDF*?*

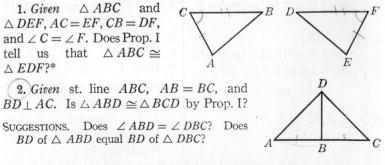

2. *Given* st. line *ABC*, $AB = BC$, and $BD ⊥ AC$. Is △ *ABD* ≅ △ *BCD* by Prop. I?

SUGGESTIONS. Does ∠ABD = ∠DBC? Does *BD* of △ *ABD* equal *BD* of △ *DBC*?

*Copy the triangles and mark the equal parts as was done in the Examples.

3. *Given* figure *ABCDE*, *AB* = *BC*, and ∠*E* = ∠*D*. By Prop. I, is △ *ABE* ≅ △ *BCD*?

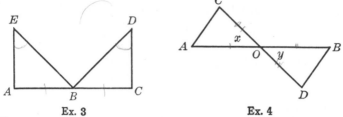

Ex. 3   Ex. 4

4. *Given* st. lines *AB* and *CD*, *AO* = *OB*, and *CO* = *OD*. What do you know about ∠*x* and ∠*y*? By Prop. I, is △ *AOC* ≅ △ *BOD*?

5. *Given* figure *ADBC* with ∠*CAB* = ∠*DAB* and ∠*CBA* = ∠*DBA*. Is △ *ABC* ≅ △ *ABD* by Prop. I?

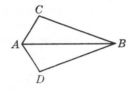

How Is the Principle of Congruence Applied in Garment Making?

62. Overlapping Triangles. Overlapping triangles are often confusing to the eye and as a result the relations between the triangles are obscured. Let us consider an example.

Given △ ABC with AD = BE and ∠ DAB = ∠ EBA. Is △ ABD ≅ △ ABE?

The triangles ABD and ABE overlap each other. They may be made to stand out by tracing them with colored crayon. For example, △ ABD could be red and △ ABE could be blue; or you could make AD and BE red, AE and BD blue, and AB yellow.

Another method of aiding the eye to visual- ize the triangles is to draw the triangles sepa- rately as shown below. By this method it is not difficult to see that the two triangles are congruent.

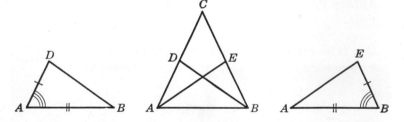

1. *Given* the figure EFGHK, st. line EK = HK, ∠ E = ∠ H, and EF = GH. Does EG = FH? Does Prop. I tell us that △ EGK ≅ △ FHK?

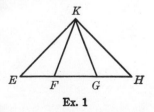

Ex. 1

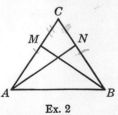

Ex. 2

2. *Given* △ ABC with AC = BC and CM = CN. Does Prop. I tell us that △ ACN ≅ BCM?

63. Corollary. A theorem that is derived from another theorem or a postulate with little or no proof is a *corollary*. The proof of the following corollary is written in full as a model. Notice especially the five parts of the demonstration—the *statement of the corollary,* the *figure, Given, To prove,* and *Proof.*

64. Corollary to Proposition I. *If two right triangles have the two legs of one equal respectively to the two legs of the other, the triangles are congruent.*

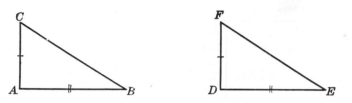

Given the two rt. ⩟ *ABC* and *DEF* with *AC = DF, AB = DE,* and ⩟ *A* and *D* the rt. ⩟.

To prove that △ *ABC* ≅ △ *DEF.*

Proof: *STATEMENTS*

STATEMENTS	*REASONS*
1. *AC = DF.*	1. Given.
2. *AB = DE.*	2. Given.
3. ∠ *A* and ∠ *D* are rt. ⩟.	3. Given.
4. ∠ *A* = ∠ *D.*	4. All rt. ⩟ are =.
5. ∴△ *ABC* ≅ △ *DEF.*	5. If two ⩟ have two sides and the included ∠ of one = respectively to two sides and the included ∠ of the other, the ⩟ are ≅.

65. Proof of a Corollary. A corollary is proved by showing that the hypothesis of the corollary is a special case of the hypothesis of the theorem, postulate, or other corollary which immediately precedes it. The steps needed to show that the theorem applies to the corollary are usually evident.

66. Applications of Proposition I and Corollary in § 64.

Example 1.

Given the st. lines AB and CD with $CO = OD$ and $AO = OB$.

To prove that $\triangle AOC \cong \triangle BOD$.

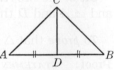

Selection of Method: 1. Known methods of proving $\triangle$ $\cong$: §§ 58, 60, 64.
   2. Method to be used: § 60.

Proof: STATEMENTS   REASONS

1. $CO = OD$.	1. Given.
2. $AO = OB$.	2. Given.
3. $\angle x = \angle y$.	3. Vertical $\angle$ are $=$.
4. $\therefore \triangle AOC \cong \triangle BOD$.	4. If two $\triangle$ have two sides and the included $\angle$ of one $=$ respectively to two sides and the included $\angle$ of the other, the $\triangle$ are $\cong$.

Example 2.

Given D, the midpoint of AB, and $CD \perp AB$.

To prove that $\triangle ADC \cong \triangle DBC$.

Selection of Method: 1. Known methods of proving $\triangle$ $\cong$: §§ 58, 60, 64.
   2. Method to be used: § 64.

Proof: STATEMENTS   REASONS

1. $CD \perp AB$.	1. Given.
2. $\angle ADC$ and BDC are rt. $\angle$.	2. The equal adjacent $\angle$ which are formed by a line and its perpendicular are rt. $\angle$.
3. $\triangle ADC$ and DBC are rt. $\triangle$.	3. Definition of a rt. $\triangle$.
4. $AD = DB$.	4. Given.
5. $CD = CD$.	5. Identity (that is, the same).
6. $\therefore \triangle ADC \cong \triangle DBC$.	6. If two rt. $\triangle$ have the two legs of one $=$ respectively to the two legs of the other, the $\triangle$ are $\cong$.

NOTE. In proving exercises the student should form the habit of indicating in the figure the parts which are given equal. Why?

EXERCISES. TRIANGLES CONGRUENT

A

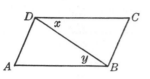

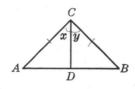

1. *Given* figure *ABCD* with *AB* = *DC* and ∠ *x* = ∠ *y*.
Prove that △ *ABD* ≅ △ *BCD*.

2. *Given* the isos. △ *ABC* with *AC* = *BC* and *CD* bisecting ∠ *ACB*.
Prove that △ *ADC* ≅ △ *DBC*.

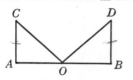

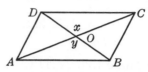

3. *Given* *CA* ⊥ *AB*, *DB* ⊥ *AB*, *CA* = *DB* and *AO* = *OB*.
Prove that △ *AOC* ≅ △ *OBD*.

4. *Given* the st. lines *AC* and *DB* with *AO* = *OC* and *DO* = *OB*.
Prove that △ *AOB* ≅ △ *DOC*.

B

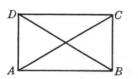

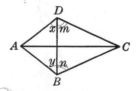

5. *Given* *AD* ⊥ *AB*, *CB* ⊥ *AB*, and *AD* = *CB*.
Prove that △ *ABD* ≅ △ *ABC*.

6. *Given* *AB* = *AD*, *BC* = *DC*, ∠ *x* = ∠ *y*, and ∠ *m* = ∠ *n*.
Prove that △ *ADC* ≅ △ *ABC*.

C

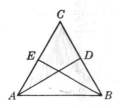

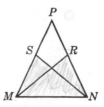

7. *Given* *AC* = *CB*, *E* the midpoint of *AC*, and *D* the midpoint of *CB*.
Prove that △ *ADC* ≅ △ *BEC*.

8. *Given* △ *MNP* with *MR* = *NS*, ∠ *MNP* = ∠ *NMP*, and ∠ *RMP* = ∠ *SNP*.
Prove that △ *MNR* ≅ △ *NMS*.

★★ Proposition II. Theorem

67. *If two triangles have two angles and the included side of one equal respectively to two angles and the included side of the other, the triangles are congruent.* (A.S.A.)

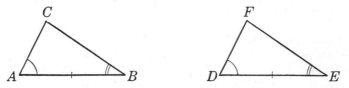

Given the △ *ABC* and *DEF* with ∠ *A* = ∠ *D*, ∠ *B* = ∠ *E*, and *AB* = *DE*.

To prove that △ *ABC* ≅ △ *DEF*.

Selection of Method: 1. Known methods of proving △ ≅: §§ 58, 60, 64.
 2. Method to be used: § 58.

Proof: *STATEMENTS*   *REASONS*

STATEMENTS	REASONS
1. *AB* = *DE*.	1. Given.
2. Place △ *ABC* on △ *DEF* so that *AB* coincides with *DE* and the point *C* falls on the same side of *DE* as the point *F*.	2. Post. 6. (Any geometric figure can be moved without changing its size or shape.) § 7. (Two = line segments can be made to coincide.)
3. ∠ *A* = ∠ *D*.	3. Given.
4. ∴ *AC* will fall along *DF*.	4. § 9. (Two = ∠ can be made to coincide.)
5. ∠ *B* = ∠ *E*.	5. Given.
6. ∴ *BC* will fall along *EF*.	6. Reason 4.
7. ∴ point *C* falls on point *F*.	7. Post. 2. (Two st. lines cannot intersect in more than one point.)
8. ∴ △ *ABC* ≅ △ *DEF*.	8. § 58. (Geometric figures that can be made to coincide are ≅.)

EXERCISES. TRIANGLES CONGRUENT

A

Use § 67 in proving the following exercises:

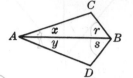

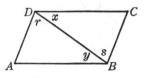

1. *Given* figure *ADBC* with ∠ *x* = ∠ *y* and ∠ *r* = ∠ *s*.
Prove that △ *ABC* ≅ △ *ADB*.

2. *Given* figure *ABCD* with ∠ *x* = ∠ *y* and ∠ *r* = ∠ *s*.
Prove that △ *ABD* ≅ △ *DBC*.

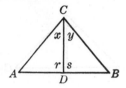

3. *Given* △ *ABC* with *CD* bisecting ∠ *ACB* and ⊥ *AB*.
Prove that △ *ADC* ≅ △ *DBC*.

B

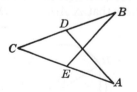

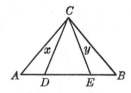

4. *Given* *AB* ⊥ *BC*, *CD* ⊥ *BC*, and *O* the midpoint of *BC*.
Prove that △ *AOB* ≅ △ *CDO*.

5. *Given* ∠ *A* = ∠ *B*, *AC* = *BC*, and ∠ *x* = ∠ *y*.
Prove that △ *ADC* ≅ △ *EBC*.

C

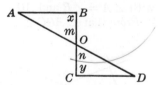

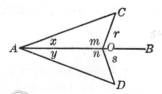

6. *Given* ∠ *A* = ∠ *B*, *AC* = *BC*.
Prove that △ *CEB* ≅ △ *CAD*.

7. *Given* *AOB* a st. line, ∠ *x* = ∠ *y*, and ∠ *r* = ∠ *s*.
Prove that △ *AOC* ≅ △ *AOD*.

ADDITIONAL EXERCISES ON CONGRUENT TRIANGLES

A

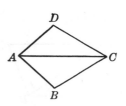

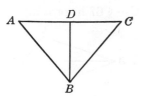

1. *Given* figure *ABCD* with *AC* bisecting ∠ *BAD* and *AB = AD*.
Prove that △ *ABC* ≅ △ *ADC*.

2. *Given* △ *ABC* with *BD* ⊥ *AC* and *AD = DC*.
Prove that △ *ADB* ≅ △ *CDB*.

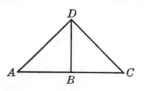

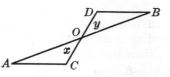

3. *Given* △ *ACD* with *DB* ⊥ *AC*, ∠ *A* = ∠ *C*, and *AB = BC*.
Prove that △ *ABD* ≅ △ *CBD*.

4. *Given* st. lines *AB* and *CD* with ∠ *A* = ∠ *B* and *AO = OB*.
Prove that △ *AOC* ≅ △ *BOD*.

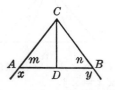

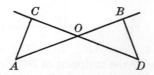

5. *Given* figure *ABC* with *AC* = *BC*, *AD = DB*, and ∠ *x* = ∠ *y*.
Prove that △ *ADC* ≅ △ *BDC*.

6. *Given* st. lines *AB* and *CD*, *AC* ⊥ *CD*, *DB* ⊥ *AB*, and *CO = OB*.
Prove that △ *AOC* ≅ △ *DOB*.

B

7. *Given* circle *ACD*, center *O*, ∠ *AOB* = ∠ *COD*, and line segments *AB* and *CD*.
Prove that △ *AOB* ≅ △ *COD*.

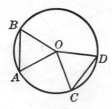

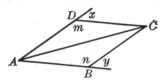

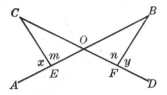

8. *Given* figure *ABCD*, *AB* = *BC* = *CD* = *DA*, and ∠ *x* = ∠ *y*. *Prove* that △ *ABC* ≅ △ *ADC*.

9. *Given* st. lines *AB* and *CD* intersecting at *O*, *EO* = *OF*, and ∠ *x* = ∠ *y*.
Prove that △ *CEO* ≅ △ *BFO*.

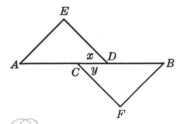

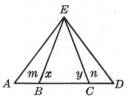

10. *Given* *ACDB* a st. line, *AC*=*DB*, ∠*A*=∠*B*, and ∠*x*=∠*y*.
Prove that △ *ADE* ≅ △ *BCF*.

11. *Given* △ *ADE*, *AC* = *BD*, *BE* = *EC*, and ∠ *x* = ∠ *y*.
Prove that △ *ABE* ≅ △ *DCE*.

C

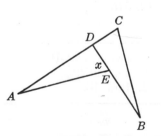

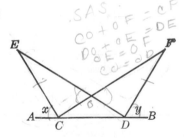

12. *Given* *DEB* a st. line, *BD* ∟ *AC*, *CD* = *DE*, and ∠ *x* = ∠ *C*.
Prove that △ *ADE* ≅ △ *BDC*.

13. *Given* *ACDB* a st. line, *CE* = *DF*, and ∠ *x* = ∠ *y*.
Prove that △ *CDE* ≅ △ *DCF*.

14. *Given* figure *ACB* with *AC* = *BC* and *AD* = *BE*.
Prove that △ *AEC* ≅ △ *BDC*.

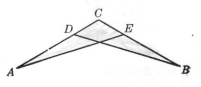

68. Corresponding Parts of Congruent Triangles. *Corresponding* (corr.) *parts* of two congruent triangles are the parts which coincide if the two triangles are made to coincide. In two congruent triangles the parts that are known to be equal are always corresponding parts, and the parts lying opposite these parts are also corresponding parts.

Thus if $AB = DE$, $\angle A = \angle D$, and $\angle B = \angle E$, the two triangles are congruent. Then $\angle C$, lying opposite AB, corresponds to $\angle F$, lying opposite DE; also AC, lying opposite $\angle B$, corresponds to DF, lying opposite $\angle E$, and, similarly, BC corresponds to EF. Does $\angle A$ correspond to $\angle D$?

69. Post. 18. *Corresponding parts of congruent polygons are equal; polygons are congruent if their corresponding parts are equal.*

This postulate is often used in proving two line segments equal or two angles equal.

Example.

Given D, the midpoint of AB and $CD \perp AB$.

To prove that $\angle A = \angle B$.

Selection of Method: 1. Known methods of proving ⧍ =: Posts. 9 and 18, §§ 31, 45, 46, 47, 48, and 49.
2. Method to be used: Post. 18.

Proof:

STATEMENTS	REASONS
1. ⧍ *ADC* and *CDB* are rt. ⧍.	1. Given.
2. ∴ ⧍ *ADC* and *CDB* are rt. ⧍.	2. Def. of a rt. △.
3. $AD = DB$.	3. Given.
4. $CD = CD$.	4. Iden.
5. Rt. $\triangle ADC \cong$ rt. $\triangle CDB$.	5. If two rt. ⧍ have the two legs of one = respectively to the two legs of the other, the ⧍ are ≅.
6. ∴ $\angle A = \angle B$.	6. Corr. parts of ≅ ⧍ are =.

EXERCISES. LINE SEGMENTS, ANGLES

A

1. State the two methods we have had of proving triangles congruent. State three methods of proving right triangles congruent.

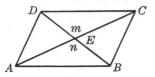

2. *Given* the st. lines *AC* and *DB* with *DE* = *EB* and *AE* = *EC*. *Prove* that *DC* = *AB*.

4. *Given* △ *ABC* with *CD* bisecting *AB* at *D* and forming = ∠ *m* and *n*. *Prove* that *AC* = *BC*.

3. *Given* the st. lines *BC* and *DA* with *DO* = *OA* and *BO* = *OC.* *Prove* that ∠ *D* = ∠ *A*.

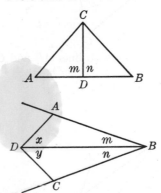

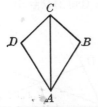

5. *Given AC* bisecting ∠ *BCD* and *BAD*. *Prove* that ∠ *B* = ∠ *D*.

6. *Given* figure *ADCB* with *AD* = *DC* and ∠ *x* = ∠ *y*. *Prove* that ∠ *m* = ∠ *n*.

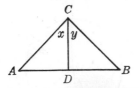

7. *Given* △ *ABC* with *CD* bisecting ∠ *ACB* and *AC* = *BC*. *Prove* that *CD* ⊥ *AB*.

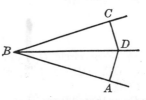

8. *Given BD* bisecting ∠ *ABC*, *CD* ⊥ *BC*, *DA* ⊥ *BA*, and *BA* = *BC*. *Prove* that *AD* = *CD*.

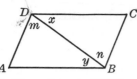

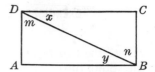

9. *Given* figure *ABCD* with ∠x = ∠y and ∠m = ∠n.
Prove that ∠A = ∠C.

10. *Given* figure *ABCD* with AD⊥DC, CB⊥AB, and ∠x=∠y.
Prove that AD = BC.

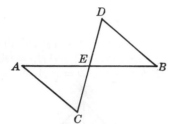

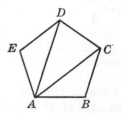

11. *Given* st. lines *AB* and *CD* bisecting each other in *E*.
Prove that AC = BD.

12. *Given* polygon *ABCDE* with equal sides and equal ∡, and line segments *AC* and *AD*.
Prove that AD = AC.

B

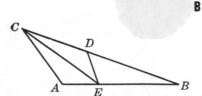

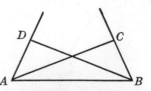

13. *Given* △ *ABC* with *CA* = *CD*, and *CE* bisecting ∠ *ACB*.
Prove that AE = DE.

14. *Given* ∠ *DAB* = ∠ *ABC* and *AD* = *BC*.
Prove that AC = BD.

15. *Given* circle *O*, radii *OA*, *OB*, *OC*, *OD*, and ∠ *AOB* = ∠ *COD*.
Prove that AB = CD.

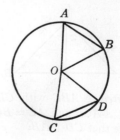

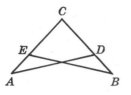

16. *Given* $AE = BD$, and $AC = BC$.
Prove that $\angle A = \angle B$.

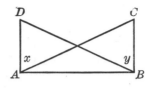

17. *Given* st. lines AC and BD, $AD \perp AB$, $BC \perp AB$ and $\angle x = \angle y$.
Prove that $\angle D = \angle C$.

C

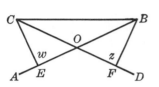

18. *Given* $CE \perp AB$, $BF \perp CD$, $BE = CF$, and $CE = BF$.
Prove that $\angle OCB = \angle OBC$.

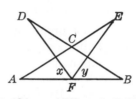

19. *Given* ACE and BCD st. lines, F the midpoint of AB, $\angle A = \angle B$, and $\angle x = \angle y$.
Prove that $AE = BD$.

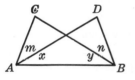

20. *Given* figure $ABDC$ with $\angle x = \angle y$ and $\angle m = \angle n$.
Prove that $\angle C = \angle D$.

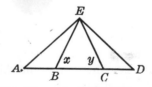

21. *Given* $\triangle ADE$, $BE = CE$, $\angle x = \angle y$, and $AC = BD$.
Prove that $AE = DE$.

22. *Given* st. line AOD, $\angle m = \angle n$, and $\angle x = \angle y$.
Prove that $CB \perp AD$.

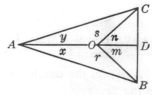

Analysis. 1. We can prove $CB \perp AD$ if we can prove $\angle ODC = \angle ODB$.

2. We can prove $\triangle ODC \cong \triangle ODB$ if we can prove $CO = OB$.

3. We can prove $CO = OB$ if we can prove $\triangle AOC \cong \triangle AOB$.

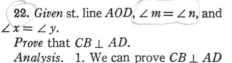

70. Directions for Proving Theorems. The demonstrations of the three propositions that we have studied in this chapter have been given in full. No specific rules for proving theorems can be given. However, the following general directions will be useful to the student and should be referred to as a model in the development of proofs. The directions will be applied to the following theorem:

If two sides of a triangle are equal, the angles opposite these sides are equal.

I. *a*. Read the theorem carefully, being certain that you know the meaning of the words used.

If you do not understand every word, refer to the index at the back of the book, where you will be directed to a definition or an explanation of the word. Probably all words in this theorem with the exception of the words "angles opposite" are understood. By looking under "Angles" in the index you will find that this expression is explained on page 78.

***b*. Determine the hypothesis and the conclusion.**

The hypothesis of the theorem is *if two sides of a triangle are equal.* The conclusion is *the angles opposite these sides are equal.* (See § 37.)

II. *a*. Draw a figure which illustrates each point, angle, and line described in the hypothesis.

***b*. Letter the figure, marking the parts which are given equal.**

△ *ABC* is the figure for the theorem.

III. From the hypothesis write what is *given* in terms of the figure.

Be sure that you make use of each relation given in the hypothesis, as it will be needed in the proof.

Then write "*Given* △ *ABC* with *AC = BC*."

IV. From the conclusion write what there is *to prove* in terms of the figure.

Then write "*To prove* that ∠ *A* = ∠ *B*."

V. Select a method of proof for the theorem.

In selecting a method of proof you should first search the axioms, postulates, definitions, and the theorems and corollaries already proved to find all known methods which might be used to prove the theorem. Then select the method most suitable to your proof.

In this theorem you wish to prove that two angles are equal. So you recall all the methods you have had of proving angles equal. These methods are: the first eight axioms, Post. 9, §§ 45, 46, 47, 48, 49, and Post. 18. You then study these methods and determine which one can be used. From a study of the axioms you find no relations by which you can prove $\angle A = \angle B$. You next try Post. 9. Since $\angle A$ and B are not right angles, Post. 9 does not apply. You refer to §§ 45, 46, 47, 48, and 49. Since $\angle A$ and B are neither vertical angles nor complements or supplements of the same angle or of equal angles, these theorems do not apply. Post. 18 states that "corresponding parts of congruent triangles are equal." Possibly you may be able to prove that $\angle A = \angle B$ if you can draw a line dividing $\triangle ABC$ into two congruent triangles. If you draw a line from C to some point D in AB, you will have two triangles with $AC = BC$ by hypothesis and $CD = CD$ by identity. You now recall the three methods of proving triangles congruent (§§ 60, 64, and 67).

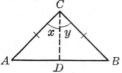

From a study of these three theorems you see that if you draw CD to bisect $\angle C$, you can prove the triangles congruent by § 60. You then draw CD bisecting $\angle C$.

VI. Write the proof, giving a reason for each statement used.

The demonstration of this theorem is given in § 72.

71. Auxiliary Lines. Lines that are introduced in a figure to assist in establishing a proof are called *auxiliary lines* (helping lines). Auxiliary lines should be dotted lines to distinguish them from the lines which are given in the hypothesis.

When drawing an auxiliary line be sure that you can give a reason why it can be drawn.

★★ Proposition III. Theorem

72. *If two sides of a triangle are equal, the angles opposite these sides are equal.*

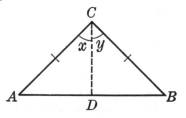

Given the △ ABC with AC = BC.

To prove that ∠ A = ∠ B.

Selection of Method: 1. Known methods of proving ⊿ =: Axs. 1–8, Posts. 9 and 18, §§ 45, 46, 47, 48, and 49.
2. Method to be used: Post. 18.

Proof: *STATEMENTS*   *REASONS*

1. Draw *CD* bisecting ∠ *C* and meeting *AB* at *D*.	1. Post. 8. (An ∠ can be bisected by one line, and only one.)
In ⊿ *ADC* and *BDC*,	
2. *AC = BC*.	2. Given.
3. *CD = CD*.	3. Identity (Iden.).
4. ∠ *x* = ∠ *y*.	4. Const. (Statement 1.)
5. ∴△ *ADC* ≅ △ *BDC*.	5. § 60. (S.A.S.*)
6. ∴ ∠ *A* = ∠ *B*.	6. Corr. ⊿ of ≅ ⊿ are =.

A test of your understanding of a theorem is to close the book and write out the complete demonstration.

★**73. Corollary.** *An equilateral triangle is equiangular.*

The proposition and corollary above give us two new methods of proving angles equal.

*See Abbreviations, p. 7.

On page 544, § 564, there is a list of methods of proving angles equal. Find on it the methods which you have already learned. Hereafter, as you learn a new method of proving angles equal, locate it on this list. When selecting a method of proof you will often find it helpful to refer to this list.

EXERCISES

A

1. State two methods of proving triangles congruent.

2. State the methods of proving line segments equal.

3. State the methods of proving angles equal.

4. State the method of proving lines perpendicular (§ 12).

5. State the method of proving a triangle isosceles (§ 55).

6. State the method of proving a triangle equilateral (§ 55).

7. If $RT = ST$ and $\angle R = 36°$, find the number of degrees in $\angle S$.

8. If $RT = ST$ and $\angle R + \angle S = 78°$, find the number of degrees in $\angle R$ and in $\angle S$.

9. If $RT = ST$, $\angle R = (3x + 6)°$, and $\angle S = (x + 46)°$, find the number of degrees in $\angle R$ and in $\angle S$.

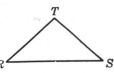

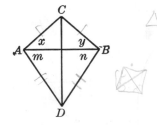

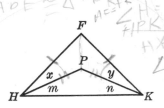

10. *Given $AC = BC$; $AD = BD$.*
   a. Prove that $\angle x = \angle y$.
   b. Prove that $\angle m = \angle n$.
   c. Prove that $\angle CAD = \angle CBD$.
   d. Prove that $\triangle ACD \cong \triangle DBC$.

11. *Given the isosceles $\triangle\ HKF$ and HKP with $HF = KF$ and $HP = KP$.*
   Prove that $\angle x = \angle y$.

12. Prove that the diagonals of a square are equal.

SUGGESTION. A square has four equal sides and four right angles.

13. In △ *ABC* below, which side is opposite ∠ *A*? ∠ *B*? ∠ *C*? Which angle is opposite side *AB*? side *BC*? side *AC*?

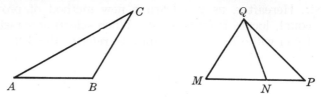

14. In △ *MNQ* which side is opposite ∠ *M*? ∠ *MQN*? ∠ *MNQ*?

15. Prove that the bisector of the vertex angle of an isosceles triangle bisects the base.

16. Prove that the bisector of the vertex angle of an isosceles triangle is perpendicular to the base.

SUGGESTIONS. Prove that it makes equal angles with the base and read the definition of a perpendicular to a line.

17. *Any point in the perpendicular bisector of a line segment is equidistant from the ends of the segment.*

18. Two isosceles triangles are congruent if the vertex angle and one of the equal sides of one are equal respectively to the vertex angle and one of the equal sides of the other.

19. The perimeter of an equilateral triangle is 168 feet. Find the length of each side.

20. *Given AC = BC and AD = EB. Prove that CD = CE.*

21. *Given CD = CE and AD = EB.*
a. *Prove that AC = BC.*
b. *Prove that ∠ A = ∠ B.*

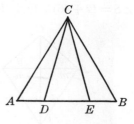

B

22. If a line is perpendicular to the bisector of an angle, it forms an isosceles triangle with the sides of the angle.

23. If the base of an isosceles triangle is trisected (divided into three equal parts), line segments drawn from the vertex to the points of division are equal.

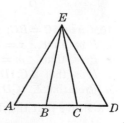

*Since this is a theorem, you are to prove it.

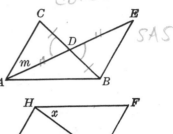

24. If the bisector of an angle of a triangle is perpendicular to the opposite side, the triangle is isosceles.

25. *Given* ⩙ *ABC* and *ABE*, *D* the midpoint of *BC*, and *AD = DE*.

  a. *Prove* that △ *ADC* ≅ △ *DBE*.

  b. *Prove* that ∠ *E* = ∠ *m*.

  c. *Prove* that ∠ *BAC* > ∠ *E*. (See Axs. 8 and 5.)

26. *Given* figure *ABFH* with *AB = HF* and ∠ *x* = ∠ *y*.

  a. *Prove* that *AH = BF*.

  b. *Prove* that ∠ *AHF* = ∠ *FBA*.

27. If two right triangles have a leg and the adjacent acute angle of one equal respectively to a leg and the adjacent acute angle of the other, the triangles are congruent.

C

28. The bisectors of two supplementary adjacent angles are perpendicular to each other.

29. The line segments joining the midpoints of the sides of an equilateral triangle form another equilateral triangle.

30. *Given* △ *ABC* with *AC = BC*, lines *AE* and *BD*, and ∠ *m* = ∠ *n*.

  Prove that *AE = BD*.

31. *Given* △ *ABC*, lines *AE* and *BD*, with *AO = BO* and ∠ *p* = ∠ *q*.

  Prove that *AD = BE*.

Exs. 30–32

32. *Given* △ *ABC* with *AC = BC*, lines *AE* and *BD*, and *CD = CE*.

  Prove that *AE = BD*.

33. The line segments bisecting the angles at the base of an isosceles triangle and terminated by the equal sides are equal.

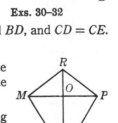

34. *Given* line segments *RN* and *MP* intersecting in *O*, *MR = PR*, and *MN = PN*.

  Prove that *RN* is the perpendicular bisector of *MP*.

★★Proposition IV. Theorem

74. *If two triangles have the three sides of one equal respectively to the three sides of the other, the triangles are congruent.* (S.S.S.)

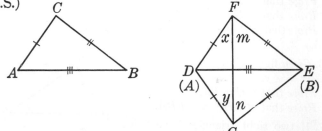

Given the △ *ABC* and *DEF* with *AB = DE*, *AC = DF*, and *CB = FE*.

To prove that △ *ABC* ≅ △ *DEF*.

Selection of Method: 1. Known methods of proving △ ≅: §§ 58, 60, 64, and 67.
2. Method to be used: § 60.

Proof: STATEMENTS   REASONS

STATEMENTS	REASONS
1. *AB = DE*.	1. Given.
2. Place △ *ABC* next to △ *DEF* so that *AB* coincides with *DE*, *A* falls on *D*, *B* on *E*, and *C* opposite *F*.	2. Post. 6; § 7.
3. Draw *FC*.	3. Post. **1.**
4. In △ *DFC*, *DF = AC*, and	4. Given.
5. ∠ *x* = ∠ *y*.	5. § 72.
6. In △ *FEC*, *FE = BC*, and	6. Given.
7. ∠ *m* = ∠ *n*.	7. § 72.
8. ∴ ∠ *x* + ∠ *m* = ∠ *y* + ∠ *n*.	8. Ax. 1.
9. ∠ *x* + ∠ *m* = ∠ *DFE*.	9. Ax. 8.
10. ∠ *y* + ∠ *n* = ∠ *ACB*.	10. Ax. 8.
11. ∴ ∠ *DFE* = ∠ *ACB*.	11. Ax. 5.
12. ∴ △ *DEF* ≅ △ *ABC*.	12. § 60.

This proposition gives us a new method of proving triangles congruent. On page 543, § 562, note the methods you have learned.

NOTE. In demonstrating a theorem the student should always give the reasons in full.

AC bisecting ∠ D
∠ ∠ x = ∠ y
A D = ∠ C

EXERCISES*

A

1. *Given* $AD = AB$ *and* $DC = BC$.
a. *Prove that* $\angle x = \angle y$.
b. *Prove that* AC *bisects* $\angle BCD$.

2. The line joining the vertex of an isosceles triangle to the midpoint of the base divides the triangle into two congruent triangles.

3. *Given* $AD = BC$ *and* $AB = DC$.
a. *Prove that* $\triangle ABD \cong \triangle BCD$.
b. *Prove that* $\angle A = \angle C$.
c. *Prove that* $\angle x = \angle y$.
d. *Prove that* $\angle m = \angle n$.
e. *Prove that* $\angle ADC = \angle ABC$.

diagonal
= △

4. *Given* $AB = BC$, $AD = CD$, *and* AC *intersecting* BD *in* E.
a. *Prove that* $\angle x = \angle y$.
b. *Prove that* $\triangle ABE \cong \triangle BEC$.
c. *Prove that* $AE = EC$.
d. *Prove that* $BE \perp AC$.

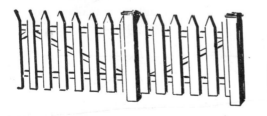

5. Why are braces needed on the fence? Which theorem states that the bicycle frame is rigid?

*If desired, pages 153–157 inclusive may be studied at this time.

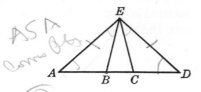

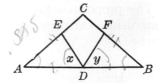

6. *Given* △ ADE with AE = DE and ∠ AEB = ∠ CED.
Prove that BE = CE.

7. *Given* △ ABC with AC = BC, AD = DB, and ∠ x = ∠ y.
Prove that DE = DF.

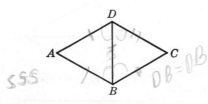

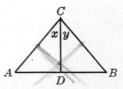

8. *Given* polygon ABCD with four equal sides.
Prove that ∠ A = ∠ C.

9. *Given* △ ABC with AC = BC and D the midpoint of AB.
Prove that ∠ x = ∠ y.

B

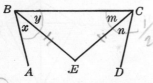

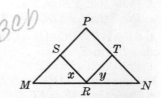

10. *Given* figure ABCDE with EB bisecting ∠ ABC, EC bisecting ∠ BCD, and EB = EC.
Prove that ∠ x = ∠ n.

11. *Given* △ MNP, MP = NP, RS bisecting MP, RT bisecting NP, and R the midpoint of MN.
Prove that ∠ x = ∠ y.

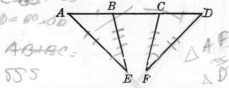

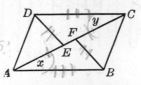

12. *Given* st. line ABCD with AC = BD, AE = DF, and BE = CF.
Prove that ∠ E = ∠ F.

13. *Given* polygon ABCD with AE = FC, DE = BF, and AB = DC.
Prove that ∠ x = ∠ y.

MISCELLANEOUS EXERCISES

1. Two boys wished to know the distance between two posts, A and B, which were located on opposite sides of a garage. They first set a stake at C. Then they set another stake at D in line with AC, making $CD = CA$. In like manner they set a stake at E in line with CB, making $CE = CB$. By measurement they found that ED was 48 feet. Prove that the distance between the two posts A and B is 48 feet.

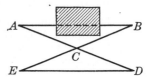

2. Some boys wished to find the distance from their camp at A to a tree at B on the opposite side of a river. They set a stake at C so that $\angle BAC = 90°$. They placed another stake at D in line with AC, making $CD = CA$. Then they stretched a tape from D, making $DE \perp AD$ and placed a stake at F, the intersection of BC and DE. They measured DF to find the length of AB. Prove that $DF = AB$.

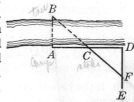

3. This is a diagram of an iron bridge. Why do you think it is composed of triangles instead of quadrilaterals (figures having four sides)? Can the bridge change its shape without breaking?

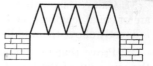

4. ABC is a wood girder for a footbridge. ADC is an iron-wire cable to make the bridge rigid. Which of the two diagrams below shows the correct method of bracing the bridge? Give reasons for your answer.

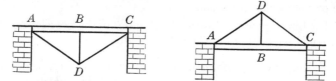

5. A contractor stood at a point P on an edge of an excavation and sighted a point Q on the opposite edge. Then, without raising or lowering his eyes, he faced about and sighted a point R on the ground. Then he measured the distance PR, which was equal to the distance across the excavation. Prove that his method is correct.

6. Before the spirit level was invented, the *plumb level* was often used. This consisted of a frame in the form of an isosceles triangle (*ABC*) and a plumb line suspended from the vertex angle (*C*). In use, the instrument was held upright with the edge *AB* resting on the surface to be leveled. Prove that when the plumb line hung directly over the midpoint *M* of *AB*, the surface upon which the edge *AB* rested was level. ("Level" means perpendicular to vertical.)

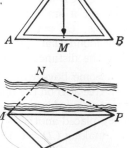

7. Make a plumb level and bring it to class.

8. Why do carpenters, in sheathing a house, often run the boards diagonally?

9. A geometry class wishing to know the distance between *M* and the inaccessible point *N*, set a stake at *Q* so that $\angle QMP = \angle PMN$ and $\angle QPM = \angle MPN$. What line should they measure to find *MN*?

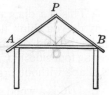

10. If the base of an isosceles triangle is extended in both directions, the angles so formed are equal.

11. Can you show that the rafters *PA* and *PB* are of equal length if the end of the ridgepole *P* is directly above the middle of the tie beam *AB*?

12. Prove that the line segments drawn from the midpoint of the base of an isosceles triangle to the midpoints of the equal sides make equal angles with the base.

13. Two oblique line segments drawn from a point on the perpendicular to a line so that they cut off equal line segments from the foot of the perpendicular are equal.

14. The bisectors of the base angles *A* and *B* of the isosceles $\triangle ABC$ cut off equal segments from *C* on *AC* and *BC*.

75. Syllogisms (*Optional*). Deductive reasoning, which we use in proving theorems and which we use in our daily conversations, can be expressed by syllogisms. A *syllogism* (sĭl'lō jĭzm) is an argument expressed in logical form and consists of three statements, the first of which is the *major premise,* the second the *minor premise,* and the third the *conclusion.*

Example 1. 1. (If) complements of the same angle are equal.
2. (If) $\angle A$ and $\angle B$ are complements of $\angle C$.
3. (Then) $\angle A = \angle B$.

In this example, statement 1 is the major premise, statement 2 is the minor premise, and statement 3 is the conclusion. Note that the minor premise states that the major premise applies to $\angle A$ and $\angle B$.

Example 2. 1. All A is B.
2. All C is A.
3. Then all C is B.

Any geometric proof may be arranged so as to consist of one or more syllogisms. The proof in Example 1, § 66, can be arranged in two syllogisms as follows:

1. Vertical angles are equal.
2. $\angle x$ and $\angle y$ are vertical angles.
3. $\angle x = \angle y$.

1. If two triangles have two sides and the included angle of one equal respectively to two sides and the included angle of the other, the triangles are congruent.
2. $CO = OD$, $AO = OB$, and $\angle x = \angle y$.
3. $\triangle AOC \cong \triangle BOD$.

Notice that in a syllogism the reason is given first.

76. Euler's Circles (*Optional*). Euler (1707–1783), a Swedish mathematician, used circles to represent deductive reasoning. Let us see how we can represent a syllogism by circles.

1. Complements of the same angle are equal.

2. $\angle A$ and $\angle B$ are complements of $\angle C$.

3. Then $\angle A = \angle B$.

Let a large circle contain all equal angles. Then we may have a smaller circle within it containing all complements of $\angle C$. Within this smaller circle we may have a third circle containing $\angle A$ and $\angle B$. Since the smallest circle is within the next larger circle and the latter is within the largest circle, we know that the smallest circle is within the largest.

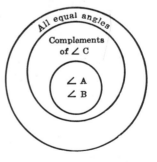

77. Reasoning in Everyday Life (*Optional*). The use of deductive reasoning is by no means confined to geometry. We constantly encounter examples of it in everyday life. In science, in business, and in industry, problems arise daily which can best be solved by this method. In public affairs and government, deductive reasoning is constantly used. No citizen can ignore its great importance.

EXERCISES

From the data given, tell which of the following conclusions are true:

1. To be eligible for the Silverdale High School football squad a boy must be less than twenty years of age, be passing in three subjects, have his parents' consent, and have a health certificate.

a. Frank is eligible for the squad because he is 15 years old, entered high school today, and has a health certificate.

b. Bill will play in the first game because he is passing in all his subjects, is on the squad, and starred last year.

c. Frank must be passing in at least three subjects since he is on the squad.

d. Ellis cannot be on the squad because he weighs only 130 pounds.

e. Dave weighs 192 pounds and is passing in four subjects. His parents are anxious for him to make the team and have secured his health certificate. Therefore he is eligible for the squad.

2. No person shall be a Senator [of the United States] who shall not have attained to the age of thirty years, and been nine years a citizen of the United States, and who shall not, when elected, be an inhabitant of that State for which he shall be chosen.

a. The above quotation from the Constitution states who shall be a Senator.

b. Mr. Perkins can never be a Senator of the United States because he was born in England.

c. Mr. Jones, if elected, can be a Senator from Ohio because he has been a citizen of Ohio the last forty years.

d. Miss Lange was born in Canada in 1915, became a citizen of the United States in 1928. She was elected to the Senate last year to represent one state while she voted in another state. She cannot take the seat in the Senate.

In the following exercises the general and specific statements are given. Supply the conclusion, if one is possible.

3. The constitution of a certain state provides that "New counties may be established by the legislature to consist of not less than 275 square miles and which shall contain a population of at least 700 qualified voters . . ."

a. The legislature wishes to establish Bluegill County which will contain 295 square miles and have a population of 2216.

b. The legislature wishes to establish Anatoras County which will contain 307 square miles and have 784 qualified voters.

4. The constitution of a certain state makes it unlawful for any subdivision to incur debts totaling more than 2% of the assessed valuation of the property in that subdivision.

a. Can Lyaston, a city in the state, which already has a debt of $48,202 and whose assessed valuation is $3,102,420, incur a further debt of $10,000?

b. Can Runnymede Park, a city in the state, which already has a debt of $492,345 and whose assessed valuation is $32,746,000, incur a further debt of $375,255?

[Lines and angles connected with triangles]

78. Median. A *median* of a tri-angle is a line segment joining any vertex to the midpoint of the opposite side. *CD* is a median of △ *ABC.* How many medians has a triangle?

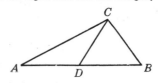

79. Altitude. An *altitude* of a triangle is a perpendicular line segment from any vertex to the opposite side.

In △ *EFG* below, *GH* is the altitude from *G* to *EF*; in △ *JKL, LM* is the altitude from the vertex *L* to the side *JK*; and in △ *RST, SW* is the altitude from *S* to *RT*. Notice that the altitude *LM* meets *JK* produced. Remember that any triangle has three altitudes.

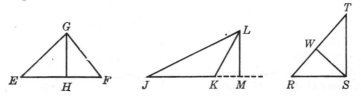

FH and *GK* are altitudes from *F* and *G* to *EG* and *EF* respectively. Note that *GK* meets *EF* produced. Will the altitude from *E* to *FG* fall within or without the triangle?

80. Angle Bisector. A *bisector* of an angle of a triangle is a line which bisects that angle. The bisector is usually regarded as being terminated by the side opposite the angle. In △ *ABC*, *CD* is the bisector of ∠ *C*. In △ *RST*, the altitude, the median, and the angle bisector are drawn from *S* to *RT*. Which is *SA*? Which is *SB*? Which is *SC*?

81. Exterior Angle. An *exterior angle* (ext. ∠) of a triangle is the angle formed by one side and another side produced. ∠ *DBC* is an exterior angle of △ *ABC*. ∡ *A* and *C* are called nonadjacent interior angles to ∠ *CBD*.

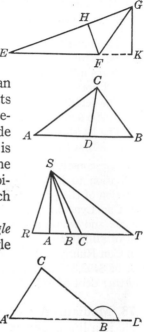

EXERCISES

A

1. In the adjoining figures, measure ∡ *x*, *A*, and *C* with a protractor. How does the size of ∠ *x* compare with that of ∠ *A*? with that of ∠ *C*? with the sum of ∠ *A* and ∠ *C*?

2. *Given* st. line *ABE* and lines *AD* and *CB* bisecting each other.

  a. *Prove* that ∠ *x* = ∠ *C*.

  b. *Prove* that ∠ *CBE* > ∠ *x*. (See Ax. 8.)

  c. *Prove* that ∠ *CBE* > ∠ *C*.

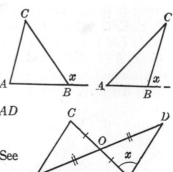

3. If the median of a triangle is also an altitude, the triangle is isosceles.

4. The median to the base of an isosceles triangle bisects the vertex angle.

5. The median to the base of an isosceles triangle is also an altitude of the triangle.

6. The bisectors of two corresponding angles of two congruent triangles are equal.

7. The corresponding medians of two congruent triangles are equal.

B

8. The vertex of an isosceles triangle lies on the perpendicular bisector of the base.

9. Line segments drawn from any point in the bisector of the vertex angle of an isosceles triangle to the extremities of the base are equal.

10. The line segments connecting the midpoints of the equal sides of an isosceles triangle with the midpoint of the base are equal.

11. A point P lies outside $\triangle ABC$ and is equidistant from BC and AB produced through B. If the perpendiculars from P to BC and AB produced form equal angles with the line PB, prove that P lies on the bisector of the exterior angle at B.

12. AE and BD, the bisectors of the base angles of isosceles $\triangle ABC$, intersect in P. Prove that $\angle CDP = \angle CEP$.

C

13. If a point in the base of an isosceles triangle is equally distant from the midpoints of the equal sides, the point bisects the base.

14. Lines drawn perpendicular to the equal sides of an isosceles triangle at their midpoints and terminated by the base are equal.

SUGGESTION. Prove that $DF = EG$.

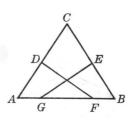

15. The medians to the equal sides of an isosceles triangle are equal.

16. The point of intersection of the perpendicular bisectors of two sides of a triangle is equidistant from the three vertices.

★ Proposition V. Theorem

82. *An exterior angle of a triangle is greater than either nonadjacent interior angle.*

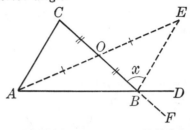

Given the △ *ABC* with the ext. ∠ *DBC*.

To prove that ∠ *DBC* > ∠ *C* and ∠ *DBC* > ∠ *A*.

Selection of Method: 1. Known methods of proving ⩘ unequal: Ax. 8.
2. Method to be used: Ax. 8.

Proof: STATEMENTS   REASONS

STATEMENTS	REASONS
1. Let *O* be the midpoint of *CB*.	1. Post. 7.
2. Join *A* to *O*.	2. Post. 1.
3. Extend *AO* to *E*, making *OE* = *AO*.	3. Post. 3.
4. Join *B* to *E*.	4. Post. 1.
5. Point *E* lies within ∠ *DBC*. Otherwise *AE* would intersect *BC* or *AD* in another point, which is impossible.	5. Post. 2.
In ⩘ *AOC* and *OBE*,	
6. *AO* = *OE* and *CO* = *OB*.	6. Const.
7. ∠ *COA* = ∠ *BOE*.	7. Why?
8. △ *AOC* ≅ △ *OBE*.	8. Why?
9. ∴ ∠ *C* = ∠ *x*.	9. Why?
10. But ∠ *DBC* > ∠ *x*.	10. Ax. 8.
11. ∴ ∠ *DBC* > ∠ *C*.	11. Ax. 5.

In like manner, by drawing a line through *C* and the midpoint of *AB* it can be proved that ∠ *ABF* > ∠ *CAB*, and hence ∠ *CBD* > ∠ *CAB*.

★83. Corollary. *There cannot be more than one perpendicular to a line from an external point.*

Given $CD \perp AB$ *and* CE *any other line from* C *to* AB.

To prove that CE is not $\perp AB$.

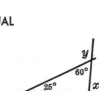

SUGGESTIONS. $\angle y$ is a rt. $\angle$. Why? $\angle x > \angle y$. Why? $\therefore \angle x$ is an obtuse $\angle$. Why?

EXERCISES [A]. ANGLES UNEQUAL

1. Is $\angle x > 25°$? Is $\angle x > 60°$? Why? How many degrees are in $\angle y$? in $\angle z$?

2. Is $\angle x + \angle y = 180°$ or $> 180°$? Why?

3. Show that $\angle x + \angle y + \angle z > 335°$.

REVIEW QUESTIONS

1. What is the name of a statement to be proved? *theorem*

2. What is the name of a geometric statement which is **accepted** *postulate* as true without proof? of a general statement? *axiom*

3. What is the name of a triangle having all sides equal? *equilateral*

4. What is the name of a triangle having two sides equal? *isosceles*

5. What is the name of the side opposite a right angle in a triangle? *hypotenuse*

6. What is the name given to the two sides that include the right angle of a right triangle? *legs*

7. What do you know about an exterior angle of a triangle? *Prop. II*

8. How many altitudes does a triangle have? How many medians? How many angle bisectors? *3*

9. What is the most common method of proving two line segments or two angles equal? *~ pts. ≅ △*

10. What are the five parts of a demonstration? *#38*

11. Are two triangles congruent if their corresponding **parts are** equal? *Post. 13*

12. What are auxiliary lines? *dotted additional explanatory lines*

SUMMARY OF PRINCIPAL METHODS OF PROOF

84. *Two triangles are congruent*

a. If two sides and the included angle of one are equal respectively to two sides and the included angle of the other.

b. If two angles and the included side of one are equal respectively to two angles and the included side of the other.

c. If the three sides of one are equal respectively to the three sides of the other.

85. *Two right triangles are congruent*

a, b, c. Same as § 84.

d. If two legs of one are equal respectively to two legs of the other.

86. *Two line segments are equal*

a. If they are corresponding sides of congruent triangles.

b. By the use of axioms.

c. By superposition.

87. *Two angles are equal*

a. If they are angles opposite equal sides in a triangle.

b. If they are corresponding angles of congruent triangles.

WORD LIST

Do you know the meaning of all the following words? Can you spell each one correctly?

acute	isosceles
altitude	median
auxiliary	miscellaneous
complementary	perimeter
corollary	polygon
corresponding	prove
equiangular	right
equilateral	scalene
exterior	superposition
hypotenuse	triangle
identity	vertices

TEST 4

Determining the Hypothesis and Conclusion (*Twenty Minutes*)

Copy these statements and underscore each hypothesis with one line and each conclusion with two lines:

1. If the three sides of one triangle are equal respectively to the three sides of another, the triangles are congruent.

2. If the bisector of an angle of a triangle is perpendicular to the opposite side, the triangle is isosceles.

3. The bisector of the vertex angle of an isosceles triangle bisects the base and is perpendicular to it.

4. If a point lies on the perpendicular bisector of a line segment, it is equidistant from the ends of the segment.

5. If the median of a triangle is also an altitude, the triangle is isosceles.

6. Two triangles are congruent if two sides and the median to one of these sides are equal respectively to two sides and the corresponding median of the other.

7. If two medians of a triangle are equal, the triangle is isosceles.

8. The bisectors of two corresponding angles of two congruent triangles are equal.

9. If two oblique line segments are drawn from a point on the perpendicular to a line so that they cut off equal line segments from the foot of the perpendicular, they are equal.

TEST 5

True-False Statements (*Six Minutes*)

Copy the numbers of these statements on your paper. Then if a statement is *always* true, write T after its number. If a statement is *not always* true, write F after its number.

1. A theorem that is derived from another theorem with little or no proof is called a postulate.

2. A triangle is a polygon.

3. If two triangles have three angles of one equal respectively to three angles of the other, the triangles are congruent.

F **4.** A median is a line joining the midpoints of two sides of a triangle.

F **5.** An equiangular triangle is isosceles.

6. Two triangles are congruent if two sides and an angle of one are equal respectively to two sides and an angle of the other.

F **7.** The sum of two sides of a triangle is greater than the third side.

8. Two right triangles are congruent if the two legs of one are equal respectively to the two legs of the other.

9. The exterior angles of a triangle are obtuse.

10. An angle less than a right angle is acute.

11. A theorem is a statement to be proved.

12. Any two altitudes of a triangle are perpendicular to each other.

TEST 6

Applications (*Twenty-five Minutes*)

1. Find the complement of an angle of 38°.

2. An angle contains 37°. Find the size of its vertical angle.

3. $\triangle ABC \cong \triangle DEF$. If $AC = 8$, $BC = 9$, $AB = 10$, and $EF = 9$, how long is DE?

4. How many degrees are in the smaller angle formed by the hands of a clock when it is 4 P.M. by the clock?

5. Through how many degrees does the minute hand of a watch pass in one hour?

6. An angle exceeds its supplement by 10°. How many degrees does it contain?

7. In polygon $ABCD$, $AB = DC = 10$ inches and $AD = BC = 8$ inches. The line BD makes $\angle ADB = 72°$. How many degrees are there in $\angle DBC$?

8. In $\triangle ABC$ the median CD is an altitude. If $\angle A = 66°$, how large is $\angle B$?

9. If two adjacent angles whose sum is 96° are bisected, how many degrees are there in the angle formed by their bisectors?

10. One of two vertical angles is represented in degrees by $\dfrac{x + 24}{4}$ and the other by $\dfrac{4x - 9}{9}$. How large is each angle?

TEST 7

Supplying Reasons (*Twenty-two Minutes*)

Supply axioms, postulates, definitions, or theorems for **the** following statements:

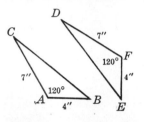

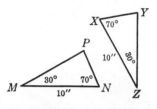

1. △ *ABC* ≅ △ *DEF.* SAS   **3.** △ *MPN* ≅ △ *XYZ.* ASA

2. ∠ *B* = ∠ *E.* Post 18   **4.** *PN* = *XY.* Post 18

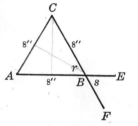

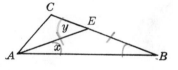

If *AC*, *ABE*, *CBF* are st. lines,   If *AE* = *EB*,

5. △ *ABC* is equiangular. SSS   **7.** ∠ *x* = ∠ *B*.

6. ∠ *r* = ∠ *s*. Vert k   **8.** ∠ *y* > ∠ *B*. Prob V

If *AC* = *AE*, *AB* = *AD*, and ∠ *CAB* = ∠ *EAD*,

9. △ *CAB* ≅ △ *EAD*. SAS

10. *CB* = *ED*. Post 18

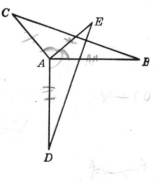

*Notice the Parallel and Perpendicular Lines in This Building on a
New England College Campus*

CHAPTER IV

Parallel and Perpendicular Lines

88. Parallel Lines. Two lines are *parallel* (‖) if they lie in the same plane and do not intersect even if extended. Thus *l* and *l'* are parallel lines.

—————————— *l*

Since in plane geometry all points and lines lie in the same plane, the words "in the same plane" are usually omitted in courses in this subject.

—————————— *l'*

89. Post. 19. *Two straight lines in the same plane are either parallel lines or intersecting lines.*

90. Angles Formed by a Transversal. A *transversal* is a line which intersects two or more lines. The line *t* is a transversal of lines *l* and *l'*. In the figure, can you name the four pairs of vertical angles? Can you name the eight pairs of supplementary angles? The ∡ *x*, *y*, *m*, and *n*, outside *l* and *l'*, are *exterior angles*. The ∡ *z*, *w*, *r*, and *s*, inside *l* and *l'*, are *interior angles*. Taken in pairs, the angles are named as follows:

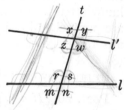

The ∡ *z* and *s* are *alternate interior* angles; also ∡ *w* and *r*.

The ∡ *y* and *m* are *alternate exterior* angles; also ∡ *x* and *n*.

The ∡ *x* and *r* are *corresponding angles*; also ∡ *y* and *s*, ∡ *n* and *w*, and ∡ *m* and *z*. Corresponding angles are often called *exterior-interior* angles. Why?

EXERCISE [A]

Draw two vertical lines cut by a transversal, letter your diagram, and name all the pairs of alternate interior angles; all the pairs of corresponding angles.

91. Indirect Method of Proof. In the theorems and exercises already studied the method of proof has been direct. The direct method consists in putting together known truths (definitions, axioms, postulates, theorems, the hypothesis), step by step, to form a proof. If the known facts are insufficient to prove a theorem directly, we can often prove it by a method known as the indirect method.

There are two forms of the indirect method—*proof by coincidence*, which will be studied on page 131, and *proof by exclusion*.

The exclusion method consists in examining all the different possible conclusions and showing that none but the one we wish to prove can be true. If there are only two conclusions possible from the facts given in the hypothesis, it is only necessary to prove that one conclusion leads to a contradiction of some known fact. For example, if we wish to prove two lines parallel, the possibilities are: (1) the lines are ∥; (2) the lines are not ∥. If we assume that the lines are not parallel and then show that this assumption leads to a contradiction of some known truth, we have established the fact that the lines are parallel. Also, if we wish to prove that $\angle A = \angle B$, there are three possibilities; (1) $\angle A = \angle B$; (2) $\angle A > \angle B$; (3) $\angle A < \angle B$.

In proof by exclusion we will use the following postulate:

Post. 20. *If a hypothetical statement leads to a contradiction of a known fact or hypothesis, the statement is false.*

To prove a theorem by the exclusion method:

1. State the conclusion and the other possibilities.
2. Show that the other possibilities lead to a contradiction of the hypothesis or of a truth previously learned.
3. The conclusion is the only remaining possibility.

The following theorem illustrates the indirect method of proof by exclusion.

★★Proposition I. Theorem

92. *If two lines form equal alternate interior angles with a transversal, the lines are parallel.*

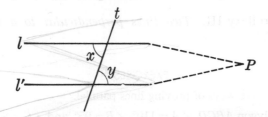

Given the lines l and l' cut by the transversal t so that $\angle x = \angle y$.

To prove that $l \parallel l'$.

Selection of Method: 1. Known methods of proving lines $\parallel$: § 88.
2. Method to be used: § 88.

Proof:

STATEMENTS	REASONS
1. l and l' are either $\parallel$ lines or intersecting lines.	1. Post. 19.
2. If l and l' intersect at some point P, a $\triangle$ is formed, and $\angle x > \angle y$.	2. § 82.
3. But $\angle x = \angle y$.	3. Given.
4. l does not intersect l'.	4. Post. 20.
5. $\therefore l \parallel l'$.	5. § 88. (Def. of $\parallel$s.)

★**93. Corollary I.** *If two lines form equal corresponding angles with a transversal, the lines are parallel.*

SUGGESTIONS. $\angle x = \angle y$. Why?
$\angle x = \angle z$. Why?
$\therefore \angle z = \angle y$. Why? Use § 92.

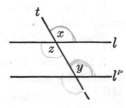

NOTE. Corollaries following a theorem proved by the *indirect method* are usually proved by the *direct method*.

★94. Corollary II. *If two lines form supplementary interior angles on the same side of a transversal, the lines are parallel.*

SUGGESTION. Show that two ∠s are supplements of the same ∠ and are therefore =.

★95. Corollary III. *Two lines perpendicular to a third line are parallel.*

EXERCISES [A]

1. Name five ways of proving lines parallel.

2. In polygon *ABCD*, $\angle A = 110°$, $\angle B = 95°$, and $\angle C = 85°$. Which two sides of the polygon are parallel? Give the reason for your answer.

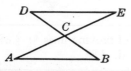

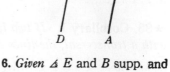

3. *Given AE* and *BD* bisecting each other in *C*.
Prove that *DE* ∥ *AB*.

4. *Given* figure *ABCE* with *BCD* a st. line, $\angle x = \angle B$, and $\angle B = \angle E$.
Prove that *EC* ∥ *AB*; *AE* ∥ *BD*.

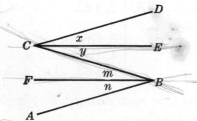

5. *Given* $\angle ABC = \angle BCD$, $\angle x = \angle y$, and $\angle m = \angle n$.
Prove that *CE* ∥ *FB*.

6. *Given* ∠s *E* and *B* supp. and $\angle B = \angle x$.
Prove that *EF* ∥ *CB*.

7. If the line *AC* of polygon *ABCD* divides the polygon into two congruent triangles with *BC* corresponding to *AD*, then *AB* ∥ *DC* and *AD* ∥ *BC*.

96. Post. 21. *Through a given point there can be only one parallel to a given line.*

Notice that this postulate does not only mean that through a given point one line can be drawn parallel to another, but states that through the point *not more than one line* can be drawn parallel to another.

Post. 21 is known as the Euclidean parallel postulate. The belief that this postulate was not as fundamental as the other postulates of geometry led many mathematicians over a period of 2000 years to try to prove or disprove this postulate by means of other postulates and axioms. Their failure to do so led to the idea that a different geometry could be constructed.

In the nineteenth century Nicholas Lobachevsky (1793–1856), a Russian professor of mathematics, and John Bolyai (1802–1860), a Hungarian army officer, independently developed a new geometry based upon the postulate *through a given point there can be any number of parallels to a given line.* A geometry of this kind is known as *non-Euclidean* geometry.

In 1854 a different non-Euclidean geometry was developed by Bernhard Riemann, a German mathematician, who assumed that any two lines in a plane intersect. A non-Euclidean geometry somewhat different from these two has been found to be of the highest importance in Einstein's theory of relativity.

However, Euclidean geometry is much simpler than non-Euclidean geometry and is the geometry used in everyday life by engineers and contractors in bridge construction, radio, transportation, etc.

★**97. Corollary.** *Two lines parallel to a third line are parallel to each other.*

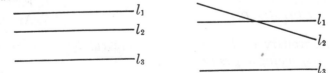

Write the complete demonstration. Use the indirect method and Post. 21.

★★Proposition II. Theorem

98. *If two parallels are cut by a transversal, the alternate interior angles are equal.*

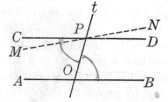

Given the two ‖s *AB* and *CD* cut by the transversal *t* at *O* and *P*.

To prove that ∠ *CPO* = ∠ *BOP*.

Selection of Method: 1. Known methods of proving ⊿ =: Axioms, Posts. 9 and 18, §§ 50 and 87.*
2. Method to be used: Ax. 9.

Proof:

STATEMENTS	REASONS
1. ∠ *CPO* and ∠ *BOP* are either = or unequal.	1. Ax. 9.
2. If ∠ *CPO* ≠ (is unequal to) ∠ *BOP*, let *MN* be another line through *P*, making ∠ *MPO* = ∠ *BOP*.	2. Ax. 9.
3. Then *MPN* ‖ *AB*.	3. § 92.
4. But *CPD* ‖ *AB*.	4. Why?
5. *CD* and *MN* are two ‖s to *AB* through *P*, which is impossible.	5. Post. 21.
6. ∴ *MPN* is not ‖ *AB*.	6. Post. 20.
7. ∴ ∠ *CPO* = ∠ *BOP*.	7. Ax. 9.

★**99. Corollary I.** *If two parallels are cut by a transversal, the corresponding angles are equal.*

*Since axioms are always known methods of proving equalities, in order to save space they will usually be omitted under "Known methods of proving . . . equal."

100. Corollary II. *If two parallels are cut by a transversal, the two interior angles on the same side of the transversal are supplementary.*

★101. Corollary III. *If a line is perpendicular to one of two parallel lines, it is perpendicular to the other.*

102. Corollary IV. *Lines perpendicular to intersecting lines will intersect.*

EXERCISES. PARALLEL LINES

A

1. If two parallels are cut by a transversal, prove that the alternate exterior angles are equal.

2. In this figure there are two parallels cut by a transversal. If ∠ s contains 51°, find the number of degrees in each of the remaining angles.

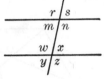

3. In the figure of Ex. 2, if ∠ r contains 118°, find the size of each remaining angle.

4. If two lines form equal alternate exterior angles with a transversal, the lines are parallel.

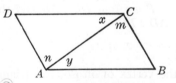 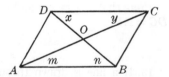

5. *Given DC ∥ AB and DC = AB. Prove that AD = BC.*

6. *Given DC ∥ AB and DC = AB. Prove that AO = OC and that DO = OB.*

7. *Given l ∥ l'.*
   a. Prove that ∠ x = ∠ m.
   b. Prove that ∠ y = ∠ n.
   c. Prove that ∠ x + ∠ y + ∠ z = 1 st. ∠.
   d. Prove that ∠ m + ∠ z + ∠ n = 1 st. ∠.

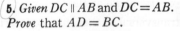

8. Why are the lines drawn with a T-square, as shown in the figure, parallel? Using the T-square, how can you draw parallel vertical lines? What other drawing instrument would be useful in drawing parallel slanting lines?

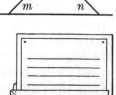

B

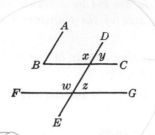

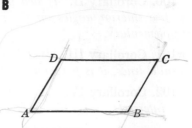

9. *Given* $AB \parallel DE$ and $BC \parallel FG$.
a. *Prove* that $\angle B = \angle z$.
b. *Prove* that $\measuredangle B$ and w are supp.

10. *Given* $AB \parallel DC$ and $AD \parallel BC$.
a. Why is $\angle A$ supp. $\angle B$?
b. Why is $\angle C$ supp. $\angle B$?
c. Why does $\angle A = \angle C$?

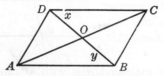

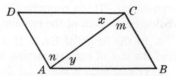

11. *Given* $DO = OB$; $AO = OC$.
Prove that $\angle x = \angle y$ and that $DC = AB$.

12. *Given* $DC = AB$; $AD = BC$.
Prove that $DC \parallel AB$ and that $AD \parallel BC$.

C

13. If a line is drawn through the vertex of an isosceles triangle parallel to the base, it bisects the exterior angle at the vertex.

14. If two parallels are cut by a transversal so that the two interior angles on the same side of the transversal contain $4x$ degrees and $(3x - 9)$ degrees respectively, find the number of degrees in each angle.

103. Right Side and Left Side of an Angle. Viewed from the vertex, the side of an angle at the right is called the *right side* of the angle and the side at the left is called the *left side* of the angle. Thus AB is the right side of $\angle A$ and AC is the left side

★Proposition III. Theorem

104. *If two angles have their sides parallel, right side to right side and left side to left side, the angles are equal.*

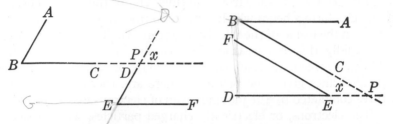

Given ∡ *B* and *E* with *BC* ∥ *EF* and *BA* ∥ *ED*.

To prove that ∠ *B* = ∠ *E*.

Selection of Method: 1. Known methods of proving ∡ =: §§ 50, 87, 98, and 99.

2. Method to be used: §§ 98 and 99.

Proof: *STATEMENTS*	*REASONS*
1. Extend *BC* and *ED*.	1. Post. 3.
2. *BC* will intersect *ED* at some point *P*.	2. §§ 89, 96.
3. *BA* ∥ *EP*.	3. Why?
4. ∴ ∠ *B* = ∠ *x*.	4. Give reason for each figure.
5. *BC* ∥ *EF*.	5. Why?
6. ∠ *E* = ∠ *x*.	6. Why?
7. ∴ ∠ *B* = ∠ *E*.	7. Why?

EXERCISES [B]

1. *If two angles have their sides parallel, right side to left side and left side to right side, the angles are supplementary.*

2. A line intersecting one of the equal sides of an isosceles triangle and parallel to the other forms a triangle having two equal angles.

105. Parallel Lines in Television. Your television screen is actually only one end of a tube, called a kinescope, which is shaped something like an ordinary electric light bulb flattened at one end. A stream of electrically charged particles, called electrons, is shot from the small end of the tube. These particles form a beam which is made to trace a series of parallel lines on the inside of the television screen (*S*). The beam moves so rapidly that it can trace 525 parallel lines on the screen 30 times a second! Each complete group, or scanning, of 525 parallel lines gives one picture. There are, therefore, 30 pictures completed by the moving beam of electrons every second.

The electrons, or electrically charged particles, which reach the inside of the screen cause that part of the screen to glow. By a special device, many of the electrons are cut off and do

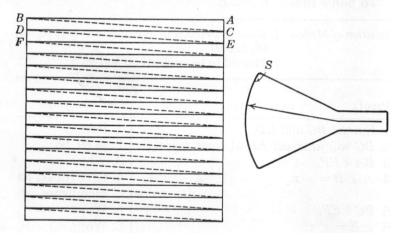

not reach the screen, and this part of the screen remains dark. It is a pattern of light and darkness which forms the images that you recognize as a picture. One picture of 525 lines replaces another so rapidly that you do not notice the end of one picture and the beginning of the next, and the effect of a motion picture is produced.

The diagram above shows the order in which the scanning beam of the television receiver forms parallel lines (only a few of the 525 lines which make up one complete picture are shown). The solid lines are those which act to form the picture on the screen, and the dotted lines show how the beam jumps back to begin scanning a new line. A complete diagram would show 525 solid lines and 525 dotted lines.

106. Indirect Reasoning in Life Situations (*Optional*). Frequently we use indirect reasoning in everyday affairs when it is impossible to reach a conclusion by direct reasoning. To reach a correct conclusion by indirect reasoning we must know all the possible conclusions and eliminate all but one as false. Suppose Mr. Clay has three friends having Brown for their surname. One day Mr. Haines passes Mr. Clay on the street and says in passing, "I saw and talked to your friend Brown at the Rotary luncheon today." Mr. Clay had no direct way of knowing which Mr. Brown might have been at the Rotary luncheon, but he knew that one Mr. Brown was out of town on vacation and another Mr. Brown was confined to bed by illness. Could Mr. Clay tell which friend Brown had been at the luncheon?

EXERCISES [A]

1. One Sunday a farmer said that he would have to go to town on an afternoon of one of the remaining days of the week. He said that he would have to go on a day that he could deliver a load of hogs at the stockyards, go to his bank, and visit his dentist. The dentist's office was open only on Monday, Wednesday, and Friday. The stockyards were not open on Monday and Saturday. The bank was not open on Wednesday and Saturday afternoons. What day did the farmer go to town?

2. Four couples, Mr. and Mrs. Smith, Mr and Mrs. Jones, Mr. and Mrs. Brown, and Mr. and Mrs. White, went into a restaurant for their dinner. They were seated at two square tables, four at each table, so that no husband and wife were at the same table. Mr. Brown and Mr. White did not sit at the same table. Mrs. Jones sat opposite Mr. Brown, and Mrs. Smith sat next to Mrs. Jones. Mr. White sat opposite his daughter. Draw a diagram showing how they were seated at the two tables.

★★Proposition IV. Theorem

107. *The sum of the angles of a triangle is a straight angle.*

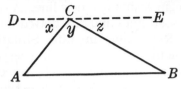

Given the △ *ABC.*

To prove that ∠ *A* + ∠ *B* + ∠ *y* = 1 st. ∠.

Selection of Method: 1. Known methods of proving the sum of *∡* = another ∠: Ax. 8.
2. Method to be used: Ax. 8.

Proof: STATEMENTS   REASONS

1. Through *C* draw *DE* ‖ *AB*.	1. Post. 21.
2. ∠ *DCE* is a st. ∠.	2. § 14.
3. ∠ *x* + ∠ *y* + ∠ *z* = 1 st. ∠.	3. Ax. 8.
4. ∠ *x* = ∠ *A* and ∠ *z* = ∠ *B.*	4. Why? Alt int ∠s
5. ∴ ∠ *A* + ∠ *y* + ∠ *B* = 1 st. ∠.	5. Why?

NOTE. The followers of Pythagoras were the first to prove this theorem.

★**108. Corollary I.** *If two angles of one triangle are equal respectively to two angles of another triangle, the third angles are equal.*

109. Corollary II. *In a triangle there can be but one right angle or one obtuse angle.*

★**110. Corollary III.** *An exterior angle of a triangle equals the sum of the two nonadjacent interior angles.*

NOTE. It is thought that Philippus was the first to prove this corollary (about 380 B.C.).

111. Corollary IV. *The acute angles of a right triangle are complementary.*

★**112. Corollary V.** *If two right triangles have the hypotenuse and an acute angle of one equal respectively to the hypotenuse and an acute angle of the other, the triangles are congruent.*

EXERCISES. ANGLES

A

1. Name all the methods we have had to prove (1) angles equal; (2) line segments equal; (3) triangles congruent; (4) angles supplementary; (5) angles complementary; (6) lines parallel; (7) lines perpendicular; (8) right triangles congruent (five ways). Have you located these methods on pages 543–546?

2. Is it possible to have two right angles in a triangle? Why?

3. Is it possible for an isosceles triangle to be a right triangle? Why?

4. One acute angle of a right triangle equals 34°. How many degrees are there in the other acute angle?

5. How many degrees are in each angle of an equilateral triangle?

6. The vertex angle of an isosceles triangle contains 40°. Find the number of degrees in each of the other angles.

7. If one of the equal angles of an isosceles triangle contains 55°, find the number of degrees in the vertex angle.

8. One of the angles of a triangle is 66°. Find each of the other two if their difference is 12°.

9. The angles of a triangle are in the ratio of 2, 3, and 4. Find the number of degrees in each angle. (Let the angles be $2x$, $3x$, and $4x$.)

10. The angles of a triangle are in the ratio of 3, 4, and 5. Find the number of degrees in each angle.

11. Find the number of degrees in each angle of an isosceles right triangle.

12. An exterior angle of a triangle contains 110° and one non-adjacent interior angle contains 31°. Find the other two angles of the triangle.

13. Find the three angles of a triangle if the second is three times the first and the third is twice the second.

14. If two angles of a triangle are complementary, prove that the triangle is a right triangle.

B

15. Prove that in an isosceles triangle the altitudes on the equal sides are equal.

16. If two right triangles have a leg and the opposite acute angle of one equal respectively to a leg and the opposite acute angle of the other, the triangles are congruent.

17. Are two triangles congruent if they have three angles of one equal respectively to three angles of the other? Explain.

18. $ABCD$ is a quadrilateral. Prove that $\angle A + \angle B + \angle C + \angle D = 2$ st. $\angle$.

19. Find the number of degrees in the angles formed by the bisectors of two of the angles of an equilateral triangle at their point of intersection.

20. The bisector of the exterior angle at the vertex of an isosceles triangle is parallel to the base.

21. The perpendiculars drawn from any point in the bisector of an angle to the sides of the angle are equal.

22. Prove that the altitude from the vertex of an isosceles triangle bisects the vertex angle.

23. If two parallels are cut by a transversal, the bisectors of the interior angles on the same side of the transversal are perpendicular to each other.

C

24. Perpendiculars drawn from any point in the base of an isosceles triangle to the equal sides make equal angles with the base.

25. If from any point outside an acute angle perpendiculars are drawn to the sides of the angle, the angle between these perpendiculars is equal to the given angle.

26. The perpendicular from the vertex of the right angle of a right triangle to the hypotenuse divides the triangle into two triangles whose corresponding angles are respectively equal.

27. If the median of a triangle is equal to half of the side to which it is drawn, the triangle is a right triangle.

★Proposition V. Theorem

113. *If two angles have their sides perpendicular, right side to right side and left side to left side, the angles are equal.*

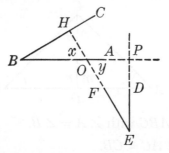

Given the $\measuredangle$ B and E with $BA \perp ED$ and $BC \perp EF$.

To prove that $\angle B = \angle E$.

Selection of Method: 1. Known methods of proving $\measuredangle$ =: §§ 50, 87, 98, 99, 104, and 108.

2. Method to be used: § 50 *b*.

Proof: *STATEMENTS*   *REASONS*

1. If necessary, prolong the sides of the $\measuredangle$ until the $\perp$ sides intersect.	1. Post. 3.
2. $\measuredangle$ B and x are comp.	2. Why?
3. $\measuredangle$ E and y are comp.	3. Why?
4. But $\angle x = \angle y$.	4. Why?
5. $\therefore$ $\angle B = \angle E$.	5. § 50 *b*.

EXERCISES [B]

If two angles have their sides perpendicular, right side to left side and left side to right side, the angles are supplementary

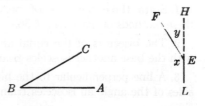

★★Proposition VI. Theorem

114. *If two angles of a triangle are equal, the sides opposite these angles are equal.*

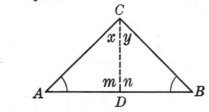

Given the $\triangle ABC$ with $\angle A = \angle B$.

To prove that $AC = CB$.

Selection of Method: 1. Known methods of proving line segments =: § 86.

2. Method to be used: § 86 *a*.

Proof: STATEMENTS	REASONS
1. Draw CD the bisector of $\angle C$.	1. Post. 8.
2. $\angle A = \angle B$.	2. Why?
3. $\angle x = \angle y$.	3. Const.
4. $\therefore \angle m = \angle n$.	4. § 108.
5. $CD = CD$.	5. Why?
6. $\therefore \triangle ADC \cong \triangle BDC$.	6. Why?
7. $\therefore AC = BC$.	7. Why?

★115. Corollary. *An equiangular triangle is equilateral.*

EXERCISES

A

1. State three methods of proving line segments equal. **Find** these methods on page 543, § 563.

2. The bisectors of the equal angles of an isosceles triangle form with the base another isosceles triangle.

3. A line perpendicular to the bisector of an angle forms with the sides of the angle an isosceles triangle (use §§ 108 and 114).

4. If the midpoints of the sides of an equilateral triangle are joined in order, four other equilateral triangles are formed.

5. *Given* $\triangle ABC$, $\angle x = \angle y$, and $AE \parallel CD$ meeting BC produced at E.

Prove that $AC = EC$.

6. A line intersecting the equal sides of an isosceles triangle and parallel to the base forms another isosceles triangle.

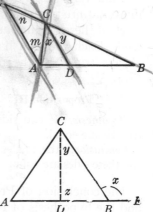

B

7. Find the angles of an isosceles triangle if one of the base angles is twice the vertex angle.

8. An exterior angle at the base of an isosceles triangle is equal to the sum of a right angle and one half the vertex angle.

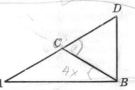

9. If an exterior angle of a triangle is supplementary to one of the nonadjacent interior angles, the triangle is isosceles.

10. If the angle at the vertex of isosceles triangle ABC is equal to four times one of the equal angles, and if perpendicular BD to base AB meets AC produced at D, then $\triangle BCD$ is equilateral.

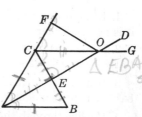

11. A line drawn through a point in the bisector of an angle parallel to one side of the angle forms with the other side and the bisector an isosceles triangle.

C

12. Prove Prop. V by drawing rays through E parallel to BA and BC.

13. *Given* the equilateral triangle ABC with AD bisecting $\angle A$, CG bisecting exterior $\angle BCF$ and $OF \perp AC$.

Prove that $AE = OF$.

SUGGESTION. Prove the four $\triangle \cong$.

14. If two lines are cut by a transversal so that the bisectors of the interior angles on the same side of the transversal are perpendicular to each other, the lines are parallel.

116. Converse Theorems. In § 30 we learned that all definitions are reversible. Thus we may say that "a perpendicular is a line that forms a right angle with another line," or "two lines that are perpendicular to each other form a right angle." Each of these definitions is a *converse* of the other, and both are true. Each theorem has a converse, but the converse is not always true. Let us now look at Prop. III, page 84, and Prop. VI, page 120.

Proposition III	Proposition VI
Hypothesis: If two sides of a triangle are equal,	*Hypothesis:* If two angles of a triangle are equal,
Conclusion: the angles opposite these sides are equal.	*Conclusion:* the sides opposite these angles are equal.

The conclusion of Prop. III is the hypothesis of Prop. VI, and the hypothesis of Prop. III is the conclusion of Prop. VI. Prop. III is called the *converse* of Prop. VI, and Prop. VI is called the *converse* of Prop. III. The *complete converse of a theorem* is the theorem obtained by interchanging all the essential facts of the hypothesis and conclusion of the original theorem.

The *partial converse of a theorem* is obtained by interchanging an equal number of facts in the hypothesis and conclusion of the original theorem. For example, the theorem "the bisector of the vertex angle of an isosceles triangle bisects the base and is perpendicular to the base" has four partial converses as follows:

1. If the bisector of the vertex angle of a triangle bisects the base, it is perpendicular to the base and the triangle is isosceles.

2. If the bisector of the vertex angle of a triangle is perpendicular to the base, it bisects the base and the triangle is isosceles.

3. If a line through the vertex of an isosceles triangle bisects the base, it is perpendicular to the base and bisects the vertex angle.

4. If a line through the vertex of an isosceles triangle is perpendicular to the base, it bisects the base and also bisects the vertex angle.

How many of these partial converses can you prove true?

EXERCISES [A]. CONVERSES

State the converses of the statements in Exs. 1–8 and determine, if you can, whether they are true or false:

1. If a man lives in Indianapolis, he lives in Indiana.

2. If two parallels are cut by a transversal, the alternate interior angles are equal.

3. If two triangles are congruent, the corresponding angles are equal.

4. If two angles have their sides parallel, right side to right side and left side to left side, the angles are equal.

5. All horses are animals.

6. Right angles are equal angles.

7. If a point lies on the perpendicular bisector of a line segment, it is equidistant from the end points of the line segment.

8. The acute angles of a right triangle are complementary.

9. Write all the partial converses of the following theorem:
The median on the base of an isosceles triangle is perpendicular to the base and bisects the vertex angle.

117. Inverse Theorems. The *inverse* (or *opposite*) *of a theorem* having one fact in the conclusion may be formed by contradicting one fact in the hypothesis and the fact in the conclusion. For example:

Theorem. If two lines form equal alternate interior angles with a transversal, the lines are parallel.

Inverse Theorem. If two lines form unequal alternate interior angles with a transversal, the lines are not parallel.

Theorem. The bisector of the vertex angle of an isosceles triangle bisects the base.

Inverse Theorem 1. The bisector of the vertex angle of a scalene triangle does not bisect the base, or

Inverse Theorem 2. If a line through the vertex of an isosceles triangle does not bisect the vertex angle, it does not bisect the base.

Theorem. If two angles of a triangle are equal, the sides opposite these angles are equal.

Inverse Theorem. If two angles of a triangle are unequal, the sides opposite these angles are unequal.

EXERCISES [A]. INVERSES

State the inverses of the following statements and determine, if you can, whether they are true or false:

1. If two angles are right angles, they are equal.

2. If two sides of a triangle are equal, the angles opposite these sides are equal.

3. When there is ice on the road, the road is slippery.

4. If a man lives in Indianapolis, he lives in Indiana.

5. If two triangles are congruent, the corresponding angles are equal.

6. If a point lies on the perpendicular bisector of a line segment, it is equidistant from the end points of the line segment.

118. Contrapositive of a Theorem. The contrapositive of a theorem is another theorem obtained from it by contradicting both the hypothesis and the conclusion and by interchanging their respective places. For example:

Theorem. If two angles are right angles, they are equal.
Contrapositive. If two angles are not equal, they are not (both) right angles.

Theorem. If two lines form equal alternate interior angles with a transversal, the lines are parallel.
Contrapositive. If two nonparallel lines are cut by a transversal, the alternate interior angles are unequal.

We shall now prove that if a theorem is true, its contrapositive is also true. Suppose that the theorem "If $A = B$, then $C = D$" has been proved.

Contrapositive. If $C \neq D$, then $A \neq B$.

Proof:

STATEMENTS	REASONS
1. Either $A = B$ or $A \neq B$.	1. Ax. 9.
2. If $A = B$, then $C = D$.	2. Theorem above.
3. But $C \neq D$.	3. Given.
4. Then $C = D$ and $C \neq D$.	4. Statements 2 and 3.
5. This is impossible, and $A \neq B$.	5. Ax. 9.

The relationships between a theorem, its converse, inverse, and contrapositive are illustrated by the following diagram:

1. Theorem ← → 3. Inverse
2. Converse ← → 4. Contrapositive

If one of the statements joined by the arrows is true, the other is true. That is, if a theorem is true, its contrapositive is true, and vice versa. Also, if the converse of a theorem is true, its inverse is true, and vice versa. Thus if we prove that a theorem and its converse are true, we know that the inverse and contrapositive are also true.

We could have proved the theorems on parallel lines differently by making use of the contrapositive. For example:

Theorem. If two intersecting lines are cut by a transversal, the alternate interior angles are unequal.

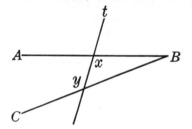

Given the intersecting lines *AB* and *CB* cut by the transversal *t*.

To prove $\angle y \neq \angle x$.

Proof: $\angle y > \angle x$ (or $\angle y \neq \angle x$). (§ 82.)

Since this theorem is proved true, we know that its contrapositive, "if two lines form equal alternate interior angles with a transversal, the lines are parallel," is true.

EXERCISES [A]. CONTRAPOSITIVES

State the contrapositives of the following statements:

1. If two angles are equal, their complements are equal.

2. If a woman is beautiful, she is young.

★★Proposition VII. Theorem

119. *If two right triangles have the hypotenuse and a leg of
one equal respectively to the hypotenuse and a leg of the other,
the triangles are congruent.*

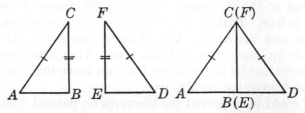

Given rt. △ *ABC* and *DEF* with ∠ *B* and *E* rt. ∠,
AC = *DF*, and *BC* = *EF*.

To prove that △ *ABC* ≅ △ *DEF*.

Selection of Method: 1. Known methods of proving △ ≅: §§ 84, 85, 112.
2. Method to be used: § 112.

Proof: STATEMENTS REASONS

1. *BC* = *EF*.	1. Why?
2. Place the two △ so that *BC* coincides with *EF*, and so that *A* and *D* lie on opposite sides of *BC*.	2. Why possible?
3. ∠ *ABC* and *DEF* are rt. ∠.	3. Why?
4. ∴ ∠ *ABD* is a st. ∠.	4. Why?
5. ∴ *ABD* is a st. line.	5. Why?
6. ∴ *ADC* is a △.	6. Why?
7. *AC* = *DC*.	7. Why?
8. ∴ ∠ *A* = ∠ *D*.	8. Why?
9. ∴ rt. △ *ABC* ≅ rt. △ *DBC* (△ *DEF*).	9. Why?

If ∠ *B* and *E* were not rt. ∠, would *ADC* be a △?

EXERCISE

If two altitudes of a triangle are equal, the triangle is isosceles.

★★ Proposition VIII.   Theorem

120.* *If one acute angle of a right triangle is 30°, the side opposite this angle is one half the hypotenuse.*

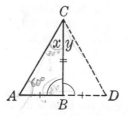

Given rt. △ *ABC* with ∠ *ACB* = 30° and ∠ *ABC* the rt. ∠.

To prove that $AB = \frac{1}{2} AC$.

Selection of Method: 1. Known methods of proving line segments =: §§ 86, 114, 115.

2. Method to be used: § 115 and axioms.

Proof: *STATEMENTS*   *REASONS*

1. Extend *AB*, making *BD* = *AB*.	1. Post. 3.
2. Draw *CD*.	2. Post. 1.
3. △ *ABC* ≅ △ *DBC*.	3. Give proof in full.
4. ∴ ∠ *D* = ∠ *A* = 60°.	4. Give proof. See § 111.
5. ∠ *y* = ∠ *x* = 30°.	5. Give proof.
6. ∴ ∠ *ACD* = 60°.	6. Why?
7. ∴ △ *ADC* is equiangular.	7. Why?
8. ∴ △ *ADC* is equilateral.	8. Why?
9. *AB* + *BD* = *AC*.	9. Why?
10. 2 *AB* = *AC*.	10. Why?
11. ∴ $AB = \frac{1}{2} AC$.	11. Why?

NOTE. Plato called the 30°-60° right triangle "the most beautiful right-angled scalene triangle."

*If desired, "Inequalities," pp. 468–474 inclusive, may be studied before Prop. VIII.

EXERCISES [A]

1. The 30°-60° right triangle and the isosceles right triangle are used in mechanical drawing. Why is $a \parallel b \parallel c$ and $d \parallel e \parallel f$?

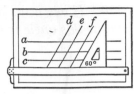

2. If one acute angle of a right triangle is twice the other acute angle, prove that the side opposite the smaller angle is half the hypotenuse.

3. If two angles of a triangle are 80° and 50°, prove that the triangle is isosceles.

4. If the exterior angle at the base of an isosceles triangle contains 135°, prove that the triangle is a right triangle.

5. If one angle of a right triangle is 30°, find the size of the angle formed by the bisectors of it and the other acute angle.

121. Analytic and Synthetic Methods of Proof. The method that you have been using for proofs is known as the *synthetic method.* Another method of proof, known as the *analytic method,* is often helpful in discovering the synthetic method.

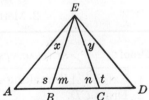

Example. *Given* $\triangle ADE$ with $AE = DE$ and $\angle x = \angle y$.

To prove that $\angle m = \angle n$.

Analysis. Let us suppose that we do not know how to prove that $\angle m = \angle n$. Before attempting to write the proof in formal order, we shall try to discover the analytic proof. We are to prove two angles equal. We recall the various methods of proving angles equal. These methods are found to be §§ 50, 87, 98, 99, and 104. After studying these methods, we believe we cannot use any but §§ 50 c and 87 a. Why can we not use § 87 b? § 50 d? We can use § 87 a if we know $BE = CE$. Why? Or we can use § 50 c if we know $\angle s = \angle t$. Why? Is $BE = CE$ if $\angle s = \angle t$? Is the converse true? We can prove $BE = CE$ if we can prove $\triangle ABE \cong \triangle DCE$. Why? $AE = DE$ and $\angle x = \angle y$. Why? To prove these triangles congruent, we need three parts of one equal respectively to three parts of the other. Now we can prove them congruent if we can show that $\angle A = \angle D$ (A.S.A.). We know that $\angle A = \angle D$. Why? Then $\angle m = \angle n$.

END Assign.

The analytic proof can be written as follows:

Analytic Proof: *STATEMENTS*   *REASONS*

1. $\angle m = \angle n$ if $BE = CE$.	1. § 87 *a.*
2. $BE = CE$ if $\triangle ABE \cong \triangle CED$.	2. § 86 *a.*
3. $\triangle ABE \cong \triangle CED$ if $\angle A = \angle D$,	3. A.S.A.
$AE = DE$,	
and $\angle x = \angle y$.	
4. $\angle A = \angle D$ if $AE = DE$.	4. § 87 *a.*
5. $AE = DE$.	5. Given.
6. $\angle x = \angle y$.	6. Given.
7. $\therefore \angle m = \angle n$.	7. Statements 1–6.

The synthetic proof can now be written by reversing the order of the above statements.

Synthetic Proof: *STATEMENTS*   *REASONS*

1. $\angle x = \angle y$.	1. Given.
2. $AE = DE$.	2. Given.
3. $\angle A = \angle D$.	3. § 87 *a.*
4. $\triangle ABE \cong \triangle CED$.	4. A.S.A.
5. $BE = CE$.	5. § 86 *a.*
6. $\angle m = \angle n$.	6. § 87 *a.*

If in the future you cannot prove a theorem by the syn
thetic method, try the analytic method.

EXERCISES

A

1. *Given* figure $ADBC$ with $AO = OB$, $\measuredangle m$ and n rt. $\measuredangle$, and AOB and COD intersecting st. lines.

Prove that $CB = AD$.

Analysis. $CB = AD$ if $\triangle COB \cong$ $\triangle AOD$. $\triangle COB \cong \triangle AOD$ if $AO = OB$, $CO = OD$, and $\angle x = \angle y$. But $AO = OB$ and $\angle x = \angle y$. Why? $CO = OD$ if $\triangle CAO \cong \triangle BOD$. Why? $\triangle CAO \cong \triangle BOD$ if $\angle m = \angle n$, $\angle AOC = \angle BOD$, and $AO = OB$. Why? But $\angle m = \angle n$, $\angle AOC = \angle BOD$, and $AO = OB$. Why?

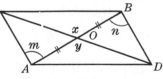

Write the **analytic** proof in full, following the model above.

assign'. #9

2. *Given* $\triangle MNP$ with $PM = PN$ and $MR = SN$.
Prove that $PR = PS$.

3. Using the figure in Ex. 2, *given* $\angle x = \angle y$ and $\angle a = \angle b$.
Prove that $\angle M = \angle N$.

4. Using the figure in Ex. 2, *given* $\angle x = \angle y$ and $MR = SN$.
Prove that $MP = NP$.

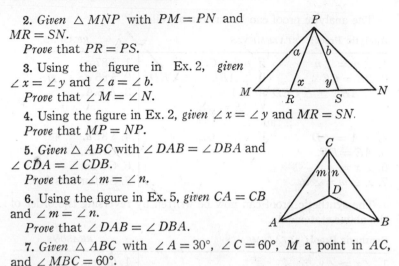

5. *Given* $\triangle ABC$ with $\angle DAB = \angle DBA$ and $\angle CDA = \angle CDB$.
Prove that $\angle m = \angle n$.

6. Using the figure in Ex. 5, *given* $CA = CB$ and $\angle m = \angle n$.
Prove that $\angle DAB = \angle DBA$.

7. *Given* $\triangle ABC$ with $\angle A = 30°$, $\angle C = 60°$, M a point in AC, and $\angle MBC = 60°$.
Prove that $AM = BM = CM$.

8. Prove that two isosceles triangles are congruent if the base and vertex angle of one are equal respectively to the base and vertex angle of the other.

9. If the altitudes drawn to two sides of a triangle are equal, the triangle is isosceles.

10. Equilateral triangles BCD and ACE are constructed outward on $\triangle ABC$.
Prove that distance $AD =$ distance BE.

11. If two lines are cut by a transversal so that the bisectors of the alternate interior angles are parallel, the lines are parallel.

12. If the sum of two exterior angles of a triangle is 270°, prove that the triangle is a right triangle.

B

13. *Given* CD intersecting AB at O, $AC \perp AB$, $DE \perp AB$, and $CD \perp DB$.
Prove that the corresponding angles of $\triangle AOC$ and DBE are equal.

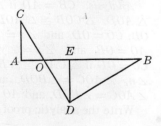

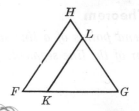

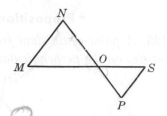

14. *Given* isosceles $\triangle FGH$ with $FH = GH$ and $KL \parallel FH$.
Prove that $KL = LG$.

15. *Given* NP intersecting MS at O with $MN = NO$ and $OP = PS$.
Prove that $MN \parallel PS$.

C

16. If the bisector of an exterior angle at one vertex of a triangle is parallel to the side opposite the vertex, the triangle is isosceles.

17. If the opposite sides of quadrilateral $ABCD$ are equal, DF and BE, the perpendiculars to the diagonal AC, are equal.

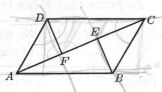

18. If, from a point within a right angle, perpendiculars are drawn to the sides of the right angle and each perpendicular is produced its own length, the line joining the extremities of the produced lines and the vertex of the right angle is a straight line.

19. *Given* the quadrilateral $ABCD$ with $AB \parallel DC$, $\angle ADC = \angle BCD$, and E and F points in CD such that $CE = DF$.
Prove that $AE = BF$.

SUGGESTIONS. Draw ⊥s from D and C to AB. Prove that $AD = BC$.

122. Proof by the Coincidence Method.
The proposition on the next page is proved by a form of indirect proof known as the *coincidence method*. It consists in drawing a geometric figure and proving that it coincides with a given geometric figure. We know that if two figures coincide, each has all the properties of the other.

In Proposition IX on the next page, we are to prove that a certain point lies on a certain line. At present we cannot prove it directly. We prove it indirectly by showing that an auxiliary line on which the given point lies coincides with the given line.

★ Proposition IX. Theorem

123. *A point equidistant from the end points of a line segment lies on the perpendicular bisector of the line segment.*

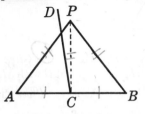

Given *CD* the ⊥ bisector of *AB*, and point *P* such that *PA = PB*.

To prove that *P* lies on *CD*.

Selection of Method: 1. No direct method known.

                             2. Method to be used: Indirect method.

Proof: *STATEMENTS*   *REASONS*

STATEMENTS	REASONS
1. Through *C*, the midpoint of *AB*, draw *PC*.	1. Posts. 7, 1.
2. *AC = CB*.	2. Why?
3. *PA = PB*.	3. Why?
4. *PC = PC*.	4. Why?
5. ∴ △ *ACP* = △ *CBP*.	5. Why?
6. ∠ *PCA* = ∠ *PCB*.	6. Why?
7. *PC* ⊥ *AB*.	7. Why?
8. ∴ *PC* coincides with *CD* and *P* lies on *CD*.	8. Post. 10.

★ 124. Corollary. *A line passing through two points each equidistant from the end points of a line segment is the perpendicular bisector of the segment.*

Suggestions. Both *A* and *B* lie
    on the ⊥ bisector of *CD*.
    Why? How many lines can
    be drawn through *A* and *B*?

Note. If desired, pages 158–166
    may be studied at this time.

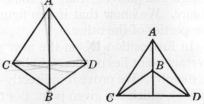

EXERCISES

A

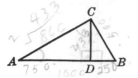

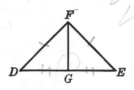

1. *Given* rt. ∠ *ACB*, ∠ *A* = 30°, *CD* ⊥ *AB*, *AC* = 866, *AB* = 1000. *Find CD*, *BC*, *DB*, and *AD*.

2. *Given* △ *DEF* with *DF* = *EF* and *DG* = *GE*. *Prove that GF* ⊥ *DE*.

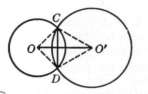

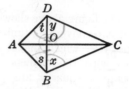

3. *Given* ⊙ *O* and *O'* intersecting at *C* and *D*. *Prove that OO'* is the ⊥ bisector of *CD*.

4. *Given* figure *ABCD* with ∠ *s* = ∠ *t* and ∠ *x* = ∠ *y*. *Prove that OB* = *OD*.

B

5. If from a point in a perpendicular to a line, equal oblique line segments are drawn to the line, they cut off equal segments from the foot of the perpendicular.

6. If a point within an angle is equidistant from the sides of the angle, it lies on the bisector of the angle.

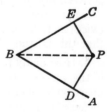

C

7. The distance of a ship, sailing in the direction *AD*, from a lighthouse can be found by the following method: At *A*, ∠ *x* is measured; the ship is steered in a straight course until a position *B* is found where ∠ *y* = 2 ∠ *x*; the distance *AB*, having been measured by the log of the ship, is said to equal the distance from *B* to the lighthouse. Can you prove that *AB* = *BC*?

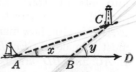

APPLICATIONS

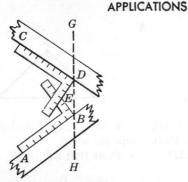

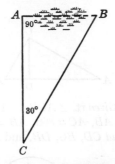

1. The figure above shows how to cut two converging timbers on a line, *GH*, which makes equal angles with the timbers. Two carpenter's squares are placed so that $BE = DE$. Prove that $\angle ABD = \angle CDB$.

2. If *A* is visible from *B* but cannot be measured on account of a swamp, show what measurements are needed in the figure above to determine *AB*. Point *C* can be determined by trial when $\angle ACB = 30°$.

3. Distances of ships from objects on land are often found in the following manner: A sailor, whose ship is at *A*, moving in direction *AC*, measures the $\angle A$ between his direction and an object *B* on shore. When he reaches a point *D* where $\angle CDB$ is twice $\angle A$, he knows that $DB = DA$. Prove that this is true. The distance *AD* is obtained from the ship's log.

4. How many pickets 2 inches wide will be needed to build a fence if the pickets are placed $1\frac{1}{2}$ inches apart between 2 posts 100 feet apart on level ground? Will more pickets be required if the fence goes over a hill?

5. A real-estate man wishes to divide the plot of ground *ABDC* into lots by constructing lines parallel to the street, *AC*. If $\angle ACE$ is 110°, how many degrees must he make $\angle CEF$, *EGH*, etc.? If *AC* and *BD* are $\perp$ *AB*, how many degrees are in $\angle CDB$?

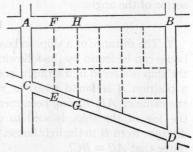

6. Explain by an illustration what measurements a carpenter could make to saw a board at a 45° angle.

7. At what angle must a carpenter cut each of two 2 × 4's to form a right angle as shown in the figure?

8. The timber *BF* supports a stairway and makes an angle of 150° with the floor *AB*. What size must the carpenter make the angles *CBD* and *CDB* of △ *CBD* so that *CB* ⊥ *AB* and *CD* ∥ *AB*? Compare the lengths of *BC* and *BD*.

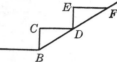

9. An ironing board is supported as shown in the figure. If *AO* = *OD* and *BO* = *OC*, prove that the ironing board *CD* is parallel to the floor *AB*. How do the lengths of *AB* and *CD* compare? Is the ironing board raised or lowered when *C* remains fixed and *D* is moved away from *C*?

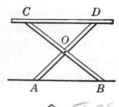

10. The rafters of a roof make an angle of 35° with the level line. What angle do the rafters form at the ridge? Why are the rafters of equal length?

11. In making a sawbuck a boy nails two pieces of wood together so that *AO* = *OC*, *OD* = *OB*, and ∠ *AOC* = 50°. At what angle must he cut the pieces of wood at *A* and *C* so that they will stand firmly on a floor? How many degrees must ∡ *D* and *B* contain in order that *DB* be parallel to *AC*? Where should he brace the sawbuck to make it more rigid?

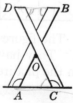

12. The figure at the right illustrates an instrument that can be used to find half an angle. The pin at *E* moves in a slot cut in bar *AC*. *AD* = *DE*. Prove that if *BDE* is adjusted to fit an angle, the angle at *A* is half of it.

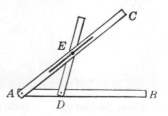

13. Show how a carpenter's square can be used to draw perpendiculars and parallels, to bisect angles, and to make angles of 45°, 30°, and 60°

125. Symmetry. A geometric figure is said to be *symmetric* with respect to a line as an axis if this line bisects all line segments perpendicular to the line and terminated by the figure.

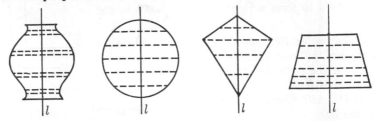

The figures above are symmetric with respect to the line *l*. Each figure has *axial* symmetry. Notice that in each case *l* is the perpendicular bisector of the dotted line segments.

A geometric figure is symmetric with respect to a point if the point bisects all line segments which pass through it and are terminated by the figure.

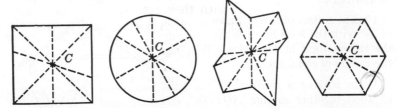

The figures above are symmetric with respect to the point *C*. They have *central* symmetry. The natural objects shown in the pictures below also have central symmetry.

Spencer; Platt; A.M.N.H.

Cross Section of an Orange   *Individual Blossom of the Fireweed*   *A Protozoan, a Microscopic Animal*

Brooklyn Botanic Garden; A.M.N.H.

Sugar-maple Leaf   *Swallowtail Butterfly*

Nature has made abundant use of symmetry in both plant and animal life, as the illustrations on these pages suggest. The beauty of a plant or animal is due, to a large extent, to the symmetry which gives it balance. Flowers, fruits, and the lower forms of animal life often possess central symmetry. Leaves, trees, landscapes with their reflections in still water, and higher forms of animal life often possess axial symmetry.

EXERCISES [A]

1. Which of the figures in the first two rows on the opposite page have both axial and central symmetry?

2. Where is the axis of symmetry of the letter A? of the letter D? of the letter M?

3. Name two letters of the alphabet which have two axes of symmetry.

4. Name two letters of the alphabet which have central symmetry.

5. Complete: If a figure is symmetric with respect to a line as an axis, the axis divides it into two __?__ parts.

Solids as well as plane figures can have symmetry. A solid can be symmetric with respect to a point, a line, or a plane. For example, a sphere is symmetric with respect to its center, it is symmetric with respect to any of its diameters as an axis, and it is symmetric with respect to any plane passing through its center.

126. Location of Points. The location of all the points which satisfy certain given conditions has always been a very interesting topic of mathematics. At this time we shall consider some simple problems on the location of points. These problems will lead us to discover some important theorems which we shall prove later.

Example. Locate ten points which are equidistant from two given parallel lines.

Solution. Locate point E which seems to be equidistant from AB and CD. Likewise locate nine other points. We see that these ten points appear to lie in a straight line parallel to AB and CD and midway between them.

EXERCISES [A]

1. How many points can you locate which are equidistant from AB and CD above? Will these points all lie in a straight line?

2. A point P moves so that it is always halfway between two parallel lines. What is its path?

3. Draw ∠ ABC. Locate within the angle a point P that seems to be equidistant from the two sides. In the same manner locate five other points. How many points can be found that are equidistant from AB and CB? Where will these points lie?

4. A boy on a hike comes to a fork in the road and decides to go through the fields, keeping the same distance from the two roads. What is his path?

5. Two parallel lines, AB and CD, are 3 inches apart. Locate several points that are twice as far from AB as from CD. What is the path of a point that moves so that it is twice as far from AB as from CD?

6. Locate a point P equidistant from M and N. Locate several other points equidistant from M and N. Do these points all lie in a straight line? What relation does the line containing all points equidistant from M and N have to the line segment joining M and N?

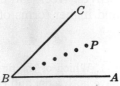

7. What is the path of a point on this page if the point moves so that it is always 1 inch from an edge?

8. A treasure is located on the bank of a river R and at equal distances from two trees, T and T'. How would you locate the treasure?

9. Locate a point A that is 2 inches from another point O. Locate another point B that is 2 inches from O. In like manner locate ten other points that are 2 inches from O. Do these points lie in a straight line or in a curve line? If point A moves so that it is always 2 inches from O, what is the name of the path it will form?

10. What is the path of the center of an automobile wheel as the car runs on a straight, level road?

11. All the points which satisfy certain conditions form a figure which is called a *locus*. What is the locus of points equidistant from two parallel lines?

12. What is the locus of points within an angle equidistant from the sides of the angle?

13. What is the locus of points 1 inch from a given point?

14. What is the locus of points equidistant from two given points?

15. What is the locus of the center of a circle that rolls on the outside of a larger circle?

16. What is the locus of the tip of the hour hand of a watch?

MISCELLANEOUS EXERCISES

B

1. It is shown in physics that when a ray of light from a candle C strikes a plane mirror at A, it is reflected along AE (E being the position of the observer's eye) in such a way that the *incident ray CA* and the *reflected ray AE* make equal angles, x and y, with the mirror. $A'E'$ is another reflected ray, which meets AE in C'. Prove that CC' is $\perp AA'$ and that $CB = BC'$.

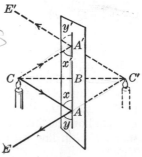

2. Prove that any other reflected ray seems to come from C', called the image of C

3. In this figure, m and n represent two plane mirrors set at an angle of 100°. From E a candle appears to be at C'', C'' being the image of C' in m, and C' being the image of C in n. What is the path of the ray of light from C reflected by both mirrors to E? How many degrees are in $\angle x$ if $\angle y = 50°$? if $\angle y = 40°$?

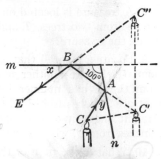

4. In the figure of Ex. 3, find $\angle y$ if $\angle x = 24°$.

5. In this figure, m and n are two parallel plane mirrors. Show that the incident ray CA is parallel to the reflected ray BE.

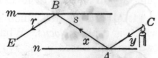

6. If the lower ends of two ladders having equal lengths are so placed that they are equidistant from a high wall, prove that the upper ends of the ladders will reach the same height on the wall.

7. If two plane mirrors, m and n, are perpendicular, show that the incident ray CA is parallel to the reflected ray BE.

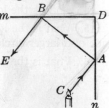

SUGGESTION. Extend lines BD and CA so that they meet.

8. Show that if two plane mirrors are set at an angle of 60° with each other, the final reflected ray makes an angle of 60° with the initial incident ray.

9. Sometimes in surveying, a triangle is formed as follows: A line segment AB, 50 feet long, is measured on a given line; the point C is located by the midpoint of a 100-foot tape whose ends are held at A and B. How many degrees are there in each of $\measuredangle A$, B, and C?

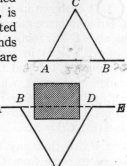

10. Forming a triangle by the method explained in Ex. 9, a surveyor is able to extend a line AB beyond an obstacle and to determine the distance from B to D. Explain how the line is extended and prove that DE is in line with AB. How is BD found?

11. In △ ADE, if AE = DE and ∠ x = ∠ y, prove that

a. ∠ h = ∠ k.
b. ∠ m = ∠ n.
c. BE = CE.

12. In the figure of Ex. 11, if ∠ r = ∠ s and ∠ x = ∠ y, prove that BE = CE.

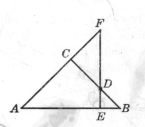

13. In the figure of Ex. 11, if AC = BD and AE = DE, prove that ∠ m = ∠ n.

14. The exterior angle at the base of an isosceles triangle is equal to the angle formed by the bisectors of the base angles.

15. If from the vertex of one of the equal angles of an isosceles triangle a perpendicular is drawn to the opposite side, it makes with the base an angle equal to one half the vertex angle of the triangle.

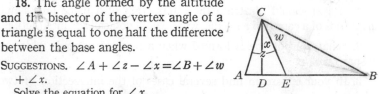

16. If through any point D in one of the equal sides BC of an isosceles △ ABC, DE is drawn ⊥ to the base AB, meeting AC extended at F, then △ CFD is isosceles.

17. D is any point in the base AB of isosceles △ ABC. The side CB is extended from B to E so that BE = BD. Then ED is drawn and extended to meet AC at F.
    Prove that ∠ CFE = 3 ∠ CEF.

18. The angle formed by the altitude and the bisector of the vertex angle of a triangle is equal to one half the difference between the base angles.

SUGGESTIONS. ∠A + ∠z − ∠x = ∠B + ∠w + ∠x.
    Solve the equation for ∠ x.

19. An altitude of a triangle divides the vertex angle into two parts whose difference equals the difference of the base angles.

*Space Geometry (Optional).** The figures we have studied are called *plane* figures, since all the points and lines of each figure lie in the same plane. In space geometry the figures also consist of points and lines, but not all the points and lines of each figure necessarily lie in the same plane.

Figures in a plane have one or two dimensions. A line has one dimension (length) and a rectangle has two dimensions (length and width). Figures in space have one, two, or three dimensions. A cube has three dimensions (length, width, and thickness).

127. Plane Surfaces. Since we have dealt with lines in our plane geometry, we may define a plane as being a surface such that a straight line joining any two points of the surface lies wholly in the surface. Although a plane is indefinite in extent, in space we usually picture it as a rectangle seen obliquely. The quadrilateral *ABCD* represents a plane. This plane may be referred to as plane *AC*, or as plane *p*. The lines *AB* and

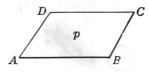

BC are drawn heavier than *AD* and *DC* to make the plane appear horizontal.

EXERCISES

1. If you should illustrate the intersection of a plane and a line by means of a card and a needle, what would you call the intersection?

2. What kind of line is formed when a piece of paper is folded in a sharp crease?

3. In your classroom find several cases of the intersection of two planes.

*The work on space geometry on pages 142–147 and elsewhere in the book is optional.

4. Can two different planes contain the same two lines?

5. How many straight lines can be drawn through one point? through two points? through any three points?

6. How many planes can contain a given point? two given points? three given points not in a straight line?

7. How many planes can contain a given straight line? two given intersecting straight lines? two parallel lines?

8. How many planes can contain a given straight line and a given point without the line?

9. How many dimensions has a line? a plane?

128. Fundamental Properties of Planes. From the preceding exercises the following postulates on planes will be apparent:

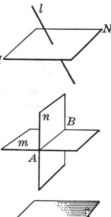

a. The intersection of a straight line and a plane is a point.

If there were two points in common, the line would lie in the plane.

b. The intersection of two planes is a straight line.

The intersection of planes *m* and *n* is the straight line *AB*.

c. A plane is determined by three points not in the same straight line.

The figure at the right shows the plane surface of a sheet of plate glass resting on three pegs.

d. A plane is determined by a line and a point without the line.

The figure at the right above shows the plane surface of a sheet of glass resting on the point of a tack and one straight edge of a bar.

e. *A plane is determined by two intersecting lines.*

f. *A plane is determined by two parallel lines.*

SUGGESTIONS. What are parallel lines? Can a plane contain both l_1 and l_2? Show that no other plane can contain l_1 and a point in l_2.

EXERCISES

1. Can you hold two pencils in such a manner that they do not lie in a plane?

2. Why is it that a table with three legs will always stand firmly on a level floor and that a table with four legs will sometimes rock?

3. Why are tripods used for the support of a surveyor's transit and a camera?

4. Are all triangles plane figures? Why?

5. Is any figure having four sides necessarily a plane figure?

6. How many applications of a straightedge are necessary to determine whether or not a surface is a plane surface?

7. Draw two intersecting planes.

8. AB, AC, and AD are three straight lines through point A but not in the same plane. How many planes are determined by these lines if they are taken two at a time?

9. AB, CD, and EF are three parallel lines, but not in the same plane. How many planes are determined by these lines if they are taken two at a time?

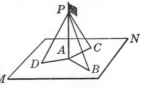

10. In the figure a flagpole PA is shown as perpendicular to plane MN representing the ground. Three wires PD, PB, and PC brace the flagpole. (*a*) Is $PA \perp AD, AB$, and AC? (*b*) If $PA = 150$ feet and $AB = 80$ feet, how long is PB? (*c*) If $AB = AC$, prove that $PB = PC$.

129. Foot of a Line. The point of intersection of a straight line and a plane is called the *foot* of the line.

130. Line Perpendicular to a Plane. A *line* is *perpendicular to a plane* if it is perpendicular to every line in the plane passing through its foot. If a line meets a plane and is not perpendicular to it, it is said to be *oblique* to the plane.

131. Theorem 1. *If a line is perpendicular to each of two intersecting lines at their point of intersection, it is perpendicular to the plane of the two lines.*

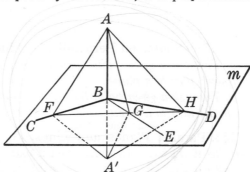

Given AB ⊥ BC and *BD*, and *m* the plane of the intersecting lines *BC* and *BD*.

To prove AB ⊥ plane *m*.

SUGGESTIONS.

1. Through *B* draw any other line *BE* in plane *m*. Why possible?
2. Draw any line intersecting *BC* at *F*, *BE* at *G*, and *BD* at *H*. **Why** possible?
3. Extend *AB* to *A'* so that *BA' = BA* and draw *AF, AG, AH, A'F, A'G,* and *A'H*. Why possible?
4. *AF = A'F, AH = A'H,* and *FH = FH*.
5. △ *AFH* ≅ △ *A'FH*.
6. Then ∠ *AFG* = ∠ *A'FG* and △ *AFG* ≅ △ *A'FG*.
7. *AG = A'G, BG ⊥ AB,* and *AB ⊥ m*.

EXERCISES

1. *Given PO ⊥* plane *m* at *O,* the center of a circle in the plane.

Prove that *PA = PB* and ∠ *PAO* = ∠ *PBO*.

2. In a plane, how many lines may be drawn perpendicular to a given line at a given point in the line?

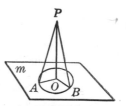

3. In space, how many lines may be drawn perpendicular to a given line at a given point in the line?

4. Are all lines perpendicular to a vertical line horizontal?

5. Are all lines perpendicular to a horizontal line vertical?

6. Can two flagpoles at opposite ends of a large building be both parallel and vertical?

In the following exercises, illustrate by means of cardboard and pencil:

7. How many lines may be drawn perpendicular to a plane at a given point in the plane? through a given external point?

8. How many planes may be drawn perpendicular to a line at a point in the line? through an external point?

132. Postulates on Perpendicular Lines and Planes.
a. Through a given point there can be one line, and only one, perpendicular to a plane.

b. Through a given point there can be one plane, and only one, perpendicular to a line.

133. Parallel Planes and Lines.
A *line* and a *plane* are *parallel* if they do not meet even if extended. Two *planes* are *parallel* if they do not meet even if extended.

134. Skew Lines.
Two lines in space that are neither parallel nor intersecting are called *skew lines*. Skew lines cannot lie in the same plane. Why?

EXERCISES

1. Are two plumb lines parallel?

2. Can two skew lines intersect? be perpendicular to each other?

3. Can two skew lines both be vertical? horizontal?

4. If two planes are parallel, is every line in one of the planes parallel to the other plane?

135. Theorem 2.
Two planes perpendicular to the same line are parallel.

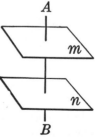

Given planes *m* and *n* each ⊥ *AB*.

To prove m ∥ n.

SUGGESTION. Prove indirectly, using §§ 132 *b* and 133.

136. Theorem 3. *If two parallel planes are cut by a third plane, the lines of intersection are parallel.*

Given the ∥ planes *m* and *n* intersected by plane *r* in *AB* and *CD* respectively.

To prove AB ∥ CD.

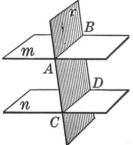

Proof: STATEMENTS   REASONS

1. *AB* and *CD* lie in the same plane *r*.	1. Given.
2. *AB* in *m* cannot meet *CD* in *n*.	2. § 133.
3. *AB* ∥ *CD*.	3. § 88.

137. Theorem 4. *A line perpendicular to one of two parallel planes is perpendicular to the other.*

Given the ∥ planes *m* and *n* and *AB* ⊥ *m*.

To prove AB ⊥ n.

Proof: STATEMENTS   REASONS

1. Through *AB* pass plane *r* intersecting *m* and *n* in *CE* and *DG* respectively. Also through *AB* pass plane *s* intersecting *m* and *n* in *CF* and *DH* respectively.	1. §§ 128 *b*, 128 *d*.
2. *CE* ∥ *DG* and *CF* ∥ *DH*.	2. § 136.
3. *AB* ⊥ *CE* and *CF*.	3. § 130.
4. ∴ *AB* ⊥ *DG* and *DH*.	4. § 101.
5. ∴ *AB* ⊥ *n.*	5. § 131.

138. Corollary. *Through a point outside a plane there can be one plane, and only one, parallel to a given plane.*

REVIEW QUESTIONS

1. What do you know about two perpendiculars to the same line at different points in the line? at the same point in the line?

2. Through a point outside a line how many lines can be drawn parallel to the line?

3. How many acute angles has every triangle?

4. What is the name of a triangle having two acute angles and one right angle? two acute angles and one obtuse angle? three acute angles?

5. What is the sum of the angles of a triangle?

6. What kind of theorem is formed by interchanging the hypothesis and conclusion of a given theorem?

7. What kind of theorem is formed by negating the hypothesis and conclusion of a given theorem?

8. Under what conditions is an exterior angle of a triangle an acute angle? a right angle?

9. What is the location of points that are equidistant from two given points?

10. If one angle of a triangle is a right angle, what is the relation between the other two angles?

11. In an isosceles right triangle how many degrees are there in each angle?

12. When two parallel lines are cut by a transversal, what pairs of angles are equal?

13. In what right triangle is one leg equal to one half the hypotenuse?

14. How many degrees are there in one angle of an equilateral triangle?

15. How many degrees are there in the angle formed by the bisectors of the two acute angles of a 30°-60° right triangle?

16. The vertex angle of an isosceles triangle is one fourth of a base angle. How many degrees are there in each angle?

17. What is the difference between axial symmetry and central symmetry?

18. State five ways of proving right triangles congruent.

SUMMARY OF PRINCIPAL METHODS OF PROOF

139. *Two right triangles are congruent*

a. If the hypotenuse and an acute angle of one are equal respectively to the hypotenuse and an acute angle of the other.

b. If the hypotenuse and a leg of one are equal respectively to the hypotenuse and a leg of the other.

140. *Two line segments are equal*

If they are sides opposite equal angles in a triangle.

141. *Two angles are equal*

a. If they are alternate interior or corresponding angles of parallel lines.

b. If their sides are parallel (or perpendicular), right side to right side and left side to left side.

c. If they are the third angles of two triangles having two angles of one equal respectively to two angles of the other.

142. *Two lines are perpendicular*

a. If one of them is parallel to a third line and the other is perpendicular to the third line.

b. If two points of one line are equidistant from two points of the other.

143. *Two lines are parallel*

a. If they do not intersect even if extended.

b. If a pair of (1) alternate interior angles or (2) corresponding angles are equal.

c. If two interior angles on the same side of the transversal are supplementary.

d. If they are perpendicular to a third line.

e. If they are parallel to a third line.

144. *Two angles are complementary*

If they are the acute angles of a right triangle.

145. *Two angles are supplementary*

If they are the interior angles on the same side of a transversal of two parallel lines.

WORD LIST

Can you spell and use all the following words correctly?

alternate	consecutive	interior	parallel
analytic	indirect	locus	synthetic

TEST 8

Supplying Reasons (*Ten Minutes*)

Supply axioms, postulates, definitions, or theorems for the following statements:

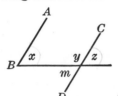
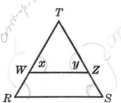

If *AB* ∥ *CD*,

1. ∠ *x* = ∠ *z*. **2.** ∠ *m* = ∠ *x*.

3. ∠ *x* and ∠ *y* are supp.

4. ∠ *m* = ∠ *z*.

If *RT* = *TS* and *WZ* ∥ *RS*,

5. ∠ *x* = ∠ *R*. **7.** ∠ *y* = ∠ *S*.

6. ∠ *R* = ∠ *S*. **8.** ∠ *x* = ∠ *y*.

9. *WT* = *TZ*.

TEST 9

Drawing a Figure for a Theorem and Stating the Hypothesis and Conclusion (*Twenty Minutes*)

Draw the figure for each of the following theorems and state accurately, in terms of the letters on the figure, the hypothesis and conclusion:

1. If a line intersects the equal sides of an isosceles triangle and is parallel to the base, the new triangle formed is also isosceles.

2. If an acute angle of one right triangle equals an acute angle of another right triangle, the remaining acute angles are equal.

3. The three altitudes of a triangle bisect the angles of the triangle formed by joining the feet of the altitudes.

4. If two lines are cut by a transversal so that the bisectors of two corresponding angles are parallel, the lines are parallel.

TEST 10

Applications (*Twenty Minutes*)

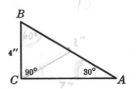

1. How many degrees are there in ∠ B? in ∠ C?

2. How many inches are there in *AB*?

3. A wheel makes 30 revolutions per minute. Through how many degrees does it turn in one second?

4. How many degrees are there in each base angle of an isosceles right triangle?

5. If *AB* ∥ *CD* and *MN* = *PN*, how many degrees are there in ∠ *x*? in ∠ *z*? in ∠ *r*?

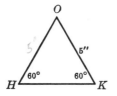

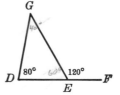

6. How many inches are in *HO*?

7. How many degrees are in ∠ *G*?

8. If *x* represents the number of degrees in an angle, what represents the number of degrees in its complement?

9. If two parallels are cut by a transversal, how many degrees are in the angle formed by the bisectors of two interior angles on the same side of the transversal?

10. If the vertex angle of an isosceles triangle is 40°, how many degrees are in the angle included by the bisectors of the base angles?

11. One acute angle of a right triangle is half the other. How many degrees are there in each acute angle?

In Making Constructions Are You Careful to Hold Your Compasses as Shown in the Picture Above?

CHAPTER V

Constructions

146. Construction Problems. In § 36 a problem is defined as a *geometric construction to be made or a computation to be performed.* For example, we may be asked to construct the altitude of a given equilateral triangle or to compute the length of the altitude. The word "construct," as used in geometry, means to draw accurately. The only instruments used in constructions are the straightedge for drawing straight lines and the compasses for drawing arcs and measuring the lengths of line segments. In construction work, remember:

1. Before drawing a line, it is necessary to locate two of its points.
2. A point is located by finding the intersection of two straight lines, two arcs, or a straight line and an arc.

147. Parts in the Solution of a Construction Problem.

I. A statement of the problem.
II. A representation of the given parts.
III. A statement of what is given in terms of the drawing.
IV. A statement of what is to be constructed.
V. The construction, with a description of and an authority for each step.
VI. A statement that the required construction has been made.
VII. A proof of the statement in part VI.

148. Discussion of a Problem. It is often desirable to discuss the solution of a problem as to the number of solutions, special cases, limitations, and applications.

★★ Proposition I. Problem

149. *To construct a triangle, given the three sides.*

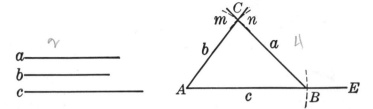

Given a, b, and *c,* the sides of a △.

To construct the △.

Construction:

STATEMENTS	REASONS
1. On any line AE construct $AB = c$.	1. § 23 a.
2. With A as a center and a radius $= b$ draw an arc m.	2. Post. 5.
3. With B as a center and a radius $= a$ draw an arc n intersecting arc m at C.	3. Post. 5.
4. Draw AC and BC.	4. Post. 1.

Then ABC is the required △.

Proof:

△ ABC has sides $= a$, b, and c.	Const.

Discussion. If $a + b < c$ or if $a + b = c$, the construction is impossible. Why?

NOTE. In studying the solution of a problem, first draw the *given* parts on a piece of paper and then construct the parts of the figure as you read the statements in the *construction*.

EXERCISES [A]. CONSTRUCTIONS

1. Construct an equilateral triangle given one side.

2. Construct a triangle having sides of $1\frac{1}{2}$, 2, and 3 inches respectively.

★★Proposition II. Problem

150. *To bisect a given angle.*

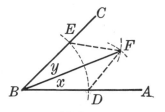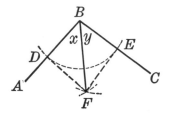

Given ∠ *ABC.*

To construct its bisector.

Construction: *STATEMENTS*   *REASONS*

1. With *B* as a center and any radius draw an arc intersecting *BA* at *D* and *BC* at *E*.	1. Post. 5.
2. With *D* and *E* as centers and with = radii draw arcs which will intersect at *F*.	2. Post. 5.
3. Draw *BF*.	3. Post. 1.

Then BF is the required bisector.

Proof:

1. Draw *DF* and *EF*. In ▲ *BDF* and *BEF*,	1. Post. 1.
2. *BD* = *BE* and *DF* = *EF*.	2. Const.
3. *BF* = *BF*.	3. Why?
4. ∴ △ *BDF* ≅ △ *BEF*.	4. Why?
5. ∴ ∠ *x* = ∠ *y*.	5. Why?
6. ∴ *BF* bisects ∠ *ABC*.	6. Why?

NOTE. This is the method of constructing the bisector of an angle mentioned in Post 8.

EXERCISES [A]. CONSTRUCTIONS

1. Draw four angles having different sizes and positions and construct their bisectors.

2. Draw an acute triangle and construct the bisectors of its angles. Do the same for a right triangle and an obtuse triangle.

★★ Proposition III. Problem

151. *With a given vertex and a given side to construct an angle equal to a given angle.*

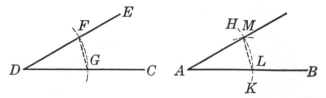

Given vertex A, side AB, and $\angle CDE$.

To construct an $\angle = \angle CDE$ and having A as the vertex and AB as one side.

Construction: *STATEMENTS* *REASONS*

STATEMENTS	REASONS
1. With D as a center and any radius draw an arc intersecting DE at F and DC at G.	1. Post. 5.
2. With A as a center and a radius $= DF$, draw arc HK intersecting AB at L.	2. Why possible?
3. With L as a center and a radius $= GF$, draw an arc intersecting $\overarc{HK}$ at M.	3. Why possible?
4. Draw AM.	4. Why possible?

Then $\angle BAM = \angle CDE$.

Proof: (The proof is left to the student.)

SUGGESTION. Draw GF and LM.

EXERCISE [A]. CONSTRUCTIONS

With a given vertex and a given side construct an angle equal to a given obtuse angle.

152. Construction Problems in Proofs. The statements of construction problems may be used as reasons in proofs in the same way as theorems are used. The wording is usually changed. For example, Prop. III may be stated, "An angle can be constructed equal to a given angle."

★★Proposition IV. Problem

153. *To construct a triangle, given two sides and the in-cluded angle.*

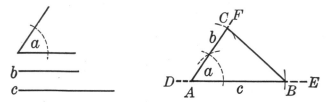

Given sides b and c and the included $\angle a$.

To construct the $\triangle$.

Construction: STATEMENTS	REASONS
1. On any line DE construct $AB = c$.	1. § 23 a.
2. At A construct $\angle BAF = \angle a$.	2. § 151.
3. On AF construct $AC = b$.	3. Why possible?
4. Draw BC.	4. Why possible?

Then ABC is the required $\triangle$.

Proof: (The proof is left to the student.)

★★Proposition V. Problem

154. *To construct a triangle, given two angles and the in-cluded side.*

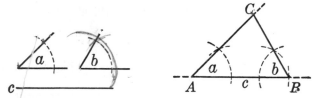

Given $\angle\!\!\!\angle\ a$ and b and the included side c.

To construct the $\triangle$.

(The construction and proof are left to the student.)

★★ Proposition VI. Problem

155. *To construct the perpendicular bisector of a given line segment.*

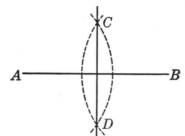

Given the line segment *AB*.

To construct the ⊥ bisector of *AB*.

Construction: *STATEMENTS*   *REASONS*

1. With *A* and *B* as centers and with = radii draw arcs intersecting at *C* and *D*.	1. Post. 5.
2. Draw *CD*.	2. Why possible?

Then CD is the ⊥ bisector of AB.

Proof:

1. *C* is equidistant from *A* and *B*.	1. Const.
2. *D* is equidistant from *A* and *B*.	2. Why?
3. ∴ *CD* is the ⊥ bisector of *AB*.	3. § 124.

EXERCISES [A]. CONSTRUCTIONS

1. Can the method of § 155 be used to bisect a line segment? to construct a perpendicular?

2. See if you can construct the perpendicular bisector of a line segment by locating two points on the same side of the line segment and each equidistant from the end points of the line segment.

3. Construct a right angle.

4. Construct a right triangle, having given the two legs.

5. Divide a line segment into four equal parts.

★★Proposition VII. Problem

156. *To construct a perpendicular to a given line from a given point without the line.*

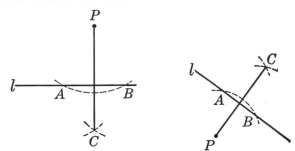

Given line *l* and point *P* without *l*.

To construct a ⊥ to *l* from *P*.

Construction: *STATEMENTS* *REASONS*

1. With *P* as a center draw an arc that will intersect *l* in two points, *A* and *B*.	1. Post. 5.
2. With *A* and *B* as centers and with = radii, draw arcs intersecting at *C*.	2. Why possible?
3. Draw *PC*.	3. Why possible?

Then PC ⊥ AB.

Proof: (The proof is left to the student.)

SUGGESTION. Show that *P* and *C* are each equidistant from *A* and *B*.

EXERCISES [B]. CONSTRUCTIONS

1. Construct perpendiculars to the sides of an angle from a point within the angle.

2. Construct the three altitudes of an acute triangle.

3. Construct the three altitudes of an obtuse triangle.

4. Construct a right triangle and then construct its three altitudes.

5. From Exs. 2, 3, and 4, what common relation do the altitudes of a triangle seem to have?

★★Proposition VIII. Problem

157. *To construct a perpendicular to a given line at a given point in the line.*

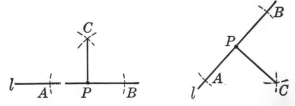

Given line *l* and point *P* in line *l*.

To construct a ⊥ to *l* at *P*.

(The construction and proof are left to the student.)

EXERCISES. CONSTRUCTIONS

A

1. Construct a 45° angle. (What part of a right angle is this?)

2. Construct a 60° angle. (Construct an equilateral △.)

3. Construct a 30° angle; a 15° angle.

4. Construct a 75° angle. (75° = 60° + 15°.)

5. Construct the bisectors of the angles of an acute triangle; of a right triangle; of an obtuse triangle. What common relation do the bisectors of the angles of a triangle seem to have?

B

6. Construct perpendiculars to the sides of a triangle from a point without the triangle.

7. Construct a right triangle and then construct the perpendicular bisectors of its legs.

8. Construct the perpendicular bisectors of the sides of an acute triangle; of an obtuse triangle. What common relation do the perpendicular bisectors of the sides of a triangle seem to have?

9. Construct a square (a quadrilateral having four equal sides and a right angle).

★★Proposition IX. Problem

158. *Through a given point to construct a line parallel to a given line.*

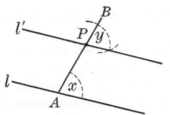

Given the point P and the line l.

To construct the line through $P \parallel l$.

Construction: *STATEMENTS*   *REASONS*

1. Draw BA through P and any point A in l.	1. Why possible?
2. With P as the vertex and PB as a side construct $\angle y = \angle x$.	2. § 151.

Then $l' \parallel l$.

Proof:

1. $\angle y = \angle x$.	1. Const.
2. $\therefore l' \parallel l$.	2. Why?

EXERCISES [A]. CONSTRUCTIONS

1. Make the construction for Prop. IX by constructing a pair of equal alternate interior angles.

2. Make the construction for Prop. IX by constructing a perpendicular from P to l and then constructing a perpendicular to this perpendicular at P.

3. Construct a line through the vertex of a triangle parallel to the base.

4. Through the vertices of a triangle construct parallels to the opposite sides.

5. Construct a polygon of four sides having the opposite sides parallel.

159. Directions for the Solution of Construction Problems. If the solution of a construction problem is not apparent, the following directions will be found useful:

---

1. Sketch (do not construct) the figure as it will appear when completed.
2. In the sketch indicate the parts of the figure that are given.
3. Study the sketch to discover (a) which given part should be constructed first; (b) how the additional parts can be constructed by means of known constructions and theorems.
4. After determining the method, construct the figure.

Example. Construct a right triangle, given the hypotenuse and an acute angle.

Given the hypotenuse c and an acute $\angle B$.

To construct the rt. $\triangle$.

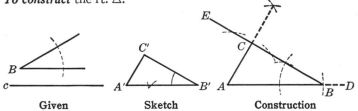

| Given | Sketch | Construction |

Analysis. At this point in the solution of the problem we determine the method of construction and perform the construction, proceeding according to the directions above as follows:

1. We sketch the $\triangle$ as it will appear when completed and label its vertices A', B', and C'.

2. In the sketch we indicate the given hypotenuse and the given $\angle B'$ by heavy lines, colored lines, or check marks.

3 and 4. From a study of the sketch we see that we can now construct the hypotenuse c and its adjacent $\angle B$. On AD we construct $AB = c$ (§ 23 a) and $\angle ABE = \angle B$ (§ 151). It remains to locate point C on BE. From the sketch we know that $\angle C'$ is a rt. $\angle$. Then $A'C' \perp B'C'$. This suggests the construction of a $\perp$ from A to BE. We next construct this $\perp$ from A to BE (§ 156), completing the required rt. $\triangle ABC$.

We are now ready to write the *construction* and *proof* of the problem.

EXERCISES. CONSTRUCTIONS

A

1. Construct a right triangle, given one leg and the adjacent acute angle.

2. Bisect one side of a given triangle. Through this point of bisection construct a line parallel to another side of the triangle.

3. Construct the three medians of a triangle. (Do the medians appear to meet in a point?)

4. Construct an isosceles triangle, given the base and altitude.

5. Construct an isosceles triangle, given one of the equal sides and the vertex angle.

6. Construct an isosceles triangle, given the base and the sum of its equal sides.

7. Construct an isosceles right triangle, given a leg.

B

8. Construct an angle equal to the sum of two given angles. (Construct two adjacent angles equal respectively to the given angles.)

9. Construct an angle equal to the sum of the angles of a given triangle.

10. Given an acute scalene triangle ABC. Construct the altitude on AB, the median on AB, and the bisector of angle C.

11. Construct one of the base angles of an isosceles triangle, given the vertex angle. (What is the sum of the three angles of a triangle?)

12. Construct a 30°-60° right triangle, given the hypotenuse.

13. Construct a right triangle, given the hypotenuse and one leg.

14. Construct a 30°-60° right triangle, given the shorter leg.

C

15. Construct $\triangle ABC$, given AB, AC, and the median on AB.

16. Divide a line segment into eight equal parts.

17. Construct an equilateral triangle, given the altitude.

18. Construct an isosceles triangle, given one of the equal sides and the altitude to the base.

19. Construct a triangle, given two angles and the side opposite one of them.

160. Trisection of an Angle. The *trisection of any given angle* (division of an angle into three equal parts), the *duplication of the cube* (the construction of $\sqrt[3]{2}$, or finding the side of a cube whose volume is double that of a given cube), and the *quadrature of the circle* (squaring a circle, or finding the square whose area is equal to that of a given circle) are the three famous geometric problems of antiquity.

It can be proved that these problems cannot be solved by using only the straightedge and compasses, but the proofs are beyond the scope of high-school mathematics. The early Greeks must have known of the impossibility of trisecting an angle by the use of the straightedge and compasses because they constructed other curves to use in the trisection of an angle.

Nicomedes (about 180 B.C.) invented a curve known as the *conchoid* by which an angle can be trisected and a cube can be duplicated. No doubt he invented this curve for one or both of these constructions.

Trisecting an Angle Using the Conchoid.* Let $\angle ABC$ be the given angle to be tri-sected. From D, any point in AB, draw $DE \perp BC$. Taking P_1, any point on DE, draw BP_1. Extend BP_1 so that $P_1P = 2BD$. Then P is a point on the upper branch of the conchoid. Other points, such as M, N, and Q, of the curve may be located in the same manner, and a smooth curve may be drawn

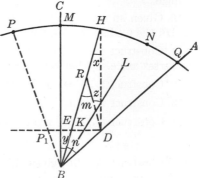

connecting them. The curve $PMNQ$ is part of the conchoid.

At D erect a $\perp$ to ED intersecting the conchoid at H. Draw BH intersecting ED at K. Draw BL bisecting $\angle ABH$. Then BL and BH trisect $\angle ABC$.

*The algebraic equation of the conchoid is $x^2y^2 = (b + y)^2(a^2 - y^2)$.

Proof. Take R, the midpoint of KH. Draw DR. $DH \parallel BC$. Why? $\angle x = \angle y$. Why? $RD = RH$ (see § 188). $\angle x = \angle z$. Why? $DB = DR$ (Ax. 6). $\angle n = \angle m$. Why? But $\angle m = \angle x + \angle z$. Why? Then $\angle n = \angle m = \angle x + \angle z = 2 \angle x = 2 \angle y$. Then $\angle HBC = \angle LBH = \angle ABL$, and $\angle ABC$ is trisected.

Since there are an infinite number of points of the curve and only a finite number of them can be constructed, this method of trisection is not a purely geometric one.

MISCELLANEOUS EXERCISES [C]

1. The figure below shows how to trisect an angle ABC by means of an instrument known as an angle trisector. BE and BF are the lines of trisection. Make a trisector and trisect an angle with it. Prove the construction correct.

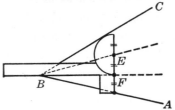

2. Construct a right angle and trisect it by using the angle trisector.

3. Construct a 60° angle and trisect it by using the angle trisector.

4. Use the angle trisector to trisect the three angles of a given triangle.

5. A ray of light starting from C is reflected by a plane mirror AB to point E. Locate the point where the ray strikes the mirror. (See Ex. 1, p. 139.)

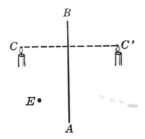

6. Charles, standing 10 feet in front of a plane mirror, sees in the mirror an object located 6 feet in front of the mirror. Construct the paths of the incident and reflected rays, using a scale of 1 inch = 4 feet.

7. Two plane mirrors are perpendicular to each other. A ray of light from an object C is reflected by the mirrors to the eye E. Construct the path of the ray of light.

8. Two plane mirrors are parallel. A ray of light from an object O is reflected by the mirrors to the eye at E. Construct the path of the ray.

9. A man sees his eye reflected by two plane mirrors placed at an angle of 60°. Construct the path of the ray of light which starts from his eye and after being reflected by the two mirrors returns to his eye

10. A billiard ball driven against the side of the table rebounds at an acute angle equal to the angle at which it strikes the side. A player wishes to drive a ball *A* against the side *CD* in such a way that it will rebound and strike ball *B*. Show how to locate the point on *CD* where the ball must strike.

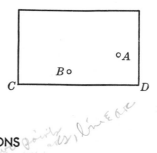

REVIEW QUESTIONS

1. How is a line located?

2. How is a point located?

3. Explain the difference between a problem and a theorem.

4. Name in order the seven steps in the solution of a problem.

5. Make the following constructions:

a. Construct a triangle, given the three sides.

b. Bisect a given angle.

c. With a given vertex and a given side construct an angle equal to a given angle.

d. Construct a triangle, given two sides and the included angle.

e. Construct a triangle, given two angles and the included side.

f. Construct the perpendicular bisector of a given line segment.

g. Construct a perpendicular to a given line from a given point without the line.

h. Construct a perpendicular to a given line at a given point in the line.

i. Through a given point construct a line parallel to a given line.

WORD LIST

Can you spell and use all the following words correctly?

adjacent	included	parallel	solution
construction	isosceles	perpendicular	trisection
discussion	miscellaneous	problem	vertex

SUMMARY OF CONSTRUCTIONS

161. *Bisectors*

a. To bisect a given angle.
b. To construct the perpendicular bisector of a given line segment.

162. *Perpendiculars*

a. To construct a perpendicular to a given line from a given point without the line.
b. To construct a perpendicular to a given line at a given point in the line.

163. *Parallel*

Through a given point to construct a line parallel to a given line.

164. *Equal angles*

With a given vertex and a given side to construct an angle equal to a given angle.

165. *Triangles*

a. To construct a triangle, given the three sides.
b. To construct a triangle, given two sides and the included angle.
c. To construct a triangle, given two angles and the included side.

TEST 11

Constructions (*Twenty-five Minutes*)

Make the following geometric constructions as accurately as you can:

1. Construct a triangle congruent to a given triangle.
2. Construct an altitude of a given triangle.
3. Construct a circle having a given diameter.
4. Construct a line passing through a given point and parallel to a given line.
5. Construct an isosceles triangle, given one of the equal sides and the vertex angle.

Notice the Many Polygons in the Structure of This Parachute Jump at an Amusement Park

CHAPTER VI

Polygons

166. Polygon. A *polygon* is a closed broken line in a plane. *ABCDE* is a polygon. Points *A, B, C, D,* and *E* are the *vertices* of the polygon, and *AB, BC, CD, DE,* and *EA* are the *sides*. The *perimeter* of a polygon is the sum of its sides. A *diagonal* of a polygon is a line segment joining any two nonadjacent vertices, as *AD*.

167. a. Polygons Classified as to Angles. An *equiangular* polygon is a polygon having all its angles equal. A *convex* polygon is a polygon having each angle less than a straight angle. A *concave* polygon is a polygon having at least one angle greater than a straight angle. Unless otherwise stated, "polygon" will mean "convex polygon."

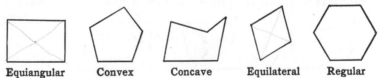

Equiangular   Convex   Concave   Equilateral   Regular

b. Polygons Classified as to Sides. An *equilateral* polygon is a polygon having all its sides equal. Polygons are named according to the number of sides, as follows:

Number of Sides	Kind of Polygon	Number of Sides	Kind of Polygon
3	Triangle	8	Octagon
4	Quadrilateral	9	Nonagon
5	Pentagon	10	Decagon
6	Hexagon	15	Pentadecagon
7	Heptagon	n	n-gon

Polygons in an Egyptian Ceiling Pattern (Second Century A.D.)

168. Regular Polygon. A *regular* polygon is a polygon which is both equilateral and equiangular.

169. Parallelogram. A *parallelogram* ($\square$) is a quadrilateral having two pairs of parallel sides. A *rhombus* is a parallelogram that has two equal adjacent sides. A *rectangle* is a parallelogram having one right angle. The corollary in § 175 proves that all angles of a rectangle are right angles. A *square* is a rectangle having two equal adjacent sides. Remember that a square is a special rectangle and also a special rhombus.

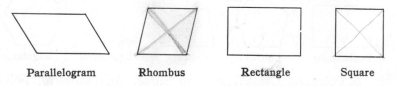

Parallelogram   Rhombus   Rectangle   Square

NOTE. Since a rhombus and a rectangle are parallelograms, every theorem which applies to a parallelogram will also apply to a rhombus and a rectangle. Also, any theorem which applies to a rhombus or a rectangle will apply to a square.

170. Base and Altitude of a Parallelogram. Any side of a parallelogram may be considered as its *base*. It is usually the side on which the figure is supposed to stand. The *altitude* of a parallelogram is the perpendicular to the base from any point in the opposite side.

★Proposition I. Theorem

171. *A diagonal of a parallelogram divides it into two congruent triangles.*

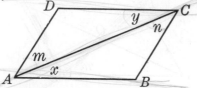

(The demonstration is left to the student.)

SUGGESTIONS. Why is $AB \parallel DC$? $AD \parallel BC$?

★★172. Corollary I. *The opposite sides of a parallelogram are equal.*

★★173. Corollary II. *The opposite angles of a parallelogram are equal.*

174. Corollary III. *Any two consecutive angles of a parallelogram are supplementary.*

(The proof of this corollary is based on § 100.)

175. Corollary IV. *All angles of a rectangle are right angles.*

176. Corollary V. *Segments of parallels included between parallels are equal.*

177. Corollary VI. *Two parallels are everywhere equidistant.*

NOTE. From Cor. VI we know that the altitudes of a parallelogram are equal.

178. Corollary VII. *All sides of a rhombus are equal.*

EXERCISES [A]

1. Which corollary states that all sides of a square are equal?

2. If points E and F trisect the diagonal AC of $\square\, ABCD$, then $BE = DF$.

3. Draw a rhombus $ABCD$. Prove that the altitude from C to AB equals the altitude from C to AD.

4. Two opposite angles of a parallelogram contain $(8x - 3)°$ and $(5x + 9)°$. How many degrees are there in each angle?

★Proposition II. Theorem

179. *The diagonals of a parallelogram bisect each other.*

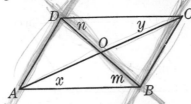

Given the ▱ *ABCD* with the diagonals *AC* and *BD* intersecting at *O*.

To prove that *AO* = *OC* and *BO* = *OD*.

Selection of Method: 1. Known methods of proving line segments =:
§§ 86, 140, 172, 176, 177, 178.
2. Method to be used: § 86 *a*. p. 100

Proof: (The proof is left to the student.)

Proposition III. Theorem

180. *The diagonals of a rhombus are perpendicular to each other.*

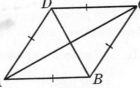

Given the rhombus *ABCD* with the diagonals *AC* and *BD*.

To prove that *AC* ⊥ *BD*.

Selection of Method: 1. Known methods of proving lines ⊥: §§ 51, 142.
2. Method to be used: § 142 *b*. p. 149

Proof: (The proof is left to the student.)

EXERCISES. PARALLELOGRAMS

A

1. Name the methods you have learned in this chapter for proving
a. Two line segments equal.   *d.* Two lines perpendicular.
b. Two angles equal.   *e.* Two angles supplementary.
c. Two triangles congruent.
Have you found these methods on pages 543–546?

2. If one angle of a parallelogram contains 65°, how many degrees are there in each of the other angles?

3. One angle of a parallelogram is three times as large as another. Find the number of degrees in each of the angles of the parallelogram.

4. Is a square a rectangle? a parallelogram? a rhombus?

5. Is a rectangle a square? a parallelogram? a rhombus?

6. Name some of the properties of a square.

7. The diagonals of a rhombus bisect the angles through which they pass.

8. The diagonals of a rectangle are equal.

B

9. Perpendiculars drawn to a diagonal of a parallelogram from opposite vertices are parallel and equal.

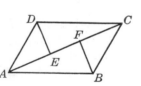

10. The diagonals of rhombus *ABCD* intersect in *O*. *BO* is 6 inches and ∠ *ADC* is 120°. Find *DO*, *AD*, and *DC*.

11. If the bisectors of two opposite angles of a parallelogram are terminated by the sides, the bisectors are parallel and equal.

C

12. If from any point in the base of an isosceles triangle parallels to the equal sides are drawn, a parallelogram is formed whose perimeter is equal to the sum of the equal sides.

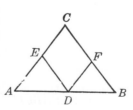

13. The bisectors of two consecutive angles of a parallelogram are perpendicular.

★★Proposition IV. Theorem

181. *If the opposite sides of a quadrilateral are equal, the figure is a parallelogram.*

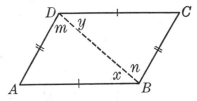

Given quadrilateral *ABCD* with *AB = DC* and *AD = BC*.

To prove that *ABCD* is a ▱.

Selection of Method: 1. Known methods of proving that a quadrilateral is a ▱: § 169.
2. Method to be used: § 169.

Proof:

STATEMENTS	REASONS
1. Draw *BD*.	1. Why possible?
In △ *ABD* and *BCD*,	
2. *AD = BC* and *AB = DC*.	2. Why?
3. *BD = BD*.	3. Why?
4. ∴ △ *ABD* ≅ △ *BCD*.	4. Why?
5. ∴ ∠ *x* = ∠ *y*.	5. Why?
6. ∴ *AB* ∥ *DC*.	6. Why?
7. ∠ *m* = ∠ *n*.	7. Why?
8. ∴ *AD* ∥ *BC*.	8. Why?
9. ∴ *ABCD* is a ▱.	9. § 169.

EXERCISES [A]. PARALLELOGRAMS

1. Name two methods of proving that a quadrilateral is a parallelogram.

2. *Given AD = BC and ∠ x = ∠ y.*
Prove that ABCD is a ▱.

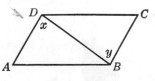

★★ Proposition V. Theorem

182. *If two sides of a quadrilateral are equal and parallel, the figure is a parallelogram.*

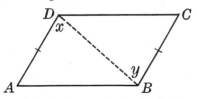

Given quadrilateral *ABCD* with *AD* = *BC* and *AD* ∥ *BC*.

To prove that *ABCD* is a □.

Selection of Method: 1. Known methods of proving that a quadrilateral is a □: §§ 169, 181.
                      2. Method to be used: § 181 or § 169.

Proof: (The proof is left to the student.)

Proposition VI. Theorem

183. *If the diagonals of a quadrilateral bisect each other, the figure is a parallelogram.*

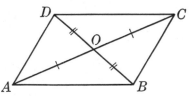

Given quadrilateral *ABCD* with *AO* = *OC* and *DO* = *OB*.

To prove that *ABCD* is a □.

Selection of Method: 1. Known methods of proving that a quadrilateral is a □: §§ 169, 181, 182.
                      2. Method to be used: § 181 or § 182.

Proof: (The proof is left to the student.)

184. Discovering a Proof. Pupils often say, "I can understand a proof after it has been demonstrated, but I do not know how to discover it when working alone." Others say, "It takes me too long to find the proof." If you belong to either of these types of pupils or if you wish to review the methods of discovering a proof, you should make a careful study of what follows in this article.

The six general statements on making a proof which are given on pages 82 and 83 are restated below with comments:

I. Read the theorem carefully, being certain that you know the meaning of each word used. Determine which is the hypothesis and which is the conclusion.

II. Draw a figure to illustrate each point, angle, and line described in the hypothesis. Make the figure as general as possible. For example, when a triangle is given, do not draw an isosceles triangle.

Letter the figure, using capital letters for points and small letters (lower case) for angles. If you wish to name a line by one letter, use a small letter.

III. From the hypothesis state in terms of the figure what is given.

IV. From the conclusion state in terms of the figure what you are to prove.

V. Select a method of proof for the theorem. (This is discussed in detail below.)

VI. Give the proof. Remember that each statement in the argument must be a complete sentence and that it must be supported by some fact that has already been proved or accepted as true without proof. Each reason must be a definition, axiom, postulate, theorem, corollary, identity, or "given."

Selecting the Method. At this time in your study of geometry you should be able to state all six steps listed above. However, the selection of a method of proof and the completion of the proof are often difficult for many pupils. The ability to discover complicated proofs is acquired slowly. To secure this ability, you must have patience and be willing to work hard.

As you have already learned, there are four kinds of proof: proof by superposition, the indirect proof, the synthetic proof, and the analytic proof.

You should remember that you can always try the indirect method when the synthetic and analytic methods fail. The indirect method is often useful in proving a theorem when its converse has been proved. In such a case you show by its converse that one of the possibilities is false.

In using the synthetic method of proof you start with the *given* facts and work toward the conclusion. In using the analytic method you start with the conclusion, saying that it is true if other facts are true, that these facts are true if others are true, and so on until you arrive at the *given* facts.

The best method of discovering a proof is the analytic-synthetic method, which is a combination of the analytic and synthetic methods. Discovering a proof in geometry may be compared to finding an automobile route from one city to another. If you wish to select an automobile route from the town "Given" to another town "Conclusion" (see page 179), you study your map to see which roads lead out of Given towards Conclusion and see which roads lead into Conclusion from the direction of Given. Then you select the best of these roads going into Conclusion and connect it with a road coming from Given. Study the following example, using the road diagram on page 179.

Given $\triangle ABC$ with $AD = DC$, $BE = EC$, and line segment DE.

To prove that $DE \parallel AB$.

First write the *given* facts as the first steps of the proof and the conclusion as the last step of the proof, namely:

Proof: *STATEMENTS*   *REASONS*

1. ABC is a $\triangle$.	1. Given.
2. $AD = DC$ and $BE = EC$.	2. Given.
$DE \parallel AB$.	

There is no statement (road) that leads directly from the given to the conclusion. By referring to § 143 we find that there are six ways of proving lines parallel, none of which leads directly from what is given. This fact suggests the use of construction lines. Since we have been studying parallelograms, let us try making a parallelogram, and perhaps we can use § 169 to arrive at the conclusion.

Draw $EF \parallel DA$. The figure $AFED$ looks like a $\square$. We can prove that it is a $\square$ if we can show that $EF = DA$, or its equal CD. We can show that $EF = CD$ if we can prove $\triangle FBE \cong \triangle DEC$. But we must stop here, for we are unable to prove the $\triangle \cong$.

Let us try another way of making a parallelogram. Extend DE to H so that $EH = DE$. Draw BH. From the figure we know that $\angle x = \angle y$ and that the two triangles are congruent (S.A.S.). It seems that we can prove that $ABHD$ is a $\square$ and then we shall know that $DE \parallel AB$.

There are four ways of proving that a quadrilateral is a parallelogram. What are they? We cannot use § 169. Why? We cannot use §§ 181, 183. Why? Let us try § 182. We know that $DC = BH$. Therefore $AD = BH$. If we can prove $AD \parallel BH$, $ABHD$ is a $\square$. There are six ways of proving two lines parallel. Since $\angle m = \angle H$, $AD \parallel BH$. Why? Then $ABHD$ is a $\square$ and $DE \parallel AB$.

The synthetic arrangement of the proof follows:

Proof:

STATEMENTS	REASONS
1. ABC is a $\triangle$.	1. Given.
2. $AD = DC$ and $BE = EC$.	2. Given.
3. Extend DE to H, so that $EH = DE$.	3. Post. 3.
4. Draw BH.	4. Post. 1.
5. $\angle x = \angle y$.	5. § 50 d.
6. $\triangle CDE \cong \triangle BHE$.	6. S.A.S.
7. $DC = BH$.	7. § 86 a.
8. $\therefore AD = BH$.	8. Ax. 6.
9. $\angle m = \angle H$	9. § 87 b.
10. $\therefore AD \parallel BH$.	10. § 143 b(1).
11. $\therefore ABHD$ is a $\square$.	11. § 182.
12. $\therefore DE \parallel AB$.	12. § 169.

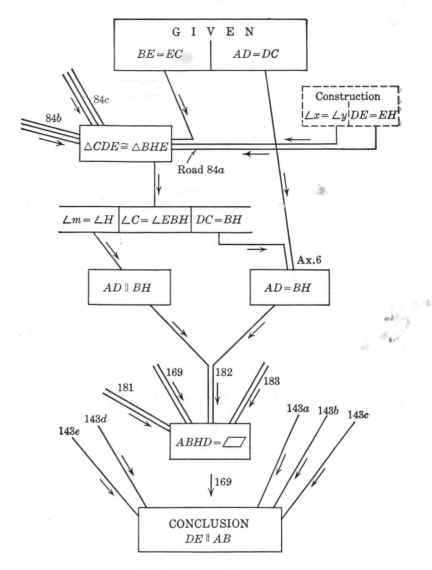

A Road Map for Reasoning

RULES OF TRAFFIC. All traffic must follow arrow signs. A two-lane road must have two cars (facts) side by side, and a three-lane road must have three cars abreast. No detours are permitted

EXERCISES. PARALLELOGRAMS

A

1. Name the four methods of proving that a quadrilateral is a parallelogram. Have you found these methods on page 547?

2. If on the same line segment as a base two congruent isosceles triangles are drawn with their vertices on opposite sides of the base, a rhombus is formed.

3. A rectangle is a square if it has perpendicular diagonals.

4. If the median of a triangle is produced its own length through the side to which it is drawn, and the extremity of the part produced is joined to the ends of the side, a parallelogram is formed.

B

5. *Given* *ABCD*, a quadrilateral, with *AB ∥ DC*, *AE = ED*, *EF ∥ AB*, *GH ∥ AD*, and *DC* produced to *H*.
　Prove that
　a. *AGFE* and *EFHD* are ▱.
　b. *GF = FH*.
　c. △ *GBF* ≅ △ *FHC*. SAS

6. This is a diagram of an extension gate. Why is it necessary to have slots in *AB* and *CD*? Prove that *AFEB* always remains a parallelogram.

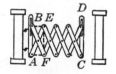

C

7. If the midpoints of the four sides of a parallelogram are joined in order, another parallelogram is formed.

8. A parallelogram is a rectangle if its diagonals are equal.

9. The bisectors of the angles of a parallelogram which is not a rhombus form a rectangle.

10. If the midpoints of the four halves of the diagonals of a parallelogram are joined in order, another parallelogram is formed.

11. *Given* ▱ *ABCD* with sides extended in succession so that *EA = CG* and *BF = DH*.
　Prove that *EFGH* is a ▱.

ENO ASSIGN #12

★★Proposition VII. Theorem

185. *If parallels intercept equal segments on one transversal, they intercept equal segments on any transversal.*

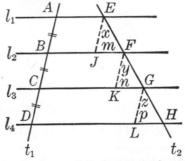

Given the ‖s l_1, l_2, l_3, and l_4 intersecting the = segments AB, BC, and CD on transversal t_1, and another transversal t_2.

To prove that $EF = FG = GH$.

Selection of Method: 1. Known methods of proving line segments =: §§ 86, 140, 172, 176, 177, 178, 179.

        2. Method to be used: § 86 *a*.

Proof:

STATEMENTS	REASONS
1. l_1 ‖ l_2 ‖ l_3 ‖ l_4.	1. Why?
2. Draw EJ, FK, and GL each ‖ t_1.	2. § 158.
3. $ABJE$, $BCKF$, and $CDLG$ are ▱.	3. Why?
4. ∴ $EJ = AB$, $FK = BC$, and $GL = CD$.	4. Why?
5. But $AB = BC = CD$.	5. Why?
6. ∴ $EJ = FK = GL$.	6. Why?
7. EJ ‖ FK ‖ GL.	7. Why?
8. ∴ $\angle x = \angle y = \angle z$.	8. Why?
9. $\angle m = \angle n = \angle p$.	9. § 141 *b*.
10. ∴ $\triangle EJF \cong \triangle FKG \cong \triangle GLH$.	10. Why?
11. ∴ $EF = FG = GH$.	11. Why?

186. Corollary. *If a line bisects one side of a triangle and is parallel to a second side, it bisects the third side.*

SUGGESTION. Through the vertex draw a line parallel to the base.

★Proposition VIII. Theorem

187. *The line segment joining the midpoints of two sides of a triangle is parallel to the third side and equal to one half of it.*

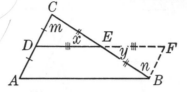

Given △ *ABC* with *CD* = *DA* and *CE* = *EB*.

To prove that *DE* ∥ *AB* and *DE* = ½ *AB*.

Selection of Method: 1. Known methods of proving (*a*) lines ∥: §§143, 169; (*b*) line segments =: §§ 86, 140, 172, 176, 177, 178, 179, 185, 186.

2. Methods to be used: (*a*) § 169; (*b*) § 172 and Ax. 4.

Proof:

STATEMENTS	REASONS
1. Extend *DE* to *F* so that *EF* = *DE*.	1. Why possible?
2. Join *B* to *F*.	2. Why possible?
3. △ *CDE* ≅ △ *EBF*.	3. Give full proof.
4. ∴ *CD* = *BF* and ∠ *m* = ∠ *n*.	4. Why?
5. ∴ *AD* = *BF* and *AC* ∥ *BF*.	5. Give reasons.
6. ∴ *ABFD* is a ▱.	6. Why?
7. ∴ *DF* or *DE* ∥ *AB*.	7. Why?
8. *DF* = *AB*.	8. Why?
9. ∴ *DE* = ½ *AB*.	9. Why?

NOTE. This theorem has many applications, not all easily recognized. Watch for figures in which the midpoints of two sides of a triangle are given.

EXERCISES. LINE SEGMENTS

A

13

1. In the figure above, find *DE* if *AB* = 26.

2. In the figure above, find *AB* if *DE* = 13.25.

26.50

3. The three sides of a triangle are 8, 10, and 13. Find the lengths of the line segments joining the midpoints of the sides.

4. *Given* $AB \parallel EF$, C the midpoint of AE, D the midpoint of BF, EF and AD produced, meeting at G.

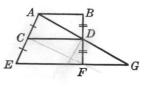

    a. *Prove* that $AB = FG$.
    b. *Prove* that $CD = \frac{1}{2} EG$.
    c. *Prove* that $CD = \frac{1}{2}(AB + EF)$.

5. The perpendiculars drawn from the midpoints of two sides of a triangle to the third side are equal.

B

6. The line segment joining the midpoints of two adjacent sides of a quadrilateral is equal and parallel to the line segment joining the midpoints of the other two sides. (Draw a diagonal.)

7. The line segments joining the midpoints of the sides of a quadrilateral, taken in order, form a parallelogram.

8. The line segments joining the midpoints of the opposite sides of a quadrilateral bisect each other. (Base the proof on Ex. **7.**)

188. Theorem. *The midpoint of the hypotenuse of a right triangle is equidistant from its vertices.*

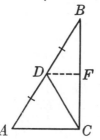

SUGGESTIONS. Draw $DF \parallel AC$. $DF \perp BC$. Why? Can you prove $DC = AD = DB$ if $\triangle CDF \cong \triangle DFB$? How many ways do you know of proving right triangles congruent? Can you prove $CF = FB$?

189. Trapezoids. A *trapezoid* is a quadrilateral having one and only one pair of parallel sides. The parallel sides are called the *bases*. The *altitude* of a trapezoid is a perpendicular to one base from any point in the other base. The *median* is the line segment joining the midpoints of the nonparallel

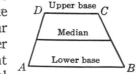

sides. An *isosceles* trapezoid is one that has equal nonparallel sides.

Proposition IX. Theorem

190. *The median of a trapezoid is parallel to the bases and equal to one half their sum.*

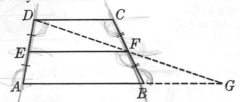

Given the trapezoid *ABCD* with the median *EF*.

To prove that *EF* ∥ *AB* and *DC*, and $EF = \frac{1}{2}(AB + DC)$.

Selection of Method: 1. Known methods of proving (*a*) lines ∥: §§ 143, 169, 187; (*b*) one line segment $= \frac{1}{2}$ another: §§ 120, 187.
2. Method to be used: (*a*) § 187; (*b*) § 187.

Proof:

STATEMENTS	REASONS
1. Draw *DF*.	1. Why possible?
2. Extend *DF* to meet *AB* produced at *G*.	2. Why possible?
3. △ *FCD* ≅ △ *FBG*.	3. Give full proof.
4. ∴ *DF = FG* and *DC = BG*.	4. Why?
5. *EF* ∥ *AG*.	5. § 187.
6. Then *EF* ∥ *DC*.	6. Why?
7. $EF = \frac{1}{2} AG$, or $\frac{1}{2}(AB + BG)$.	7. Why?
8. ∴ $EF = \frac{1}{2}(AB + DC)$.	8. Why?

EXERCISES. TRAPEZOIDS

A

$\frac{18}{2} = 9''$

1. The bases of a trapezoid are 8 and 10 inches respectively. Find the median.

$\frac{28}{2} = 14''$

2. The parallel sides of a trapezoid are 12 and 16 inches respectively and the nonparallel sides are 3 and 5 inches. Find the median.

3. The median of a trapezoid is 18 feet and the upper base is 12 feet 8 inches. Find the other base. 23.4″

sum: bases 35
36′
upper 12′.8″
lower 23.4″

Can You See the Trapezoids in This Picture?

4. The angles adjacent to one of the nonparallel sides of a trapezoid are supplementary.

5. The median of a trapezoid bisects each diagonal.

6. A line parallel to the bases of a trapezoid and bisecting one of the nonparallel sides bisects the other nonparallel side.

B

7. The nonparallel sides of an isosceles trapezoid make equal angles with either base.

8. The diagonals of an isosceles trapezoid are equal.

9. If the midpoint of the base of an isosceles triangle is joined to the midpoints of the equal sides, a rhombus is formed.

C

10. State and prove the converse of Ex. 7.

11. In this figure, $AB \perp BC$, $AE \perp EC$, BD bisects AC, and $BD = 12$ inches. Find ED.

12. The bisectors of two exterior angles of a triangle meet at an angle which is equal to one half the third exterior angle.

★Proposition X. Theorem

191. *The sum of the exterior angles of a polygon, formed by extending each of its sides in succession, is two straight angles.*

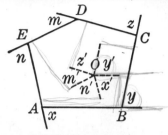

Given the polygon *ABCDE* with ext. ∠s *x, y, z, m,* and *n.*

To prove that ∠ *x* + ∠ *y* + ∠ *z* + ∠ *m* + ∠ *n* = 2 st. ∠s.

Selection of Method: 1. Known methods of proving a sum of angles = 2 st. ∠s: Post. 12.
2. Method to be used: Post. 12.

Proof:	STATEMENTS	REASONS

1. Through some point *O* draw lines ‖ the sides of the polygon.	1. Why possible?
2. ∠*x'* + ∠*y'* + ∠*z'* + ∠*m'* + ∠*n'* = 2 st. ∠s.	2. Post. 12.
3. ∠*x'* = ∠*x*, ∠*y'* = ∠*y*, ∠*z'* = ∠*z*, etc.	3. § 141 *b.*
4. ∴ ∠*x* + ∠*y* + ∠*z* + ∠*m* + ∠*n* = 2 st. ∠s.	4. Why?

192. Corollary. *Each exterior angle of a regular polygon of n sides contains* $\dfrac{360°}{n}$.

EXERCISES [A]. EXTERIOR ANGLES

1. Imagine a regular polygon drawn on the floor. Starting at any point in a side, walk once around the polygon. Through what angle do you turn at each vertex? Through how many degrees do you turn in making the circuit?

2. Name the polygons having 3, 4, 5, · · ·, 10 sides and state the sum of the exterior angles of each polygon.

3. Why are two of the exterior angles of a right triangle obtuse?

Post. 12 — The sum if all the ∠s about a point is two straight ∠s.

★Proposition XI. Theorem

193. *The sum of the interior angles of a polygon having* *n* *sides is* $(n-2)$ *straight angles.*

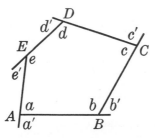

Given the polygon *ABCDE* with angles *a*, *b*, *c*, *d*, and *e*.

To prove that $\angle a + \angle b + \angle c + \angle d + \angle e = (n-2)$ st. ∡.

Selection of Method: 1. Known methods of proving values of sums of angles: Post. 12, §§ 52, 53, 107, 110, 144, 145, 191.
2. Method to be used: § 191.

Proof: *STATEMENTS*	*REASONS*
1. Extend the sides of *ABCDE* in succession to form the exterior ∡ *a'*, *b'*, *c'*, *d'*, and *e'*.	1. § 81; Post. 3.
2. $\angle a + \angle a' = 1$ st. $\angle$; $\angle b + \angle b' = 1$ st. $\angle$; $\cdots$.	2. Post. 14.
3. $\angle a + \angle a' + \angle b + \angle b' + \angle c + \angle c' + \cdots$ $= n$ st. ∡.	3. Ax. 1.
4. But $\angle a' + \angle b' + \angle c' + \angle d' + \angle e' = 2$ st. ∡.	4. § 191.
5. ∴ $\angle a + \angle b + \angle c + \angle d + \angle e$ $= (n-2)$ st. ∡.	5. Ax. 2.

NOTE. If we represent the sum of the interior angles by *I* and the sum of the exterior angles by *E*, statements 3, 4, and 5 of the proof above may be summarized as follows: $I + E = n$, and $E = 2$. Then $I = n - 2$.

194. Corollary. *Each interior angle of a regular polygon of* *n* *sides contains* $\dfrac{180(n-2)^\circ}{n}$.

EXERCISES. ANGLES OF POLYGONS

A

Example 1. Find the number of degrees in each interior angle of a regular nonagon.

Solution. From § 194, each int. $\angle = \dfrac{180(n-2)^\circ}{n}$.

Substituting $n = 9$,   each int. $\angle = \dfrac{180(9-2)^\circ}{9}$;

whence   each int. $\angle = 140^\circ$.

Example 2. Find the number of sides of a regular polygon if each interior angle is 135°.

Solution.   Each ext. $\angle = 180^\circ - 135^\circ = 45^\circ$.

By § 192, no. of degrees in each ext. $\angle = \dfrac{360}{n}$.

$$\therefore 45 = \frac{360}{n};$$

whence $45\,n = 360,$

and $n = 8$, no. of sides.

Example 3. Find the number of sides of a polygon if the sum of the interior angles is 1080°.

Solution.   Let $n =$ no. of sides of the polygon.

From § 193, $(n-2)180 =$ no. of degrees in the sum of the int. $\angle$.

Substituting, $(n-2)180 = 1080,$

or $180\,n - 360 = 1080;$

whence $180\,n = 1440,$

and $n = 8$, no. of sides.

1. How many degrees are there in the sum of the exterior angles of a triangle? of a quadrilateral? of any polygon?

2. Using § 192, find the number of degrees in each exterior angle of an equilateral triangle; a regular pentagon; a regular hexagon.

3. Find the number of straight angles in the sum of the interior angles of a quadrilateral; a pentagon; a hexagon; a heptagon; an octagon; a nonagon; a decagon. Find the number of degrees in the sum of the interior angles of each polygon.

4. Find the number of degrees in each interior angle of a regular pentagon; a regular hexagon; a regular heptagon; a regular octagon; a regular polygon of fifteen sides.

5. How many degrees are there in the sum of the interior angles of a parallelogram? a rhombus? a trapezoid?

6. The sum of three angles of a trapezoid is 290°. How many degrees are there in the fourth angle?

7. As the number of sides of a regular polygon increases, does an exterior angle increase or decrease? an interior angle?

8. A surveyor gave the following measurements for a field in the form of a quadrilateral: $AB = 18$ rods, $\angle B = 128°$; $BC = 12.5$ rods, $\angle C = 102°$; $CD = 21$ rods, $\angle D = 56°$; $DA = 26.3$ rods, $\angle A = 72°$. Can you find an error in his work?

B

9. How many sides has a regular polygon if each exterior angle contains 40°? 45°? 60°? $51\frac{3}{7}$°? 120°?

10. How many sides has a regular polygon if each interior angle contains 108°? 144°? 150°? 162°? (First find the exterior angle.)

11. Find the number of sides of a polygon if the sum of its interior angles is 540°; 900°; 8 rt. $\angle$; 7 st. $\angle$.

12. Two exterior angles of a triangle contain 200°. How many degrees are there in the third exterior angle?

13. If the sum of seven angles of an octagon is 1000°, find the number of degrees in the remaining angle.

14. How many sides has an equiangular polygon if one of its exterior angles is 22.5°?

15. What is the smallest angle that any equiangular polygon may have? What is the largest exterior angle that any equiangular polygon may have?

16. Find the number of sides of a polygon if the sum of its interior angles is twice the sum of its exterior angles.

17. *If the opposite angles of a quadrilateral are equal, the figure is a parallelogram.*

18. Prove Prop. XI using the accompanying figure.

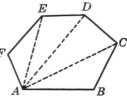

SUGGESTIONS. From any vertex, as A, draw diagonals as shown. If the polygon has n sides, show that $(n - 2)$ triangles are formed. What is the sum of the angles of $(n - 2)$ triangles?

C

19. Linoleum designs and tiled floors are often made of regular polygons. How many squares must be placed about a point to fill the plane about it? How many equiangular triangles? What other regular polygon can be used to fill the plane about a point?

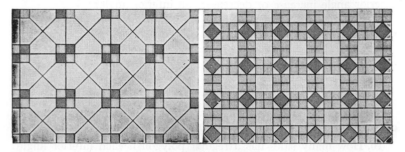

20. Show that a square and two regular octagons can be used to fill the plane about a point.

21. *Given* isos. $\triangle ABC$ with P any point in AB, $PD \perp AC$, $PE \perp BC$, and $AF \perp BC$.
Prove that $AF = DP + PE$.

22. If from a point within a given angle perpendiculars are drawn to the sides, the angle formed by the perpendiculars is a supplement of the given angle.

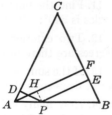

23. The bisector of the right angle of a right triangle bisects the angle included by the altitude and median on the hypotenuse.

24. *Given* $\triangle ABC$ with AD and BD the bisectors of $\angle A$ and B respectively, and $EDF \parallel AB$.
Prove that $EF = AE + BF$.

25. The difference between two consecutive angles of a parallelogram is 80°. Find all the angles.

26. *Given* $\square ABCD$ with E and F the midpoints of AD and BC respectively, and the diagonal BD.
Prove that AF and EC trisect BD.

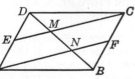

★★ Proposition XII. Problem

195. *To divide a given line segment into any number of equal parts.*

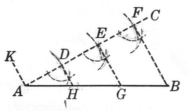

Given the line segment AB.

To divide AB into any number of = parts (as three).

Construction:

STATEMENTS	REASONS
1. Draw a line from A to some point C not in AB.	1. Why possible?
2. Construct three = line segments, AD, DE, and EF on AC.	2. Why possible?
3. From the last point of division F, draw FB.	3. Why possible?
4. Through E and D draw lines ∥ FB, intersecting AB at G and H respectively.	4. Why possible?

Then $AH = HG = GB$.

Proof:

1. Through A draw AK ∥ BF.	1. Why possible?
2. AK ∥ DH and EG.	2. Why?
3. $AD = DE = EF$.	3. Why?
4. ∴ $AH = HG = GB$.	4. Why?

EXERCISES [A]. CONSTRUCTIONS

1. In the figure above, after point G is found, show two ways of finding H without drawing a line through D parallel to FB.

2. Divide a line segment into four equal parts by two methods.

3. Divide the base of a given triangle into five equal parts.

no proof required

Quilt Designs

CONSTRUCTION EXERCISES

A

Before attempting these exercises, review § 159.

Construct a square, given

1. One side.
2. The perimeter.
3. The diagonal.
4. The sum of its diagonals.

Construct a rectangle, given

5. Two adjacent sides.
6. One side and a diagonal.
7. The diagonals and the angle between them.

Construct a rhombus, given

8. The diagonals.
9. The perimeter and one diagonal.
10. One side and one angle.

Construct a parallelogram, given

11. Two adjacent sides and the included angle.
12. The diagonals and the angle between them.

Construct a quadrilateral, given

13. The four sides and the angle between two adjacent sides.
14. Two adjacent angles and the three sides which include them.
15. Three angles and the two sides included by them.

B

Construct a square, given

16. The sum of the diagonal and one side.

17. The difference between the diagonal and one side.

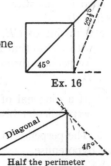

Ex. 16

Construct a rectangle, given

18. One side and the angle formed by the diagonals.

(**19.** The perimeter and one diagonal.

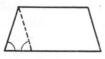

Ex. 19

Construct a rhombus, given

20. One angle and a diagonal.

21. The altitude and one diagonal.

C

Construct a parallelogram, given

(**22.** One side, one angle, and one diagonal.

23. Two adjacent sides and an altitude.

24. One side and the diagonals.

Construct a trapezoid, given

25. Four sides.

(**26.** The bases and the diagonals.

27. The bases and lower base angles.

28. The nonparallel sides and the difference of the bases.

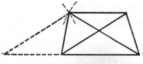

Ex. 26

Construct an isosceles trapezoid, given

29. The bases and the altitude.

30. The bases and one angle.

31. The median, altitude, and one of the bases.

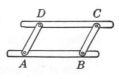

Ex. 30

MISCELLANEOUS EXERCISES [B, C]

1. Why is the edge *DC* of the parallel ruler shown in the figure always parallel to the edge *AB*?

2. If a diagonal of a parallelogram bisects one angle, the figure is a rhombus.

3. A man wishing to build a fence through C parallel to AB proceeded in this way: He set stakes at two points, D and E, on line AB, another at F, the midpoint of CE, and another at G in line with DF so that $FG = DF$. Prove that a fence passing through C and G is parallel to AB.

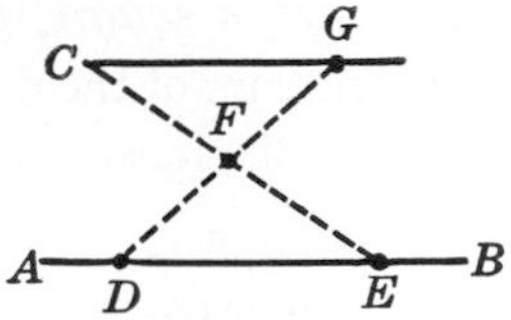

4. If a diagonal of a quadrilateral bisects two of its angles, it is the perpendicular bisector of the other diagonal.

5. The perpendicular bisector of one leg of a right triangle bisects the hypotenuse.

6. The line segments joining the midpoints of the sides of a triangle divide the triangle into four congruent triangles. (See § 187 and § 171.)

7. The line segments joining the midpoints of the sides of a rhombus, taken in order, form a rectangle.

8. Perpendiculars drawn from the end points of the base of a triangle to the median on the base are equal.

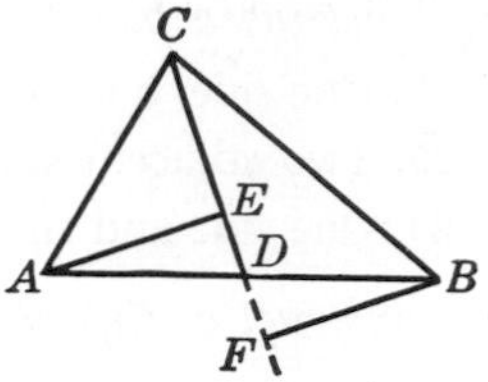

9. In the figure of Ex. 8, draw AF and BE. Prove that $AFBE$ is a parallelogram.

10. Show that the greatest number of diagonals possible in a polygon of n sides is $\dfrac{n(n-3)}{2}$.

11. A quadrilateral in which two pairs of adjacent sides are equal is called a *kite*. Prove that the longer diagonal divides the kite into two congruent triangles. Prove that the shorter diagonal divides the kite into two isosceles triangles.

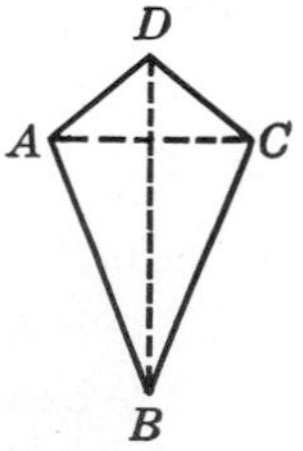

12. Through any point P within $\triangle ABC$ construct a line forming equal angles with AB and BC.

13. If the diagonals of a parallelogram are perpendicular to each other, the parallelogram is a rhombus.

14. The bisector of one angle of a triangle and the bisector of an exterior angle at a second vertex form an angle equal to one half the third angle of the triangle.

END ASSIGN # 13

EXERCISES. PRACTICAL PROBLEMS

1. Explain how you can determine by the use of cord whether or not a table top is rectangular.

2. Explain how you can determine by cord whether or not the table will stand on a level floor without rocking.

3. At the right is a diagram of a curtain stretcher. The stretcher consists of four boards which are held together by small bolts at *A*, *B*, *C*, and *D*. A curtain is fastened to the stretcher by small nails. Explain what precautions are needed to have the curtain dry in rectangular form.

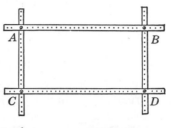

4. A boy, wishing to find the distance between two points, *A* and *B*, on opposite sides of a building, set one stake at *C*, another at *D*, the midpoint of *CA*, and one at *E*, the midpoint of *CB*. He then measured *DE*. If *DE* measured 36 feet, what was the length of *AB*?

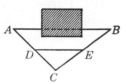

5. Explain why the floor board of a lawn swing remains parallel to the ground. Prove that the hangers, *AD* and *BC*, must be parallel if the floor board *AB* is parallel to the ground and equal to the distance *DC* between the supports of the hangers.

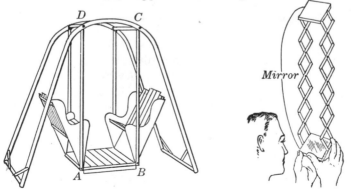

Mirror

6. At the right above is shown a collapsible periscope with which one may see over the heads of a crowd. Explain how it is made and what geometric principles are involved in its use.

196. Dihedral Angles. Since two intersecting lines determine a plane, the angles we have studied so far are plane angles. An angle formed by two planes that meet is a *dihedral angle*. The two planes are called the *faces*, and their line of meeting is called the *edge*, of the dihedral angle. A dihedral angle may be read by naming a point in one face, the edge, and a point in the other face, as dihedral ∠ *A-BC-D*. When there is no doubt as to the meaning, a dihedral angle may be read by naming its edge, as dihedral ∠ *BC*.

197. Perpendicular Planes. Two *planes are perpendicular* to each other if one of them forms two equal adjacent dihedral angles with the other.

EXERCISES

Using two rectangular pieces of cardboard, represent

1. Two perpendicular planes.

2. A right dihedral angle; an acute dihedral angle; an obtuse dihedral angle.

3. Two supplementary adjacent dihedral angles.

In the figure at the right, two planes, *EF* and *GH*, are cut by a third plane, *MN*.

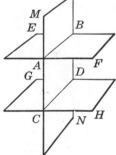

4. Name two pairs of alternate interior dihedral angles; two pairs of alternate exterior dihedral angles.

5. Name two pairs of corresponding dihedral angles.

6. Name two pairs of vertical dihedral angles.

7. If planes *EF* and *GH* are parallel, do you think that the alternate interior dihedral angles are equal? the corresponding dihedral angles are equal?

Using pencils, rectangular cardboards, and a desk top as illustrations, answer the following questions:

8. Through a line perpendicular to a plane, how many planes perpendicular to the given plane may be drawn?

9. Through a line oblique to a plane, how many planes perpendicular to the given plane may be drawn?

10. Through a line parallel to a plane, how many planes perpendicular to the given plane may be drawn?

11. If a line is parallel to a given plane, is a plane that is parallel to the line parallel to the given plane also?

12. If two intersecting planes are perpendicular to a third plane. is their intersection perpendicular to the third plane?

13. Are two planes parallel to each other if they are parallel to a third plane?

14. Are two planes parallel to each other if they are perpendicular to the same plane?

15. Are two lines parallel if they are parallel to the same plane?

16. Are two lines parallel if they are perpendicular to the same plane?

17. If one of two parallel lines is perpendicular to a plane, is the other perpendicular to the plane?

18. Is it possible for a line to be perpendicular to each of two skew lines?

19. How many intersecting lines may be parallel to a line?

20. How many intersecting lines may be parallel to a plane?

21. How many intersecting planes may be parallel to a line?

22. Can a line be perpendicular to two lines in a plane?

23. When can a plane be perpendicular to both a given plane and a given line?

24. Through a given point outside a given plane how many planes may be drawn parallel to the given plane?

25. Are two lines parallel if they are parallel to the same line?

26. What is the shortest line segment that can be drawn from a point to a plane?

27. Are two parallel planes everywhere equidistant?

198. Errors in Reasoning (*Optional*). One of the principal goals of education is to learn to think logically, without bias and emotion, and to evaluate the thinking of others.

In order to reason effectively we should make use of the methods of reasoning we use in proving theorems. Each conclusion we make should be based upon a general statement that is acceptable both to ourselves and to our hearers. This general statement in logic is called the major premise; in geometry it may be an axiom, postulate, theorem, or definition.

The reasoning in life situations is often difficult to analyze. One of the reasons for this is that we make use of hidden assumptions. We shall now briefly consider some common errors that occur in everyday thinking.

199. Reasoning with False Major Premises (*Optional*). A proof of a theorem may be logical, but the conclusion may not be true because one or more of the axioms, postulates, definitions, and theorems used in the proof is not true.

Likewise, the correctness of any conclusion arrived at in any non-geometric situation depends upon the general statement upon which the conclusion is based. Faulty generalizations make for loose thinking.

Example. Frank said, "My father should permit me to smoke, if I want to, because I am a senior." He used the hidden assumption (major premise) "All seniors should be permitted to smoke." If this premise was true and Frank was a senior, then his conclusion was true; but if the premise was false, his conclusion was not logical. Unless both Frank and his father could agree upon the major premise, they could not be sure of an agreement on the conclusion.

False major premises are often used in reasoning when we *reason from special cases.* When we take note of one or more special cases, make a generalization (major premise), and then apply this generalization to a particular case, we are reasoning from special cases.

Example. Mrs. Frank said that Mr. Winkel was a grafter because he was a policeman. Her major premise was "All policemen are grafters." She arrived at this generalization by noting that two policemen accepted tips from a storekeeper.

Assuming the converse of a true statement may lead to a false conclusion, because the converse of a true statement is not necessarily true.

Reasoning by analogy often leads to incorrect conclusions. It is based upon the assumption that if two things agree in one or more ways, they agree in other ways. Of course any conclusion based upon this assumption is not always true. The reasoning is bad even though the conclusion is true. We often encounter this type of reasoning in advertising.

Example. John said, "Frank and I make the same grades in school, have the same I.Q.'s, and look enough alike to be twins. If he can get a contract to appear on television, I can too." Do you see that John used an incorrect generalization in arriving at his conclusion?

200. Error Due to Lack of Agreement of Minor Premise and Major Premise (*Optional*). Whenever the minor premise does not agree with all the conditions of the major premise, we cannot be sure of the correctness of the conclusion.

Example. Bessie said that there will not be a frost tonight because there is seldom one when the sky is cloudy. Her conclusion was faulty because she forgot the word "seldom."

EXERCISES (Optional)

Discuss the reasoning used in each of the following:

1. I heard over the radio that Arthrito relieves rheumatism. I am going to buy a bottle of it to cure my grandfather's rheumatism.

2. Bill's father bought a Roxie television set and he had all kinds of trouble with it. I do not want a Roxie.

3. Miss Webb will not call on me to recite today because she called on me yesterday.

4. Any good citizen tries to obey the laws of his city, state, and country. Dick is not a good citizen because he drove through a red traffic signal.

5. The punishment for stealing an automobile is a minimum of five years in prison. Bill's brother will have to go to prison because he was arrested for stealing an automobile.

6. Sue does not live according to the Golden Rule because she sold me her scarf for $4 and she paid only $3 for it.

7. A public official should be honest, efficient, and courageous. Mr. Black should make a good governor because he is honest, efficient, and courageous.

8. Miss Webb is a poor geometry teacher because she does not explain the theorems.

9. Wilson's dog will not bite anyone because the dog always barks when you go near it.

10. The government should not own the coal mines, railroads, and telegraph systems because every time that a government has attempted to provide greater benefits for more people through centralized authority, it took away man's freedom, lowered the standard of living, and finally ceased to exist.

11. A good mathematics teacher should know her subject well. My sister Eunice will make a good mathematics teacher because she is graduating from college this June with honors in mathematics.

12. When the battery is dead, the car will not start. I know our battery is dead because the car would not start this morning.

13. All members of the trigonometry class must belong to and attend the XYZ Club. Jane belongs to the XYZ Club, so she must be studying trigonometry.

14. By using Reduco, Clara reduced her weight from 140 pounds to 125 pounds. I am going to be slender because I am using Reduco.

15. Prove to yourself in a 30-day test that Dentflorine is beneficial for your teeth. Brush your teeth after each meal with Dentflorine and see the beneficial effects of it.

REVIEW QUESTIONS

1. What facts have you proved about parallelograms? about rectangles? about trapezoids?

2. Name the methods of proving that a quadrilateral is a parallelogram.

3 In what quadrilaterals do the diagonals bisect the angles?

4. In what quadrilaterals are the diagonals equal?

5. In what quadrilaterals do the diagonals bisect each other?

6. In what quadrilaterals are the diagonals perpendicular to each other?

7. What two facts may be stated about the diagonals of a rectangle?

8. What three facts may be stated about the diagonals of a rhombus?

9. What four facts may be stated about the diagonals of a square?

10. As the number of sides of a polygon increases, does the sum of the exterior angles increase or decrease?

11. What is the sum of the interior angles of a quadrilateral? of a triangle? of a pentagon? of a hexagon?

12. What is the sum of the exterior angles of a polygon having six sides? eight sides? ten sides?

13. What do you know about the median of a trapezoid?

14. What do you know about the line segment connecting the midpoints of two sides of a triangle?

15. What is the name of a polygon in which the sum of the interior angles equals the sum of the exterior angles?

16. What propositions on constructions have you had? Can you do the constructions?

17. What is the name of the quadrilateral having one, and only one, pair of parallel sides?

18. What is the perimeter of the triangle formed by joining the midpoints of the sides of a triangle whose perimeter is 192 inches?

19. What is the relation between any interior angle of a polygon and its adjacent exterior angle?

20. *Prove:* If the diagonals of a parallelogram are equal, the parallelogram is a rectangle.

21. One angle of a triangle is 20°. How large is the angle formed by the bisectors of the other two angles?

22. In $\triangle ABC$, $AC = BC$ and $\angle A = 45°$. How large is $\angle C$?

23. $\angle B$ of $\square ABCD$ is 110°. How large is $\angle C$?

24. $\angle C$ of $\square ABCD$ is four times as large as $\angle D$. How large is $\angle B$?

25. How many degrees are there in each interior angle of a regular polygon having 18 sides?

26. How many sides has a regular polygon if each exterior angle contains 24°?

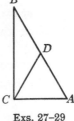

In $\triangle ABC$, $AD = DB$ and $\angle C = 90°$.

27. Find BD if $\angle B = 30°$ and $AC = 10$ inches.

28. Find CA if $CD = 8$ inches and $\angle A = 60°$.

29. Find CD if $AB = 16$ inches and $\angle A = 75°$.

30. The sum of two angles of a triangle is 108° and their difference is 16°. How many degrees are there in each angle of the triangle?

Exs. 27–29

31. In $\square ABCD$, $\angle A = 30°$, $BC = 18$ inches, and $DC = 20$ inches. Find the altitude upon AB as the base.

32. The diagonal AC of rhombus $ABCD$ is $\frac{1}{4}$ the perimeter. How large is $\angle C$?

The median EF of trapezoid $ABCD$ intersects AC in R and BD in S.

33. If $DC = 8$ and $AB = 12$, find EF; ER; SF; RS.

34. If $EF = 24$ and $AB = 30$, find DC; ER; SF; RS.

35. If $ER = 5$ and $RF = 7$, find DC; AB; SF; RS.

36. One angle of a parallelogram is 4 times as large as another. How large is each angle of the parallelogram?

37. In rhombus $ABCD$, $\angle A = 60°$ and $AB = 10$ inches. Find BD.

38. In $\square ABCD$, $\angle B = 150°$ and $AD = 12$ inches. Find the altitude from D to AB.

39. How many diagonals has a decagon?

SUMMARY OF PRINCIPAL METHODS OF PROOF

201. *Two triangles are congruent*

If they are formed by a diagonal of a parallelogram.

202. *Two line segments are equal*

a. If they are opposite sides of a parallelogram.
b. If they are segments of parallels included between parallels.

c. If they are segments of a diagonal of a parallelogram formed by the intersection of the other diagonal.

d. If they are intercepted on a transversal by parallel lines which intercept equal segments on another transversal.

e. If they are segments of one side of a triangle formed by a line which bisects a second side and is parallel to the third side.

203. *One line segment is equal to one half another*

a. If one joins the midpoints of two sides of a triangle and the other is the third side of the triangle.

b. If one is the median of a trapezoid and the other is equal to the sum of the bases of the trapezoid.

204. *Two angles are equal*

If they are opposite angles of a parallelogram.

205. *Two lines are perpendicular*

a. If they are diagonals of a rhombus.

b. If they are adjacent sides of a rectangle.

206. *Two lines are parallel*

a. If they are opposite sides of a parallelogram.

b. If one is a line connecting the midpoints of two sides of a triangle and the other is the third side of the triangle.

c. If they are the bases of a trapezoid.

d. If one is the median of a trapezoid and the other is one of the bases.

207. *Two angles are supplementary*

If they are two consecutive angles of a parallelogram.

208. *A quadrilateral is a parallelogram*

a. If the opposite sides are parallel.

b. If the opposite sides are equal.

c. If two sides are equal and parallel.

d. If the diagonals bisect each other.

209. *Construction*

To divide a given line segment into any number of equal parts.

WORD LIST

Can you spell and use each of the following words?

alternate	equilateral	oblique	perimeter
complementary	hexagon	octagon	rhombus
converse	hypotenuse	opposite	supplementary
corollary	infinite	parallel	trapezoid
decagon	intercept	parallelogram	trisect
diagonal	mathematics	pentadecagon	trisection
equiangular	nonagon	pentagon	vertices

TEST 12

Multiple-Choice Statements (*Ten Minutes*)

On your paper write the word or group of words printed in boldface type which makes each statement true:

1. A pentagon is a polygon having 3 sides **5 sides** 7 sides 9 sides.

2. A rectangle is a **square** **trapezoid** **parallelogram** **rhombus.**

3. The diagonals of a **rectangle** **polygon** **quadrilateral** **parallelogram** **rhombus** bisect each other and are perpendicular to each other.

4. The sum of the exterior angles of a hexagon is **180** **360** **540** **900** **1080** degrees.

5. The segments of parallels included between **two parallels** **two perpendiculars** **two obliques** are equal.

6. The diagonals of a parallelogram **are perpendicular to each other** **bisect each other** **are equal.**

7. The opposite angles of a parallelogram are **equal** **complementary** **supplementary.**

8. The line segment joining the midpoints of two sides of a triangle is equal to **one third** **one half** **two thirds** the third side.

9. The median of a trapezoid is equal to **the sum of the nonparallel sides** **one half the sum of the diagonals** **one half the sum of the parallel sides.**

10. Each interior angle of a regular octagon is equal to **108** **120** **135** **140** **144** degrees.

$$\frac{180(8-2)}{8} \qquad 8\sqrt{10\overline{\underset{8}{}}} \qquad \frac{180}{6} \qquad 135$$

TEST 13

Constructions (*Twenty-five Minutes*)

Make the following constructions as accurately as you can:

1. Divide a given line segment into five equal parts.
2. Construct a square, given one side.
3. Construct a rectangle, given one side and a diagonal.
4. Construct a rhombus, given the diagonals.
5. Construct an equilateral triangle, given the line segment joining the midpoints of two of the sides.

TEST 14

Applications (*Twenty-seven Minutes*)

1. If one angle of a parallelogram contains 40°, how many degrees are there in each of the other three angles?
2. If one side of a rhombus is 6 inches long, how many inches are there in the perimeter?
3. In the figure, $AB = 8$ inches, $BC = 6$ inches, $AC = 5$ inches, and D, E, and F are the midpoints, respectively, of AB, BC, and AC. Find the perimeter of $\triangle DEF$.

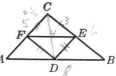

4. How many degrees are there in the sum of the interior angles of a polygon having seven sides?
5. How many degrees are there in the sum of the exterior angles of a polygon having eleven sides?
6. If the diagonals, AC and BD, of a square $ABCD$ intersect at O, and $AO = 6$ inches, how many inches are there in the sum of the diagonals?
7. How many degrees are there in each interior angle of a regular polygon of ten sides?
8. How many degrees are there in each exterior angle of a regular polygon of eleven sides?
9. If one angle of a rhombus contains 30° and an altitude is 6 inches long, how many inches are there in one side?

10. How many inches are there in the perimeter of a parallelogram formed by joining the midpoints of the sides of a quadrilateral whose diagonals are 11 inches and 7 inches respectively?

11. If the median to the hypotenuse of a right triangle is 5 inches long, how many inches are there in the hypotenuse?

12. How many degrees are there in the angle formed by two diagonals drawn from the same vertex of a regular pentagon?

TEST 15

Drawing the Figure for a Theorem (*Thirteen Minutes*)

Draw a figure for each of the following theorems:

1. The bisectors of the four angles of a parallelogram which is not a rhombus form a rectangle.

2. The line joining the midpoints of the nonparallel sides of a trapezoid bisects the diagonals.

3. If perpendiculars are drawn from the end points of the shorter base of an isosceles trapezoid to the other base, two congruent triangles are formed.

4. If perpendiculars are drawn from the four vertices of a parallelogram to any line outside the parallelogram, the sum of the perpendiculars from one pair of opposite vertices equals the sum of the perpendiculars from the other pair.

5. If the sides, AB and DC, of a quadrilateral $ABCD$ meet when produced at a point E, and AD and BC produced meet at a point F, then $\angle FCE = \angle F + \angle E + \angle A$.

TEST 16

Converses, Inverses, Contrapositives, Hypotheses, and Conclusions (*Ten Minutes*)

1. State the hypothesis of statement 2, Test 15.

2. State the converse of statement 2, Test 15.

3. State the converse of statement 3, Test 15.

4. State the inverse of statement 2, Test 15.

5. State the contrapositive of statement 2, Test 15.

6. State the conclusion of statement 5, Test 15.

Bureau of Reclamation
Shasta Dam on the Sacramento River in California

Shasta Dam, the next to the highest concrete dam in the world, is 602 feet high. Its crest length is 3500 feet. In its construction 6,000,-000 cubic yards of concrete were used. Shasta Lake, which is formed by the dam, has an area of 46 square miles. The water from the lake flows 500 miles through rivers and canals to irrigate the San Joaquin Valley. At Shasta Dam the water is used to generate electric power.

The project of which this dam is a part was built under the direction of the Bureau of Reclamation, Department of the Interior.

Each step in the construction of a great engineering project of this kind requires the constant use of mathematics.

CHAPTER VII

Areas of Polygons

210. Measurement of a Surface. A line segment is measured by finding how many times it contains a unit of measure. Thus a line segment is 16 inches long if it contains the inch unit 16 times. An angle is measured by finding how many times it contains a unit angle. For example, an angle contains 25° if it contains the 1° angle 25 times. In the same manner, a *surface is measured* by finding how many times it contains a unit for measuring surfaces.

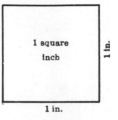

211. Unit of Area. A *unit of area* is a surface enclosed by a square each of whose sides is some unit of length. Thus a surface enclosed by a square each of whose sides is one inch is a unit of area called a *square inch.* Other common units of area are the *square foot,* the *square yard,* the *square centimeter,* and the *square mile.* Can you name still other common units of area?

212. Area of a Figure. The *area of a plane figure* in terms of a unit of area is the number of times the figure contains the unit. The rectangle *ABCD* contains 3 rows of squares, each row containing 5 units. The area of the rectangle is 3 × 5, or 15, units. If each of the units were a square inch, the area of the rectangle would be 15 square inches.

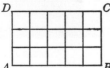

If the base of a rectangle contains $5\frac{1}{4}$ units of length and the altitude contains $3\frac{1}{2}$ units of length, the area of the rectangle is $3\frac{1}{2} \times 5\frac{1}{4}$, or $18\frac{3}{8}$, square units.

If the base is 6 and the altitude is $\sqrt{3}$, the area is $6\sqrt{3}$.

213. Ratio. The _ratio_ of one quantity to another like quantity is the numerical value of the _first_ quantity divided by the numerical value of the second, both expressed in terms of a common unit. The ratio of 3 to 4 is $\frac{3}{4}$ and the ratio of 4 to 3 is $\frac{4}{3}$. The ratio of 2 pounds to 6 pounds is $\frac{2}{6}$, or $\frac{1}{3}$; and the ratio of 5 inches to 2 feet is $\frac{5}{24}$. We cannot find the ratio between two unlike quantities, such as the ratio of 3 books to 5 chairs.

The colon (:) and the division sign (÷) can also be used to denote ratio. Thus, $\frac{3}{4}$, 3 : 4, and 3 ÷ 4 denote the ratio of 3 to 4. Since ratios are really fractions, all the principles of fractions apply to them.

NUMERICAL EXERCISES [A]

1. Reduce each of the following ratios to lowest terms:

   a. $\dfrac{4}{6}$.   *b.* $\dfrac{a^2}{4\,a^2}$.   *c.* $\dfrac{5\,x}{10\,x^2}$.   *d.* $\dfrac{6\,x^2}{12\,xy}$.   *e.* $8\,a^2 : 16\,a^3$.
                                                                f. $(a^2 - b^2) : (a - b)^2$.

2. Express in lowest terms the ratio of
a. 30° to 90°.   *c.* 2 inches to 1 foot.
b. A right angle to a straight angle.   *d.* 5° to 30′.
e. One angle of an equilateral triangle to the sum of the other two.
f. The perimeter of a regular hexagon to one of its sides.

3. If $5\,x = 7\,y$, find the ratio of x to y; of y to x.

4. Two quantities are in the ratio of 4 : 5. If $4\,x$ represents the first quantity, what represents the second?

5. Separate 105 into two parts which are in the ratio of 2 : 5. (Let $2\,x =$ the smaller part.)

6. Find the angles of a triangle if they are in the ratio of 3 : 5 : 7.

214. Radicals. As you probably remember, a _radical_ is an indicated root of a number, as $\sqrt{5}$, $\sqrt[3]{b}$, and $\sqrt{\frac{1}{2}}$. A radical is expressed in its _simplest form_ when the _radicand_ (the quantity under the radical sign) is a whole number and as small as possible.

Two important principles of radicals are:

Principle I. $\sqrt{ab} = \sqrt{a}\sqrt{b}$ and $\sqrt{a}\sqrt{b} = \sqrt{ab}$.

Principle II. $\sqrt{\dfrac{a}{b}} = \dfrac{\sqrt{a}}{\sqrt{b}}$ and $\dfrac{\sqrt{a}}{\sqrt{b}} = \sqrt{\dfrac{a}{b}}$.

Example 1. Simplify $\sqrt{49}$.

Solution. $\sqrt{49} = 7$.

Example 2. Simplify $\sqrt{50}$.

Solution. $\sqrt{50} = \sqrt{25}\,\sqrt{2} = 5\sqrt{2}$.

Example 3. Simplify $\sqrt{\tfrac{3}{8}}$.

Solution. $\sqrt{\tfrac{3}{8}} = \sqrt{\tfrac{6}{16}}$. Then $\sqrt{\tfrac{6}{16}} = \dfrac{\sqrt{6}}{\sqrt{16}} = \dfrac{\sqrt{6}}{4} = \tfrac{1}{4}\sqrt{6}$.

EXERCISES [A]

Simplify the following radicals:

1. $\sqrt{8}$.   5. $\sqrt{72}$.   9. $2\sqrt{16}$.   13. $\sqrt{\tfrac{1}{2}}$.   16. $\sqrt{\tfrac{9}{25}}$.

2. $\sqrt{25}$.   6. $\sqrt{81}$.   10. $3\sqrt{8}$.   14. $\sqrt{\tfrac{1}{3}}$.   17. $\sqrt{\tfrac{3}{5}}$.   19. $\sqrt{\tfrac{1}{a}}$.

3. $\sqrt{32}$.   7. $\sqrt{18}$.   11. $5\sqrt{75}$.   15. $\sqrt{\tfrac{2}{3}}$.   18. $\sqrt{\tfrac{1}{7}}$.   20. $\sqrt{\tfrac{1}{a^3}}$.

4. $\sqrt{60}$.   8. $\sqrt{20}$.   12. $\sqrt{16}$.

215. How to Find the Square Root of a Number. The method of finding square root will now be illustrated.

Example 1. Find the positive square root of 841.

Solution. We first separate the number into groups of two figures each, beginning at the decimal point.

$$2 \times 2 = 4. \quad \begin{array}{r} 2\,9. \\ \hline \sqrt{8\,41.} \\ 2\,|\,4 \\ \hline 49\,|\,4\,41 \\ \quad\,|\,4\,41 \end{array}$$

Example 2. $\sqrt{165} = ?$

Solution.

$$\begin{array}{r} 1\,2\,.\,8\;4\;5\,+ \\ \hline \sqrt{1\text{`}65,\,00\text{'}00\text{'}00} \end{array}$$

$2 \times 1 = 2.$

$2 \times 12 = 24.$

$2 \times 128 = 256.$

$2 \times 1284 = 2568.$

$$\begin{array}{r} 1\,|\,1 \\ \hline 22\,|\,65 \\ \,|\,44 \\ \hline 248\,|\,21\,00 \\ \,|\,19\,84 \\ \hline 2564\,|\,1\,16\,00 \\ \,|\,1\,02\,56 \\ \hline 25685\,|\,13\,44\,00 \\ \,|\,12\,84\,25 \end{array}$$

In Example 2 the answer is given to three decimal places. To the nearest hundredth it is 12.85 and to the nearest tenth it is 12.8.

In many exercises involving square root, time can be saved by referring to the table of square roots on page 563.

216. Quadratic Equations. A *quadratic equation* is one which when simplified contains the second power, but no higher power, of the unknown. We shall now briefly review the algebraic methods of solving quadratic equations.

217. Incomplete Quadratic Equations. An *incomplete quadratic* equation is a quadratic equation in which the first power of the unknown is absent. $7x^2 - 175 = 0$ and $3m^2 + m^2 = 256$ are incomplete quadratic equations.

To solve an incomplete quadratic equation:

1. Solve the equation for the square of the unknown.

2. Find the square root of each member.

Example 1. Solve

$$4x^2 - 144 = 0.$$

Solution. $4x^2 - 144 = 0.$
$$4x^2 = 144.$$
$$x^2 = 36.$$
R₂, $$x = \pm 6.$$

Example 2. Solve $x^2 + 4x^2 = 64$.

Solution. $x^2 + 4x^2 = 64.$
$$5x^2 = 64.$$
$$x^2 = \tfrac{64}{5}.$$
R₂, $$x = \pm \sqrt{\frac{64}{5}} = \pm \sqrt{\frac{64 \times 5}{25}}$$
$$= \pm \tfrac{8}{5}\sqrt{5}.$$

EXERCISES [A]

Solve:

1. $x^2 = 25$.

2. $4x^2 = 100$.

3. $x^2 + 25 = 75$.

4. $3y^2 - 192 = 0$.

5. $x^2 - \dfrac{x^2}{4} = 100$.

6. $4x^2 - \tfrac{1}{9} = 0$.

7. $\dfrac{2x^2 - 7}{5} - \dfrac{x^2 - 4}{3} + \dfrac{8}{5} = 0$.

8. $\dfrac{x^2 - 1}{4} + \dfrac{3x^2 + 3}{10} = 5$.

9. $(x - 2)^2 + 4x = 16$.

218. Complete Quadratic Equations. A *complete quadratic equation* is one that contains both the second and first powers of the unknown. We shall now review three methods of solution.

a. Solution by Factoring. The factoring method is the simplest of the three, when it can be used.

To solve an equation by factoring:

1. If necessary, transform it so that the right member is zero.

2. Factor the left member and equate to zero.

3. Equate each factor containing the unknown to zero.

4. Solve the resulting equations.

Example. Solve $2x^2 - 4x = 6$.

Solution. Making the right member zero, $2x^2 - 4x - 6 = 0$.
Factoring the left member, $2(x - 3)(x + 1) = 0$.
Setting the factors containing x equal to zero, we have $x - 3 = 0$
and $x + 1 = 0$. Solving these two equations, $x = 3$ and $x = -1$.

EXERCISES [A]

1. $x^2 - x - 6 = 0$.

2. $x^2 + x = 30$.

3. $2x^2 + 5x = 3$.

4. $3x^2 + 14x = 5$.

5. $x^2 - 25 = 0$.

6. $y^2 - 2y = 24$.

7. $x^2 - 8x = 0$.

8. $3x^2 = 15x$.

9. $12x^2 + 11x = 5$.

10. $6x^2 - x - 1 = 0$.

11. $\dfrac{y^2}{3} - \dfrac{y}{2} = 5\frac{5}{6}$.

b. Solution by Completing the Square. Any complete quadratic equation can be solved by completing the square.

To solve a quadratic equation by completing the square:

1. Write the equation in the form $x^2 + bx = c$.

2. Add to each member the square of half of b.

3. Find the square root of each member, placing the $\pm$ sign before the square root of the right member.

4. Solve the two resulting equations.

Example 1. Solve $2x^2 - 12x = 32$.

Solution. $\qquad\qquad 2x^2 - 12x = 32$.

$\mathrm{D_2}, \qquad\qquad\qquad x^2 - 6x = 16$.

Adding to each member the square of half of -6, which is 9,

$$x^2 - 6x + 9 = 25.$$

$\mathrm{R_2}, \qquad\qquad\qquad x - 3 = \pm 5$.

Solving the two equations, $\quad x = 3 \pm 5$; $\ x = 8$ or -2.

Example 2. Solve $2x^2 - 5x = -1$.

Solution. $\qquad\qquad 2x^2 - 5x = -1$.

$\mathrm{D_2}, \qquad\qquad\qquad x^2 - \frac{5}{2}x = -\frac{1}{2}$.

$$\left[\tfrac{1}{2} \text{ of } -\tfrac{5}{2} = -\tfrac{5}{4} \text{ and } \left(-\tfrac{5}{4}\right)^2 = \tfrac{25}{16}.\right]$$

$\mathrm{A_{\frac{25}{16}}}, \qquad\qquad x^2 - \frac{5}{2}x + \frac{25}{16} = \frac{17}{16}$. $\qquad\qquad \left[\tfrac{25}{16} - \tfrac{1}{2} = \tfrac{17}{16}.\right]$

$\mathrm{R_2}, \qquad x - \frac{5}{4} = \pm \frac{1}{4}\sqrt{17}$; $\ x = \frac{5}{4} \pm \frac{1}{4}\sqrt{17}$, or $\frac{1}{4}\left(5 \pm \sqrt{17}\right)$.

c. Solution by Formula. Any complete quadratic equation can be written in the form $ax^2 + bx + c = 0$. From this we obtain the formula for the roots: $x = \dfrac{-b \pm \sqrt{b^2 - 4ac}}{2a}$.

Example. Solve $3x^2 - 4x = 2$.

Solution. Changing the equation into the form $ax^2 + bx + c = 0$, $3x^2 - 4x - 2 = 0$. In this equation $a = 3$, $b = -4$, and $c = -2$. Substituting these values of a, b, and c in the formula, we get

$$x = \frac{4 \pm \sqrt{16 - 4(3)(-2)}}{6} = \frac{4 \pm \sqrt{40}}{6} = \frac{4 \pm 2\sqrt{10}}{6} = \frac{2 \pm \sqrt{10}}{3}.$$

EXERCISES [A]

Solve either by completing the square or by the formula. Express roots containing radicals correct to the nearest tenth.

1. $x^2 + 2x = 8$.
2. $x^2 + 16x = 36$.
3. $4x^2 + 20x = 11$.
4. $x^2 - 6x - 7 = 0$.
5. $x^2 - 40x = 41$.
6. $m^2 + 8m - 9 = 0$.
7. $x^2 + 4x = 7$.
8. $2x^2 + 5x + 1 = 0$.
9. $y^2 + 3y - 1 = 0$.

219. Figures Equal in Area (Equivalent). Figures equal in area are not necessarily congruent, but congruent figures are always equal in area. "Equal" often means "equal in area."

EXERCISES [A]

1. Find the area of each of the seven polygons below by counting the small squares. (Estimate the area of any incomplete squares.)

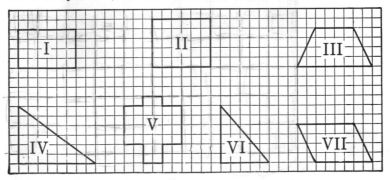

2. Which of the polygons in Ex. 1 have the same shape? Which are congruent? Which are equal in area?

3. Draw two polygons which have the same shape but are not congruent. Could they be equal in area?

4. If two polygons have the same shape and are equal in area, are they congruent? Is the converse true?

220. Area of a Rectangle. The examples and exercises of §§ 212 and 219 illustrate the following postulate:

Post. 22. *The area of a rectangle is equal to the product of its base and altitude, or S = bh.*

NOTE. This means that the number of square units of area is equal to the product of the number of linear units in the base and the number of linear units in the altitude. In propositions relating to areas, the word "rectangle" is commonly used for the words "area of a rectangle." The same is true for other plane figures.

EXERCISES [A]. AREAS OF RECTANGLES

1. Find the area of a rectangular lot 50 feet wide and 135 feet long.

2. Find the cost of sodding a football field 300 feet long and 160 feet wide at 18 cents a square yard.

3. Find the cost of a field 50 rods wide and 80 rods long at $80 an acre.

4. What is the cost of placing clay over a tennis court 36 feet wide and 78 feet long at 20 cents a square yard?

5. Find the altitude of a rectangle whose base is 16.5 inches and whose area is 1300.3 square inches.

6. Find the area of a rectangle whose base is $2x - 1$ and whose altitude is $x + 4$.

Example. Find the dimensions of a rectangle if the width is $\frac{2}{3}$ of its length and its area is 1574.64.

Solution. Let $x =$ the length. Then $\frac{2}{3} x =$ the width. $\frac{2}{3} x^2 = 1574.64$; $2 x^2 = 4723.92$; $x^2 = 2361.96$; $x = 48.6$, length; $\frac{2}{3} x = 32.4$, width.

7. The altitude of a rectangle is $\frac{2}{5}$ of its length. Find its dimensions if its area is 2535.

8. The ratio of the width to the length of a rectangular city lot is 3 : 8. Find the dimensions of the lot if its area is 9600 square feet.

$(2x-1)(x+4) = A$

$A = 3x(3)$ $9y = A$

9. Find the area of the cross section of the I-beam shown below if the width of each of the upper and lower rectangles is $1\frac{3}{8}$ inches.

10. If you double the altitude of a rectangle and leave the base the same, how is the area changed?

11. If both the altitude and the base of a rectangle are doubled, how is the area changed?

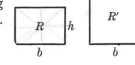

221. Corollary I. *Two rectangles having equal bases have the same ratio as their altitudes.*

Given rectangles R and R', having altitudes h and h' and equal bases b.

To prove that $\dfrac{R}{R'} = \dfrac{h}{h'}$.

$1\,{}^{3}\!/_{8}$

Proof:

STATEMENTS	REASONS
1. $R = bh$ and $R' = bh'$.	1. Why?
2. $\therefore \dfrac{R}{R'} = \dfrac{bh}{bh'}$, or $\dfrac{R}{R'} = \dfrac{h}{h'}$.	2. Why?

222. Corollary II. *Two rectangles having equal altitudes have the same ratio as their bases.*

223. Corollary III. *The area of a square is equal to the square of one of its sides.*

$4 \times 4 = 16$

EXERCISES. AREAS OF RECTANGLES [A]

1. How many tiles, each 4 inches on a side, does it take to cover a floor 12 feet 4 inches long by 10 feet 8 inches wide?

2. Find the area of a square if each of its sides is $x - 4$.

3. Rectangle AH is separated into 12 rectangles. If $AB=BC=CD=DE$ and $EF=FG=GH$, find the following ratios:

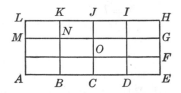

a. Rectangle AN to rectangle AK.
b. Rectangle AJ to rectangle AH.
c. Rectangle AO to rectangle AF.
d. Rectangle BI to rectangle CI.
e. Rectangle BF to rectangle CF.
f. Rectangle BO to rectangle ND.

★★ Proposition I. Theorem

224. *The area of a parallelogram is equal to the product of its base and altitude, or S = bh.*

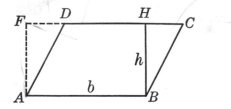

Given □ *ABCD* with base *AB*, denoted by *b*, and altitude *BH*, denoted by *h*.

To prove that the area of *ABCD* = *bh*.

Selection of Method: 1. Known methods of finding areas of polygons: §§ 220, 223.
2. Method to be used: § 220.

Proof: *STATEMENTS*   *REASONS*

STATEMENTS	REASONS
1. *HB* ⊥ *AB* and *DC*.	1. §§ 170, 142 *a*.
2. Through *A* draw *AF* ∥ *BH*, meeting *CD* extended at *F*.	2. § 96; Post. 3.
3. Then *AF* ⊥ *AB* and *FC*.	3. Why?
4. *ABHF* is a rectangle.	4. Give proof.
5. In rt. ⩜ *AFD* and *BHC*, *AD* = *BC*, and *AF* = *BH*.	5. Why?
6 ∴ rt. △ *AFD* ≅ rt. △ *BHC*.	6. Why?
7 Trapezoid *ABHD* = trapezoid *ABHD*.	7. Why?
8. ∴ rectangle *ABHF* = □ *ABCD*.	8. Ax. 1.
9. But the area of rectangle *ABHF* = *bh*.	9. § 220.
10. ∴ the area of □ *ABCD* = *bh*.	10. Why?

225. Corollary I. *Parallelograms having equal bases and equal altitudes are equal in area.*

226. Corollary II. *Two parallelograms having equal bases have the same ratio as their altitudes; and two parallelograms having equal altitudes have the same ratio as their bases.*

EXERCISES. AREAS OF PARALLELOGRAMS

A

1. Find the area of a parallelogram whose base is 18 inches and whose altitude is 12 inches.

2. The base of a parallelogram is 17.4 and the altitude is 11.4. Find the area. *198.36*

3. Find the area of a parallelogram whose base is 48 inches and whose altitude is 33 inches.

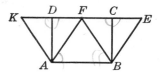

4. In the figure above, which is the largest, rectangle *ABCD*, parallelogram *ABEF*, or parallelogram *ABFK*?

5. The area of a parallelogram is 8430 square feet and the altitude is 150 feet. Find the base.

6. Find the area of this cross section of an I-beam, the steel in it being $\frac{1}{2}$ inch in thickness.

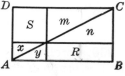

7. How many tiles each 1 inch wide and 2 inches long will be required for a fireplace hearth 2 feet wide and 5 feet 4 inches long, allowing 10 per cent of the surface for cement?

8. The ratio between the base and altitude of a parallelogram is 2 : 3. Find the base if the area of the parallelogram is 1734 square inches.

C

9. *ABCD* is a rectangle with diagonal *AC*. *R* is a rectangle, and *S* is a square.
   Prove that *S = R*.

★★Proposition II. Theorem

227. *The area of a triangle is equal to one half the product of its base and altitude.*

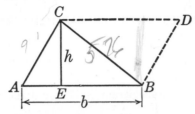

Given the △ *ABC* having its base *AB* denoted by *b* and its altitude *CE* denoted by *h*.

To prove that the area of △ *ABC* = $\frac{1}{2}$ *bh*.

Selection of Method: 1. Known methods of finding areas of polygons: §§ 220, 223, 224.
2. Method to be used: § 224.

Proof: STATEMENTS	REASONS
1. Through *C* draw a line ‖ *AB*, and through *B* draw a line ‖ *AC*.	1. Why possible?
2. These lines meet at some point *D*.	2. Why?
3. Then *ABDC* is a ▱ having base *b* and altitude *h*	3. Why?
4. △ *ABC* = $\frac{1}{2}$ ▱ *ABDC*.	4. Why?
5. Area of ▱ *ABDC* = *bh*.	5. Why?
6. Then area of $\frac{1}{2}$ ▱ *ABDC* = $\frac{1}{2}$ *bh*.	6. Why?
7. ∴ area of △ *ABC* = $\frac{1}{2}$ *bh*.	7. Why?

228. Corollary I. *Two triangles having equal bases have the same ratio as their altitudes.*

229. Corollary II. *Two triangles having equal altitudes have the same ratio as their bases.*

230. Corollary III. *The areas of two triangles have the same ratio as the products of their bases and altitudes.*

231. Corollary IV. *The area of a rhombus is equal to one half the product of its diagonals.*

232. Corollary V. *If a triangle and a parallelogram have equal bases and altitudes, the area of the triangle is half the area of the parallelogram.*

EXERCISES. AREAS

A

1. Find the area of a triangle if its base is 17 and its altitude is 12.

2. What is the area of a triangle whose base is 21.4 and whose altitude is 14.8?

3. Find the base of a triangle if its area is 576 square feet and its altitude is 9 feet.

4. Find the area of a rhombus if its diagonals are 32 feet and 40 feet.

5. The area of a rhombus is 2352 square inches and one diagonal is 56 inches. How long is the other diagonal?

6. The area of $\triangle ABC$ is 108 square inches and D, E, and F are the midpoints of the three sides. Find the area of $\triangle ABO$; of $\triangle BOC$; of $\triangle AOC$; of $\triangle ODB$; of $\triangle BOE$; of $\triangle AOF$.

7. Prove that two triangles having equal bases and equal altitudes are equal.

B

8. $ABCD$ is a parallelogram whose diagonals intersect in E. Prove that $\triangle ABE = \triangle BEC$.

9. Find the side of a square whose area equals that of a triangle with base 144 inches and altitude 72 inches.

10. The area of a rhombus is 2304. Find its diagonals if one is half the other.

11. In $\triangle ABC$, D is the midpoint of AC and E is the midpoint of BC. Find these ratios:

$$\frac{\triangle DEC}{\triangle DEA}; \quad \frac{\triangle CDE}{\triangle AEC}; \quad \frac{\triangle ACE}{\triangle ABC}; \quad \frac{\triangle DCE}{\triangle ABC}.$$

12. Find the area of $\square ABCD$ if $AB = 19$, $AD = 16$, and $\angle C = 30°$.

★★Proposition III. Theorem

233. *The area of a trapezoid is equal to half the product of its altitude and the sum of its bases, or $S = \frac{1}{2} h(b + b')$.*

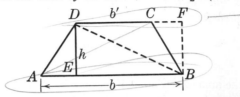

Given the trapezoid $ABCD$ having altitude DE denoted by h, base AB denoted by b, and base DC denoted by b'.

To prove that $S = \frac{1}{2} h(b + b')$.

Selection of Method: 1. Known methods of finding areas of polygons: §§ 220, 223, 224, 227, 231, 232.

2. Method to be used: § 227.

Proof: *STATEMENTS*	*REASONS*
1. Draw DB.	1. Why possible?
2. Draw $BF \perp DC$.	2. Why possible?
3. $BF = ED = h$.	3. Why?
4. Area of $\triangle ABD = \frac{1}{2} bh$.	4. Why?
5. Area of $\triangle DBC = \frac{1}{2} b'h$.	5. Why?
6. $\triangle ABD + \triangle DBC = \frac{1}{2} bh + \frac{1}{2} b'h$ $= \frac{1}{2} h(b + b')$.	6. Why?
7. But $\triangle ABD + \triangle DBC = $ trap. $ABCD$.	7. Why?
8. $\therefore S = \frac{1}{2} h(b + b')$.	8. Why?

NOTE. To remember this theorem, think of the trapezoid as two triangles.

EXERCISES. AREAS OF TRAPEZOIDS

A

1. What is the area of a trapezoid whose altitude is 18 inches and whose bases are 9 inches and 13 inches respectively?

2. Find the area of a trapezoid whose bases are 24.3 and 16.9 respectively and whose altitude is 15.7. 6.4684

3. The area of a trapezoid is 4256 square inches and the bases are 68 inches and 84 inches respectively. Find the altitude.

4. The area of a trapezoid is 504 square inches. One of the bases is 24 inches and the altitude is 18 inches. Find the other base.

5. A diagonal divides a trapezoid into two triangles which have the same ratio as the bases of the trapezoid. Why?

6. The area of a trapezoid is 651 square feet and the bases are 27 and 35 feet respectively. Find the altitude.

7. Find the height of a trapezoid if its bases are 8 inches and 20 inches respectively and its area is 96 square inches.

8. Find the area of a trapezoid if the sum of its bases is 35 and its altitude is 17.

9. *Given* trapezoid $ABCD$ with bases AB and CD and diagonals AC and BD intersecting in E.
Prove that $\triangle ADE = \triangle BEC$.

B

10. The altitude of a trapezoid is ab, one base is $2a - b$, and the other base is $2a + b$. Find its area.

11. The area of a trapezoid is 3105 square inches, one base is 155 inches, and the altitude is 34.5 inches. Find the other base.

12. The bases of a trapezoid are 26 inches and 84 inches respectively and the altitude is 24 inches. Find the side of a square that has the same area as the trapezoid.

13. The bases of a trapezoid are 25 and 28 respectively. Find its altitude if its area is equal to that of a triangle whose base is 26.5 and whose altitude is 10.

14. The altitude of a trapezoid is m and the bases are $3m + 1$ and $5m - 9$ respectively. Find the height of an equal triangle whose base is $m - 1$.

15. In trapezoid $ABCD$, base AB is 24, base DC is 10, AD is 12, and $\angle A$ is 30°. Find the area of the trapezoid.

16. What is the area of the isosceles trapezoid whose bases are 8 inches and 18 inches respectively, if the nonparallel sides make angles of 45° with the lower base?

★Proposition IV. Pythagorean Theorem

234. *The square upon the hypotenuse of a right triangle is equal to the sum of the squares upon the legs.*

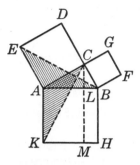

Given the rt. △ *ABC* having ∠ *ACB* the rt. ∠, and squares constructed upon the sides *AB, BC,* and *AC.*

To prove that square *AKHB* = square *ACDE* + square *BFGC.*

Selection of Method: 1. Known methods of comparing areas of polygons: §§ 221, 222, 225, 226, 228, 229, 230, 232.
2. Method to be used: § 232 and Ax. 1.

Proof: STATEMENTS	REASONS
1. Draw *CM* ∥ *AK.*	1. Why possible?
2. Draw *CK* and *BE.*	2. Why possible?
In ▲ *KAC* and *BAE,*	
3. *AK* = *AB, AC* = *AE,* and	3. Why?
4. ∠ *KAC* = ∠ *BAE.*	4. Give proof.
5. ∴ △ *KAC* ≅ △ *BAE.*	5. Why?
6. *DCB* is a st. line.	6. Give proof.
7. △ *BAE* and square *ACDE* have the same base *AE* and altitudes = *AC.*	7. § 177.

(Proof continued on opposite page.)

8. ∴ △ BAE = ½ square $ACDE$. | 8. § 232.
9. △ KAC and rectangle $KMLA$ have the same base AK and altitudes = AL. | 9. § 177.
10. ∴ △ KAC = ½ rectangle $KMLA$. | 10. Why?
11. From (5), (8), and (10), ½ rectangle $KMLA$ = ½ square $ACDE$. | 11. Why?
12. ∴ rectangle $KMLA$ = square $ACDE$. | 12. Why?
13. In like manner, rectangle $MHBL$ = square $BFGC$. | 13. Steps 1-12
14. ∴ $KMLA + MHBL = ACDE + BFGC$. | 14. Why?
15. ∴ square $KHBA$ = square $ACDE$ + square $BFGC$. | 15. Give axioms.

235. Proofs of the Pythagorean Theorem. Many proofs of the Pythagorean Theorem have been presented. The first proof of the theorem is attributed to Pythagoras about 525 B.C., but his method of demonstration is unknown. The proof of § 234 is attributed to Euclid. The proof given in § 411 is algebraic in character, while Euclid's proof is purely geometric. The statements of the theorems in § 411 and § 234 are also different. In § 411 the squares of the line segments are compared, while in § 234 the areas of the squares are compared. Below is an outline of the demonstration of the theorem as devised by President Garfield.

Given △ ABC with hypotenuse AB.
To prove that $c^2 = a^2 + b^2$.

Produce CB to D, making $b' = b$. At D construct $ED \perp BD$, making $a' = a$. Draw BE and AE. The area S of the trapezoid $CAED$ is given by the formula

$$S = \tfrac{1}{2}(a + b')(b + a') = \tfrac{1}{2}(a^2 + 2\,ab + b^2)$$
$$= \tfrac{1}{2}\,a^2 + ab + \tfrac{1}{2}\,b^2.$$

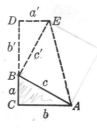

Considering the △ of the trapezoid,

$$S = \tfrac{1}{2}\,ab + \tfrac{1}{2}\,c^2 + \tfrac{1}{2}\,ab = ab + \tfrac{1}{2}\,c^2.$$
$$\therefore ab + \tfrac{1}{2}\,c^2 = \tfrac{1}{2}\,a^2 + ab + \tfrac{1}{2}\,b^2.$$

Solving, $c^2 = a^2 + b^2$.

EXERCISES [A]. PYTHAGOREAN THEOREM

In the figure below, AB is the hypotenuse of rt. $\triangle ABC$, each side of which is a side of a square, and CS is $\perp DE$.

1. Find the area of rectangle $SEBR$ if $BF = 8$.

2. If $KH = 8$ and $CG = 15$, what is the area of $ADEB$?

3. If $BC = 7$ and $AC = 9$, what is the area of $SEBR$? of $DSRA$?

4. Find AR if $AD = 30$ inches and the area of $\triangle KAB$ is 360 square inches.

5. Find the area of $ACHK$ if BC is 12 inches and RS is 20 inches.

6. Find DS if $FG = 12$ and $DE = 16$.

7. If $AK = 36$ and $RS = 39$, what is the area of $BFGC$?

8. Find the area of $ACHK$ if $AR = 12$ and $RB = 4$.

EXERCISES. RIGHT TRIANGLES

A

Example 1. Find the altitude of an equilateral triangle whose side is 7.

Solution. Let $x =$ the altitude. Then x bisects the base.

Then
$$x^2 + 3.5^2 = 7^2.$$
$$x^2 + 12.25 = 49.$$
$$x^2 = 36.75.$$
$$x = 6.06.$$

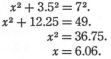

Example 2. The altitude of an equilateral triangle is 8. What is the length of a side?

Solution.
$$x^2 = (\tfrac{1}{2} x)^2 + 8^2.$$
$$x^2 = \tfrac{1}{4} x^2 + 64.$$
$$4 x^2 = x^2 + 256.$$
$$3 x^2 = 256.$$
$$x^2 = \tfrac{256}{3}.$$
$$x = \sqrt{\tfrac{256}{3}} = \tfrac{16}{3}\sqrt{3}, \text{ or } 9.24.$$

Start Assign.# 15

/ **Example 3.** In a 30°-60° triangle the short leg is 8. Find the long leg.

Solution. By § 120 the hypotenuse = 16. Let x = the long leg.

$$x^2 + 64 = 256.$$

Solving, $x = \sqrt{192} = 8\sqrt{3}$, or 13.86.

1. If c is the hypotenuse and a and b are the legs of a right triangle,
a. Find c if $a = 15$ and $b = 20$.   *c.* Find b if $a = 33$ and $c = 44$.
b. Find a if $c = 13$ and $b = 12$.   *d.* Find c if $a = 14.4$ and $b = 6$.

2. Find the diagonal of a square whose perimeter is 40.

3. Find correct to the nearest tenth the side of a square whose diagonal is 10.0 inches.

4. A ladder 20 feet long reaches a windowsill 16 feet from the ground. How far from the house is the foot of the ladder?

5. The diagonal of a square is $5\sqrt{2}$. Find a side.

6. Find the short leg of a 30°-60° triangle whose long leg is 20.

7. Find the side of a square whose diagonal is $3\sqrt{3}$.

8. Find the altitude of an equilateral triangle having a side equal to $8\sqrt{2}$.

9. Find the diagonal of a rectangle whose length is 45 inches and whose width is 24 inches.

10. The diagonal of a rectangle is 104 feet and the width is 40 feet. Find the length.

B

11. Find the side of an equilateral triangle whose altitude is 96 inches.

12. Prove that a median of a triangle bisects the triangle.

13. P is any point in the diagonal AC of $\square ABCD$. Prove that $\triangle ABP = \triangle ADP$.

SUGGESTION. Consider AP the base of each triangle.

14. What is the area of a tract of land in the shape of a right triangle if its hypotenuse is 52 feet and one of the other sides is 40 feet?

15. Write a formula for the area of the shaded surface bounded by the rectangle and square.

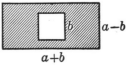

16. Find the area of an isosceles triangle whose base is b and whose other two sides are each equal to s.

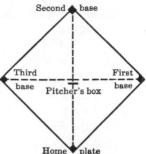

17. An 18-foot ladder resting against a house just reaches a window 16 feet above the ground. How far is the foot of the ladder from the house?

18. A baseball field is a square each side of which is 90 feet long. What is the distance from first base to third base?

19. The pitcher's box is 60 feet from the home plate. How far is it from second base? from third base?

20. The shortstop fields a batted ball at a point one third of the distance from second base to third base. How far must he throw the ball to make an out at first base?

21. A certain square field contains an acre. How many rods long is a side of the field?

C

22. Show that the altitude of an equilateral triangle having a side s is given by the formula $h = \frac{s}{2}\sqrt{3}$.

23. The difference between the base and altitude of a rectangle is 91 and a diagonal is 221. Find the base and altitude.

24. The sides of a triangle are 10, 13, and 13 respectively. Find the altitude drawn to a side 13. Find the area of the triangle.

236. Important Formulas. In the next two articles we shall develop important formulas relating to the square and equilateral triangle. You should remember these formulas, for they will be useful in solving many problems.

237. Theorem. *The diagonal of a square having a side s is given by the formula $d = s\sqrt{2}$.*

Proof: $d^2 = s^2 + s^2$.   Why?
$d^2 = 2\,s^2$.   Why?
$d = s\sqrt{2}$.   Why?

238. Theorem. *The altitude and area of an equilateral triangle having a side s are given by the formulas* $h = \frac{s}{2}\sqrt{3}$ *and* $A = \frac{s^2}{4}\sqrt{3}$.

Proof:

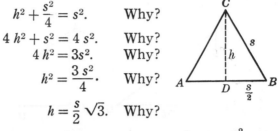

$h^2 + \frac{s^2}{4} = s^2.$	Why?
$4h^2 + s^2 = 4s^2.$	Why?
$4h^2 = 3s^2.$	Why?
$h^2 = \frac{3s^2}{4}.$	Why?
$h = \frac{s}{2}\sqrt{3}.$	Why?

Let A stand for the area. Then $A = \frac{1}{2} \times s \times \frac{s}{2}\sqrt{3} = \frac{s^2}{4}\sqrt{3}$.

EXERCISES. EQUILATERAL POLYGONS

A

Find the diagonal of a square whose side is

1. 6. 8.484   **2.** $\sqrt{2}$. = 2   **3.** 8. 11.312   **4.** $2\sqrt{3}$.

Find the altitude of an equilateral triangle whose side is

5. 10. 8.660   **6.** 18. 15.588   **7.** 15. 12.99   **8.** $14\sqrt{2}$. 9.898

Find the area of an equilateral triangle whose side is

9. 8. 27.712   **10.** 12. 62.352   **11.** 7. 21.217   **12.** $\sqrt{5}$. 96   8188

B

Example. Find the side of an equilateral triangle with area $36\sqrt{3}$.

Solution. Let $s =$ the length of each side of the $\triangle$.

Then $\frac{s^2}{4}\sqrt{3} = 36\sqrt{3}$; $s^2\sqrt{3} = 144\sqrt{3}$; $s^2 = 144$; $s = 12$.

Find the side of the equilateral triangle whose area is

13. $9\sqrt{3}$.   **15.** $\frac{1}{4}\sqrt{3}$.   **17.** 16.   **19.** 64.
14. $16\sqrt{3}$.   **16.** $\sqrt{3}$.   **18.** 20.   **20.** 100.

21. Find the area of a regular hexagon having a side of 8 inches.

Proposition V. Theorem

239. *If the sum of the squares of two sides of a triangle is equal to the square of the third side, the triangle is a right triangle.*

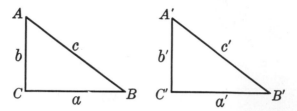

Given $\triangle ABC$, the longest side AB denoted by c, the side BC denoted by a, the side AC denoted by b, and $c^2 = a^2 + b^2$.

To prove that ABC is a right triangle.

Selection of Method: 1. Known methods of proving that triangles are right triangles: § 55 *b*.
2. Method to be used: § 55 *b*.

Proof: *STATEMENTS*   *REASONS*

STATEMENTS	REASONS
1. Construct rt. $\triangle A'B'C'$ with leg $A'C'$ $= AC$ and leg $C'B' = CB$.	1. §§ 153, 157.
2. $c'^2 = a'^2 + b'^2$.	2. Why?
3. But $a = a'$ and $b = b'$.	3. Why?
4. Then $a^2 = a'^2$ and $b^2 = b'^2$.	4. Why?
5. From (2), $c'^2 = a^2 + b^2$.	5. Why?
6. But $c^2 = a^2 + b^2$.	6. Why?
7. Then $c^2 = c'^2$.	7. Why?
8. And $c = c'$.	8. Why?
9. Then $\triangle ABC \cong \triangle A'B'C'$.	9. Why?
10. $\angle C = \angle C'$.	10. Why?
11. $\angle C'$ is a rt. $\angle$.	11. Why?
12. Then $\angle C$ is a rt. $\angle$.	12. Why?
13. Then $\triangle ABC$ is a rt. $\triangle$.	13. Why?

EXERCISES [A]

Which of the following are right triangles?

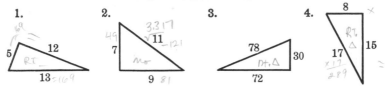

1. **2.** **3.** **4.**

240. Hero's Formula. The formula for finding the area of a triangle in terms of its sides is known as Hero's Formula. It is so named because its first appearance was in the writings of Hero about 125 B.C. Hero was a mathematician and lived in Alexandria. We shall now give the formula without proof.

241. Theorem (Hero's Formula). *The area of a triangle whose sides are a, b, and c is given by the formula*

$$A = \sqrt{s(s-a)(s-b)(s-c)}, \quad \text{where} \quad s = \tfrac{1}{2}(a+b+c).$$

Example. Find the area of a triangle whose sides are 8, 15, and 17.

Solution. $s = \tfrac{1}{2}(a+b+c) = \tfrac{1}{2}(8+15+17) = 20.$

$A = \sqrt{s(s-a)(s-b)(s-c)} = \sqrt{20(20-8)(20-15)(20-17)} = 60.$

242. Corollary. *In any triangle whose sides are a, b, and c, the altitude h on the side c is given by the formula*

$$h = \frac{2}{c}\sqrt{s(s-a)(s-b)(s-c)}.$$

EXERCISES [B]. AREAS OF TRIANGLES

Find the area of a triangle whose sides are

1. 9, 12, and 15. 4. 17.2, 12.3, and 8.5. 7. 200, 300, and 400.
2. 20, 48, and 52. 5. 65, 156, and 169. 8. $a+b$, $a-b$, $2c$.
3. 16, 30, and 34. 6. 984, 1845, and 2091. 9. $m+n$, $m+p$, $n+p$.

10. Using Hero's Formula, show that the area of an equilateral triangle having side s is $\tfrac{1}{4}s^2\sqrt{3}$.

11. The sides of a triangle are 18, 24, and 30. Find the altitude to the side 18; to the side 24; to the side 30.

243. Areas of Polygons. The area of a polygon may be found by separating it into triangles and trapezoids as shown. Any diagonal *AD* is drawn. Then perpendiculars to *AD* are drawn from *B*, *C*, *E*, and *F*, forming triangles and trapezoids.

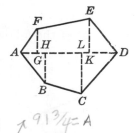

EXERCISES [C]. AREAS $\nearrow 9\,1\,3/4 = A$

1. In the figure of § 243, if $AG = 2$, $GH = 2$, $HL = 5$, $LK = 2$, $KD = 4$, $FG = 3\frac{1}{2}$, $EK = 5$, $HB = 4\frac{1}{2}$, and $LC = 6$, find the area of polygon *ABCDEF*.

2. Find the area in square miles of the state of Utah. (Obtain your measurements from a map of Utah.)

3. Find the area of the quadrilateral *ABCD* in the figure at the right.

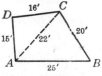

4. Find the area of quadrilateral *ABCD* if $AB = 20$ feet, $\angle B = 90°$, diagonal $AC = 24$ feet, $\angle ACD = 90°$, and $CD = 10$ feet.

5. Find the area of quadrilateral *RSTU* if $RU = 20$ inches, $TU = 16$ inches, $\angle RTU = 90°$, $RS = 11$ inches, and $ST = 5$ inches.

6. A farmer had a pentagon-shaped field of wheat which produced 324 bushels. A sketch of the field is shown at the right. He made the following measurements: $AC = 60$ rods; $EC = 70$ rods; $AE = 18$ rods; $\perp BF = 22$ rods; and $\perp DH = 14$ rods. Find the average number of bushels of wheat per acre produced by the field.

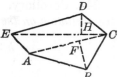

7. Prove that the area of the quadrilateral whose vertices are the midpoints of the sides of a second quadrilateral is equal to half the area of the second quadrilateral.

8. In this figure the dashed lines are perpendicular to *EH*, $EA = 60$, $FB = 80$, $GD = 40$, $HC = 56$, $EF = 45$, $FG = 8$, and $GH = 25$. Find the area of *ABCD*.

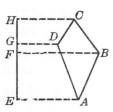

9. In △ *ABC*, *AE* and *BD* are two medians intersecting in *F*. Prove that △ *ABF* = quadrilateral *DFEC*.

EXERCISES. MISCELLANEOUS

A

1. A trunk is 30 inches long and 18 inches wide, inside measure. What is the length of the longest umbrella that will lie flat on the bottom of it?

2. A back yard is 22 feet by 34 feet. What is the length of the longest rope that can be stretched across it?

3. The legs of a right triangle are 15 and 20. Find the area of an equilateral triangle which has one of its sides equal to the hypotenuse of the right triangle.

4. If the base of a triangle is doubled and the altitude remains unchanged, how is the area changed?

5. If both base and altitude of a triangle are trebled, how is the area changed?

6. If the area of a triangle remains the same when the altitude is doubled, how is the base changed?

7. About 2000 B.C. the Egyptians knew that a right triangle could be formed by stretching around three pegs a cord measured off into 3, 4, and 5 units. Prove that a triangle with sides 3, 4, and 5 is a right triangle.

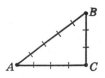

B

8. The sides of a triangle are 16 inches, 30 inches, and 34 inches respectively. Find the altitude drawn to the longest side.

SUGGESTION. Let $x =$ the altitude. Then $17 x =$ the area of the triangle. Find the area by Hero's Formula and equate the areas. Or use § 242.

9. *Prove:* Two triangles are equal in area if two sides of one are equal respectively to two sides of the other and the included angles are supplementary.

10. Write a formula for the area of a kite in terms of its diagonals, d and d'.

11. Write a formula for the area of a rhombus in terms of a side, s, when one angle contains 120°.

C

12. Find the side of an equilateral triangle that is equal in area to a square 18 inches on a side.

Proposition VI. Problem

244. *To construct a square equal to the sum of two given squares.*

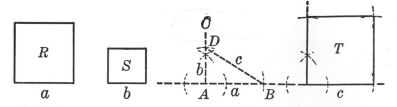

Given the squares R and S having sides a and b respectively.

To construct a square $T = R + S$.

Construction:

STATEMENTS	REASONS
1. Construct $AB = a$.	1. Why possible?
2. Construct $AC \perp AB$.	2. Why possible?
3. On AC lay off $AD = b$.	3. Why possible?
4. Draw DB.	4. Why possible?
5. Construct square T with a side $= BD(c)$.	5. Why possible?

Then square T = square R + square S.

Proof: (The proof is left to the student.)

EXERCISES [B]. CONSTRUCTIONS

1. Construct a square twice as large as a given square.

2. Construct a square equal to the sum of three given squares.

3. Construct a square equal to the difference of two given squares.

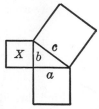

SUGGESTION. a and c are known. How can you find b, the side of the square X?

4. Construct a square three times as large as a given square.

Proposition VII. Problem

245. *To construct a triangle equal to a given polygon.**

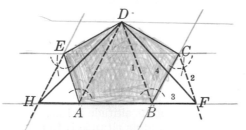

Given the polygon *ABCDE*.

To construct a △ = *ABCDE*.

Construction: *STATEMENTS*   *REASONS*

1. Draw diagonal *DB*, forming △ *BCD*.	1. Why possible?
2. Construct a line through *C* ‖ *BD*.	2. Why possible?
3. Produce *AB* to meet this line at *F*.	3. Why possible?
4. Draw *DF*.	4. Why possible?
5. In like manner, construct *HD*.	5. Statements 1–4.

Then △ *HDF* = *ABCDE*.

Proof: (The proof is left to the student.)

SUGGESTIONS. △ *BFD* = △ *BCD* since they have the same base *BD* and equal altitudes. Why are the altitudes equal? △ *BCD* is replaced by △ *BFD* of equal area. In this way the number of sides of the polygon is reduced by one. In like manner, △ *AED* is replaced by △ *AHD* of equal area. and the number of sides of the polygon *AFDE* is reduced by one.

EXERCISES [A]. CONSTRUCTIONS

1. Construct a triangle equal in area to a given square.

2. Construct a right triangle equal in area to a given triangle.

3. Construct a right triangle equal in area to a given square.

4. Construct a triangle equal in area to a given hexagon.

5. Construct a quadrilateral equal in area to a given pentagon.

*This problem may be stated "Transform a given polygon into a triangle."

EXERCISES. REVIEW

A

1. Find the area of a rectangle whose dimensions are

a. 18.2 and 16.

b. $4\frac{2}{3}$ and $7\frac{5}{8}$.

c. 4.18 and 9.32.

d. $x + 6$ and $4x - 3$.

e. $2x - 3y$ and $4xy$.

f. $x^2 + x + 1$ and $x^2 - x + 1$.

2. The area of a rectangle is $a^2 - ab - 2b^2$ and the base is $a - 2b$. Find the altitude.

3. Find the base of a parallelogram

a. If its area is 360.43 and its altitude is 13.3.

b. If its area is 10 acres and its altitude is 15 rods.

c. If its area is $4x^3 - 8x^2 + 4x$ and its altitude is $4x$.

d. If its area is $x^2 + x - 30$ and its altitude is $x - 5$.

4. Find the area of a cement walk 5 feet wide which surrounds a rectangular plot of grass 115 feet long and 82 feet wide.

5. Find the side of a square equal in area to a trapezoid whose bases are 34 feet and 62 feet and whose altitude is 27 feet.

6. *ABCD* is a parallelogram. Prove that $\triangle ABD = \triangle ABC$. diagonals $\div$ = $\triangle$

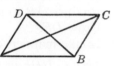

7. Find the area of a rhombus whose diagonals are 18 feet and 24 feet respectively.

8. Each side of a rhombus is 13 inches and one diagonal is 10 inches. Find the area.

9. The area of a rhombus is 384 square inches and one diagonal is 16 inches. Find the other diagonal.

10. Prove that the area of a square is equal to one half the square of a diagonal.

11. The area of a square is 60 square inches. Find its diagonal.

12. Find the area of an equilateral triangle each of whose sides is

a. 8 inches.

b. 10 inches.

c. 14 inches.

d. $3\sqrt{3}$.

e. 1.732.

f. $\frac{1}{2}\sqrt{3}$.

13. A rectangular field whose adjacent sides have the ratio 2 : 5 contains 1440 square rods. Find the dimensions of the field.

14. The sides of a rectangle whose area is 240 square feet have the ratio 3 : 5. Find the diagonal of the rectangle.

15. Find the base of a triangle whose area is $x^2 - x - 20$ and whose altitude is $x + 4$.

B

16. Find the area of an isosceles trapezoid whose bases are 20 inches and 30 inches respectively and whose nonparallel sides are each 17 inches.

17. Find the area of a trapezoid whose bases are 16 inches and 24 inches respectively if the angles at one base are each 60°.

18. Find the side of a square which is equal to a trapezoid whose bases are 40 inches and 56 inches respectively and whose altitude is $21\frac{1}{3}$ inches.

19. Prove that the line segment joining the midpoints of the bases of a trapezoid divides the trapezoid into two equal trapezoids.

20. Find the area of trapezoid $ABCD$ in which base AB is 50 inches, BC is 20 inches, $\angle B$ is 30°, and $\angle A$ is 45°.

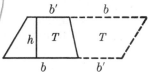

21. Prove Prop. III, using this figure.

22. The area of a trapezoid is 390 square inches and the altitude is 15 inches. Find the bases if their difference is 12 inches.

23. The area of an isosceles right triangle is 72 square inches. Find the length of each side.

24. Find the area of a rhombus whose longer diagonal is 48 inches and whose perimeter is 120 inches.

25. Find the side of a square equal in area to the sum of two squares whose areas are 121 and 135 square inches respectively.

26. Find the longest side of an isosceles right triangle if its area is 288 square inches.

27. The area of a trapezoid is 51 square inches. Its altitude is 8.5 inches and one base is 4 inches. Find the other base.

28. A living room is 12 feet wide and 24 feet long. Which would be the cheaper, and how much, to buy a rug for the room for $108 or to cover the floor with carpet at $3.25 per square yard?

29. Find the altitude of an equilateral triangle whose area is $12.25\sqrt{3}$.

30. A ladder 50 feet long is placed so that its foot is 8 feet from a building. How far must the foot of the ladder be moved from the building to lower the top of the ladder 6 feet?

31. The area of a rhombus is 150 square inches and the diagonals have the ratio 3 : 4. Find the length of each side of the rhombus.

32. The sides of a triangle are 18 inches, 20 inches, and 24 inches. Find the altitude upon the longest side.

33. The sides of a triangle are 35, 84, and 91 respectively. Find the altitude drawn to the side 91.

34. One angle of a parallelogram is 30°. If the adjacent sides are 12 feet and 16 feet respectively, what is the area of the parallelogram?

35. The shaded surface between the two squares is of uniform width. Find the area and width of the shaded surface.

36. The area of a rectangle whose base is 18 feet is 432 square feet. Find the diagonal.

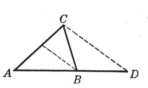

C

37. Transform △ *ABC* below into a triangle having base *AD*.

38. A diagonal of a rectangle is 25 feet. Find the area of the rectangle if its width is 9 feet.

39. Find the perimeter of a rectangular field if its area is 11.25 acres and the length is twice the width.

40. The difference between two adjacent sides of a parallelogram is 4 feet, and the included angle contains 60°. What are the lengths of its sides if its area is $126\sqrt{3}$ square feet?

41. One angle of a parallelogram contains 60°. If the adjacent sides are 12 feet and 16 feet respectively, what is the area of the parallelogram?

42. Find the area of an isosceles triangle whose perimeter is *p* and whose base is *b*.

43. Find the area of an equilateral triangle whose altitude is *h*.

44. The difference between a side and the altitude of an equilateral triangle is $2(2 - \sqrt{3})$ feet. Find the area of the triangle.

45. The shortest side of a 30°-60° right triangle is 15. Find the area.

46. The area of a 30°-60° right triangle is 17.32. Find the lengths of the three sides.

47. Using § 227, prove that the product of the legs of a right triangle is equal to the product of the hypotenuse and the altitude upon it.

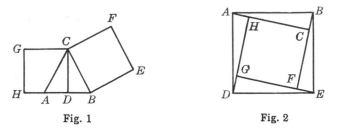

Fig. 1   Fig. 2

48. In Fig. 1, *ABC* is an equilateral triangle with altitude *CD*. If the area of square *BF* is 24 square inches, what is the area of square *DG*?

49. Using Fig. 2, see if you can prove the Pythagorean Theorem.

50. Find the area of the trapezoid *ABCD*.

SUGGESTIONS. Draw *CE* ∥ *AD*. Find the area of △ *CEB*. Find the altitude of △ *CEB* and then find the area of the parallelogram.

51. The sum of the diagonals of a rhombus is 69 inches, and one diagonal is 21 inches longer than the other. Find the area of the rhombus.

52. The area of a rhombus is 165 square inches, and one diagonal exceeds the other by 7 inches. Find the two diagonals.

53. In trapezoid *ABCD*, ∠ *A* = 60°, ∠ *B* = 90°, *AD* = 12 inches, and *BD* = 24 inches. Find the area of *ABCD*.

54. The bases of an isosceles trapezoid are 15 inches and 21 inches. If each of the nonparallel sides is 5 inches, what is the area of the trapezoid?

55. Find the diagonal of a rectangle which has an altitude of 16 feet and an area of 480 square feet.

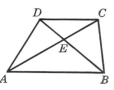

56. Given the trapezoid *ABCD*, one base *AB*, area △ *ABC* = 126, area △ *ABE* = 81. Find the area of △ *AED*.

EXERCISES. APPLICATIONS

1. A barn is 50 feet wide, 60 feet long, and 20 feet high to the eaves. The rise of the roof is 12 feet. Estimate the cost of applying two coats of paint to the barn if one gallon of paint will cover 400 square feet. The 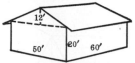 paint costs $3.50 a gallon, and the cost of labor is twice the cost of the paint. Find the cost of roofing the barn at $6 a square (100 square feet) if the roof extends beyond the siding 2 feet at each end and 18 inches at each side.

2. Find the cost of sheet roofing for the barn (Ex. 1) if the roof extends 1 foot beyond the siding on all four sides and if the roofing costs $7 a square. (1 square = 100 square feet.)

3. A tree 90 feet high is broken off 40 feet from the ground. How far from the foot of the tree will the top strike the ground?

4. A farmer wished to divide a triangular pasture field ABC into two fields having equal areas by building a fence from D, a point in AB. How did he do it?

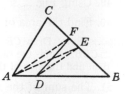

SUGGESTIONS. E is the midpoint of BC. Prove that $\triangle ADE = \triangle DEF$.

5. A farmer had a farm in the shape of the quadrilateral $ABCD$ and wished to separate it into two farms equal in area by a fence DF from D to a point in AB. How did he do it?

SUGGESTIONS. $AE = EC$. $EF \parallel DB$. $\triangle OFB = \triangle EOD$.

6. A farmer wished to run one fence from a tree T to the side CB of a field and another fence from T to the side AB and thus separate the field ABC into two fields of equal area. He ran a fence from T to D, the midpoint of BC. He then drew DE parallel to TA and ran a fence from T to E. Can you prove that polygon $EBDT =$ polygon $AETDC$?

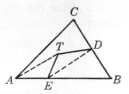

SUGGESTIONS. Draw AD and compare $\triangle ABD$ with $\triangle ADC$. How does AD divide $AEDT$?

End Assign # 15

[Space geometry. Optional]

246. Prisms and Parallelepipeds. This figure represents a prism. The top and bottom surfaces are called its *bases*. The bases lie in parallel planes. The other faces are called *lateral faces* and intersect in parallel line segments called *edges*. In a *right prism* the lateral faces and edges are perpendicular to the bases. A *regular prism* is a right prism whose bases are regular polygons. Prisms are triangular, quadrangular, pentagonal, etc., according as their bases are triangles, quadrilaterals, pentagons, etc.

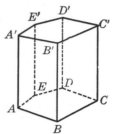

A parallelepiped is a prism whose bases are parallelograms. A *rectangular parallelepiped* is a right prism whose bases are rectangles. It is sometimes called a *rectangular solid*.

A *cube* is a parallelepiped all of whose bases are squares.

Parallelepiped

EXERCISES

1. Name several objects that are rectangular parallelepipeds; prisms.

2. How many faces has a parallelepiped? a triangular prism?

3. How many edges has a parallelepiped? a quadrangular prism?

4. How many vertices has a parallelepiped? a pentagonal prism?

5. Prove that the lateral faces of a prism are parallelograms.

6. Prove that the lateral edges of a prism are equal.

7. Prove that the lateral faces of a right prism are rectangles.

8. Prove that the bases of a triangular prism are equal.

9. A room is 24 feet long, 12 feet wide, and 8 feet high. Find the distance from a lower corner to the opposite upper corner.

10. Prove that the sum of the squares of the edges of a rectangular parallelepiped is equal to the sum of the squares of the four diagonals.

247. Area of a Prism. The *lateral area* of a prism is the sum of the areas of the lateral faces. The area of a prism means its total area and is the sum of its lateral area and the areas of its two bases.

248. Volume of a Solid. The volume of a solid is the number of cubic units of measure contained in the solid. A cubic unit of measure is a cube whose edge is one linear unit. This solid contains 12 of these cubic units of measure.

249. Postulate. *The volume of a right prism is the product of its base and altitude.*

Example. Find the volume of a regular triangular prism if its lateral edge is 10 inches and one edge of a base is 6 inches.

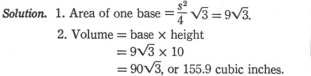

Solution. 1. Area of one base $= \dfrac{s^2}{4}\sqrt{3} = 9\sqrt{3}$.

2. Volume $=$ base $\times$ height
$$= 9\sqrt{3} \times 10$$
$$= 90\sqrt{3}, \text{ or } 155.9 \text{ cubic inches.}$$

EXERCISES

1. Find the area of a cube 6 inches on an edge. Find its volume.

2. Find the lateral area of a regular triangular prism if each of its edges is 4 inches. Find its volume.

3. Find the area and volume of a right prism whose lateral edge is 12 inches and whose base is a right triangle with legs of 8 inches and 6 inches respectively.

4. A classroom is 24 feet wide, 36 feet long, and 12 feet high. What is its volume in cubic yards? What is its lateral area in square yards?

5. Find the area and volume of a rectangular parallelepiped having an altitude of 16 inches and a base 10 inches long by 5 inches wide.

6. Find the lateral area of a regular hexagonal prism 2 feet high if one edge of a base is 6 inches.

7. How many gallons are needed to fill a pool 140 feet long and 50 feet wide to a depth of 6 feet? (231 cubic inches = 1 gallon.)

250. Pyramids. The figure below represents a *pyramid.*
One face, *ABCDE*, is a polygon called the *base* of the pyramid.
The lateral faces are triangles meeting in a
common vertex *V*. The intersections of the
lateral faces are the *lateral edges.* The *altitude*
of a pyramid is the perpendicular from the
vertex to the plane of the base. Pyramids are
called triangular, quadrangular, etc., in the
same manner as prisms.

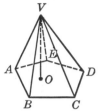

A *regular pyramid* is a pyramid whose base is a regular polygon and whose altitude is perpendicular to the plane of its
base at the point which is equidistant from the vertices of
the base.

The *slant height* of a regular pyramid is the altitude of any
of the lateral faces.

EXERCISES

1. Prove that the lateral edges of a regular pyramid are equal.

2. Prove that the lateral faces of a regular pyramid are congruent
isosceles triangles.

3. How many edges has a triangular pyramid? a hexagonal pyramid? an octagonal pyramid?

4. Find the slant height of a regular quadrangular pyramid if one
edge of the base is 16 inches and a lateral edge is 17 inches. Find
the altitude.

5. Find the slant height of a regular triangular pyramid if one
edge of the base is 6 inches and a lateral edge is 5 inches. Find the
altitude.

6. Find the lateral area of a regular pentagonal pyramid if the slant
height is 7 inches and one edge of the base is 5 inches.

7. Find the lateral area of a hexagonal pyramid whose lateral edges
are 7 inches each and whose base has sides of 6 inches each.

8. Find the area of a regular triangular pyramid if each edge is
8 inches.

9. Find the area of a regular hexagonal pyramid if each edge of
the base is 10 inches and each lateral edge is 13 inches.

251. Postulate. *The volume of a pyramid is equal to one third the product of its base and altitude.*

EXERCISES

1. Find the volume of a regular pyramid whose altitude is 3 feet and whose base is a square 2 feet on a side.

2. Find the volume of a regular quadrangular pyramid whose slant height is 26 feet and whose base is 20 feet on a side.

3. Find the volume of a regular triangular pyramid if the altitude is 20 inches and a side of the base is 8 inches.

4. Find the volume and area of a triangular pyramid if each lateral edge is 36 inches and the base is 12 inches on a side.

5. A prism and a pyramid have equal bases and equal altitudes. How do their volumes compare?

6. Why do only regular pyramids have slant heights?

252. Frustum of a Pyramid. A *frustum of a pyramid* is the part of a pyramid formed between the base of a pyramid and a plane parallel to the base. In the figure, *ABCD-EFGH* is a frustum of a pyramid.

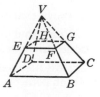

EXERCISES

1. *ABC-DEF* is the frustum of a pyramid.
a. *Prove* that *AB ∥ DE, BC ∥ EF*, and *AC ∥ DF*.
b. *Prove* that *ABED, BCFE*, and *ACFD* are trapezoids.

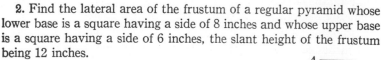

2. Find the lateral area of the frustum of a regular pyramid whose lower base is a square having a side of 8 inches and whose upper base is a square having a side of 6 inches, the slant height of the frustum being 12 inches.

3. In the figure at the right *AC* and *BD* are any two diagonals of a cube.
a. *Prove* that *AC = BD*.
b. *Prove* that *AC* and *BD* bisect each other.

EXERCISES IN REASONING (Optional)

In each of the following exercises tell whether or not the conclusion is valid and give the reason for your answer:

1. Jack is taller than Joan, and I am taller than Jack. Therefore I am taller than Joan.

2. Our basketball team won from West High 36 to 18. Beaumont won from West High 25 to 24. I know that we can defeat Beaumont.

3. Miss Jones, my new Latin teacher, is not a hard marker. I know I shall like her.

4. Mr. Wilson, our geometry teacher, gives us credit for handing in work that has been missed due to unavoidable absence. I was barred from school last week for cutting classes. Mr. Wilson will permit me to get credit for all the assignments I missed.

5. Mr. James had a cough, took some cough medicine, and was soon well. If I have a cough, some of the same medicine will help me.

6. I saw in a magazine advertisement the picture of a beautiful girl smoking a cigarette. I am going to smoke cigarettes so that I may be beautiful.

7. Our automobile shop teacher always finds jobs for his graduates. When I graduate from his course, he will find a job for me.

8. I heard over the radio that Joan Dickson, who won the prize for having the most beautiful hands, uses Derma Hand Lotion. I am going to use Derma Hand Lotion and have beautiful hands.

9. A good teacher speaks when he meets any of his pupils. My physics teacher spoke to me on the campus this morning. Therefore he is a good teacher.

10. We have a good basketball coach, good basketball material, and a fine school spirit. We should have a good team.

11. If all people are created equal, then one person can learn geometry as easily as another.

12. If our cat has one more tail than no cat, and if no cat has eight tails, then our cat has nine tails.

13. Bob French says that he spends only 30 minutes each day in preparing his college mathematics lesson and that he makes the highest grade in his class. Name three possible conclusions. Can each conclusion be partly true?

1 — whole class smart
2 — whole class dumb
3 — awfully easy math class

REVIEW QUESTIONS

1. Give formulas for the following:

a. Area of a rectangle.

b. Area of a parallelogram.

c. Area of a rhombus.

d. Area of a square. Give two.

e. Area of a triangle. Give two.

f. Area of an equilateral triangle in terms of a side.

g. Area of a trapezoid.

h. Relation between the sides of a right triangle and the hypotenuse.

i. Altitude of an equilateral triangle in terms of a side.

2. Can two squares with different perimeters have the same area? Can two triangles with different perimeters have the same area?

3. If two parallelograms have equal bases, to what is the ratio of their areas equal?

4. If two polygons are equal in area, do they have the same shape?

5. What is the name of the triangle whose altitude is one of its sides?

6. Is a triangle divided into two equal triangles by a bisector of one of its angles? by an altitude? by a median?

7. Who was Pythagoras? Euclid? Archimedes?

8. Can two rectangles have equal areas and different perimeters?

9. Can two rectangles have equal perimeters and different areas?

10. What part of a triangle is cut off by a line which is parallel to the base and bisects a side?

11. If both dimensions of a rectangle are doubled, how is its area changed?

12. If two triangles have equal bases, how do their areas compare?

13. How can you find the height of a triangle when its base and area are known?

14. How can you find a side of a square when its perimeter is given? when its diagonal is given?

15. How can you find a leg of a right triangle when the hypotenuse and the other leg are given?

16. State the converse of the Pythagorean Theorem.

17. Give a rule for finding the height of a trapezoid when its bases and area are known.

SUMMARY OF PRINCIPAL METHODS OF PROOF

253. *Equal ratios*

a. Two rectangles, parallelograms, or triangles having equal bases have the same ratio as their altitudes.

b. Two rectangles, parallelograms, or triangles having equal altitudes have the same ratio as their bases.

c. Two triangles have the same ratio as the products of their bases and altitudes.

254. *Areas*

a. A *rectangle* is equal to the product of its base and altitude.

b. A *parallelogram* is equal to the product of its base and altitude.

c. A *triangle* is equal to one half the product of its base and altitude.

d. A *triangle* whose sides are *a, b,* and *c* and whose semiperimeter is *s* is equal to $\sqrt{s(s-a)(s-b)(s-c)}$.

e. A *trapezoid* is equal to half the product of its altitude and the sum of its bases.

f. An *equilateral triangle* whose side is *s* is equal to $\frac{s^2}{4}\sqrt{3}$.

g. A *rhombus* is equal to one half the product of its diagonals.

h. A *square* is equal to the square of a side.

i. The square upon the hypotenuse of a right triangle is equal to the sum of the squares upon the legs.

255. *Polygons equal in area*

a. Two rectangles, parallelograms, or triangles are equal in area if they have equal bases and equal altitudes.

b. If a triangle and parallelogram have equal bases and equal altitudes, the area of the triangle equals half the area of the parallelogram.

256. *Constructions*

a. To construct a square equal to the sum of two given squares.

b. To construct a triangle equal to a given polygon.

WORD LIST

area	mathematics	proposition	solution
equivalent	numerator	Pythagoras	trapezoid

TEST 17

True-False Statements (*Twelve Minutes*)

Copy the numbers of these statements on your paper. Then if a statement is *always* true, write T after its number. If a statement is *not always* true, write F after its number. Do not guess.

F **1.** The area of a triangle is equal to the product of its base and altitude. *×times*

F **2.** If the dimensions of a rectangle are doubled, the area is doubled.

F **3.** The area of a trapezoid is equal to the product of the sum of its bases and its altitude.

F **4.** The area of a rhombus is equal to one half the product of the diagonals.

F **5.** The product of the legs of a right triangle is equal to the product of the hypotenuse and the altitude upon it.

T **6.** The hypotenuse of a right triangle whose legs are a and b is $\sqrt{ab}$.

T **7.** Two parallelograms having equal bases have the same ratio as their altitudes.

T **8.** Triangles that have equal bases and equal altitudes are congruent.

F **9.** In the formula $A = \sqrt{s(s-a)(s-b)(s-c)}$, $s = a + b + c$.

10. The area of a trapezoid is equal to the product of its median and altitude.

T **11.** If a side of a triangle is doubled and its altitude remains the same, its area is doubled.

12. If a side of a square is doubled, its perimeter is doubled.

F **13.** If the perimeter of a square is trebled, its area is trebled.

F **14.** Pythagoras is a theorem.

F **15.** The altitude of a triangle divides the triangle into two equal triangles.

T **16.** If the midpoints of the sides of a triangle are joined by straight line segments, the triangle formed by the segments is one fourth the original triangle.

T **17.** The triangle whose sides are 16, 30, and 34 is a right triangle.

TEST 18

Constructions (*Twelve Minutes*)

Make the following geometric constructions accurately:

1. Construct a quadrilateral equal to a given pentagon.
2. Construct a triangle equal to a given square.
3. Construct a square equal to the difference of two given squares.

TEST 19

Applications (*Thirty Minutes*)

1. The base of a parallelogram is 11 feet and the altitude is 8 feet. Find the area.
2. The base of a triangle is 6 feet and the altitude is 8 feet. Find the area.
3. The hypotenuse of a right triangle is 13 feet and one leg is 5 feet. Find the area.
4. Find the area of an equilateral triangle whose side is 10 feet.
5. The bases of a trapezoid are 14 feet and 8 feet respectively and the area is 66 square feet. Find the altitude.
6. Find the area of a square whose diagonal is 12 feet.
7. The base of a rectangle is 22 and its area is 550. Find the length of one of its diagonals.
8. Find the side of a square equal to a trapezoid whose bases are 32 and 18 and whose altitude is 9.
9. Find the area of a rhombus if a side is equal to 12 and one angle contains 30°.
10. The area of a trapezoid is 144 square inches. One base is double the other and the altitude is 8 inches. Find the bases.
11. Find the area of a triangle whose sides are 6, 8, and 12.
12. Find the area of a rhombus if the diagonals are 10 and 16.
13. Find the altitude of an equilateral triangle if a side is equal to 12.
14. The bases of an isosceles trapezoid are 12 and 18. The equal non-parallel sides are each 5. Find the area of the trapezoid.
15. The area of a rectangle is 320 and the base is five times its altitude. What is its altitude?

Electric Generators in a Powerhouse at Pickwick Landing, Tennessee

The many and varied applications of the circle in a large powerhouse
are of great interest to students of geometry

CHAPTER VIII

Circles, Angles, and Arcs

In this chapter we shall make a study of the circle and the lines and angles associated with it. The circle has many properties which no other plane figure possesses. For example, it is symmetric with respect to its center and is symmetric with respect to any of its diameters.

Of all simple geometric figures the circle is perhaps the most appealing. Used in decoration it readily harmonizes in composition with other geometric figures. It is frequently used in the designs of public buildings, churches, cathedrals, and landscape gardens.

Have you ever considered how useful the circle is? Without the circle there would be no watches, clocks, wagons, automobiles, steamships, electricity, or any modern conveniences.

257. Circle. A *circle* (⊙) is a closed plane curve all points of which are equidistant from a point within called the *center*. *Congruent* or *equal circles* are circles that can be made to coincide. If two circles coincide, their centers coincide.

258. Lines Related to the Circle. A *radius* (plural, *radii*) of a circle is a line segment connecting the center with any point on the circle.

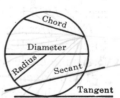

A *chord* is a line segment connecting any two points on the circle.

A *diameter* is a chord passing through the center of the circle.

A *secant* is a line which meets the circle in two points and passes through it in at least one of them.

A *tangent* is a line touching a circle at one point, and only one. This point is called the *point of tangency* or *point of contact*.

The *line of centers* of two circles is the straight line determined by the centers of the circles.

259. Angles Related to the Circle. A *central angle,* as ∠ AOB in the figure, is an angle whose vertex is the center of the circle and whose sides are radii. An *inscribed angle,* as ∠ CDE, is an angle whose vertex is on the circle and whose sides are chords.

260. Arc. An *arc* (⌒) is the part of a circle included between any two of its points. An arc is usually named by its end points or by a small letter near it.

A *semicircle* is an arc that is half of a circle.

A *quadrant* is an arc that is one fourth of a circle. A *minor arc* is one that is less than a semicircle and a *major arc* is one that is larger than a semicircle. Any two points of a circle divide the circle into two arcs. If these two arcs are unequal, one is a major arc and the other is a minor arc. From now on when two capital letters are used to name an arc the minor arc is the one intended, unless stated otherwise. Thus $\overset{\frown}{AB}$ means the minor arc AB. Every chord of a circle has two arcs. If these arcs are unequal, we shall agree that "a chord and its arc" means "a chord and its minor arc."

An angle is *inscribed in an arc* if its vertex is on the arc and its sides are chords joining the vertex to the end points of the arc. ∠ DCE is inscribed in $\overset{\frown}{DCE}$.

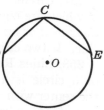

Equal arcs are arcs which can be made to coincide. It follows that they are arcs of the same circle or of equal circles.

The *midpoint of an arc* is the point which divides the arc into two equal parts. The *center of an arc* is the center of the circle of which the arc is a part. In the figure, M is the midpoint and O is the center of $\overset{\frown}{AB}$.

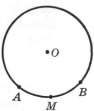

261. Circumference. The *circumference* of a circle is its length expressed in linear units (as feet and inches).

262. Postulates on the Circle.* From definitions and a study of the circle we may state the following postulates:

a. **Post. 23.** *Circles having equal radii are equal; and conversely.*

b. **Post. 24.** *A point is within, on, or outside a circle if its distance from the center is less than, equal to, or greater than the radius; and conversely.*

c. **Post. 25.** *Two minor arcs, or two major arcs, coincide if their end points and centers coincide; and conversely.*

ORAL EXERCISES [A]

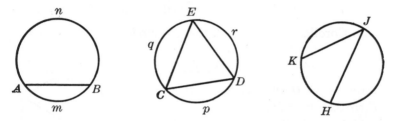

1. Name the minor arcs of the circles above; the major arcs.

2. Complete: $\angle$ __?__ is inscribed in $\widehat{CDE}$; $\angle$ __?__ is inscribed in $\widehat{CED}$; $\angle J$ is inscribed in __?__.

263. Post. 26. *In a circle or in equal circles equal central angles have equal arcs.*

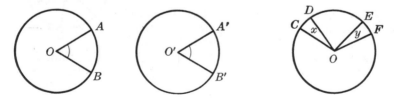

This postulate states that if $\odot O = \odot O'$ and $\angle O = \angle O'$, then $\widehat{AB} = \widehat{A'B'}$. It also states that if $\angle x = \angle y$, $\widehat{CD} = \widehat{EF}$

264. Corollary. *A diameter of a circle bisects the circle.* (What kind of central angles are formed?)

*Other postulates on the circle are given on pages 43 and 44.

265. Post. 27. *In a circle or in equal circles equal arcs have equal central angles.*

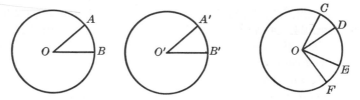

This postulate states that if $\odot O = \odot O'$ and $\overarc{AB} = \overarc{A'B'}$, $\angle O = \angle O'$. It also states that if $\overarc{CD} = \overarc{EF}$, $\angle COD = \angle EOF$. Postulates 26 and 27 can be proved by superposition.

266. Corollary. *If a chord bisects a circle, it is a diameter.*

EXERCISES [A]

1. *Given* circle O with diameters AB and CD.
Prove that $\overarc{AC} = \overarc{DB}$.

2. If a circle is divided into six equal arcs and radii are drawn to the points of division, how many degrees are there in each of the six central angles?

3. *Given* $\odot O$, radii AO, CO, and BO, and C the midpoint of $\overarc{AB}$.
Prove that CO bisects $\angle AOB$.

4. On paper locate three points, A, B, and C, not in the same straight line. Locate several points equidistant from A and B (see §§ 123 and 155). Using these points as centers, construct circles passing through A and B. In like manner, construct several circles passing through B and C. How many circles can be drawn through A, B, and C? Can a circle be drawn through A, B, and C if these points lie on a straight line? Why?

5. *Given* diameter AB of $\odot O$, radii CO and OD, and $\overarc{AC} = \overarc{BD}$.

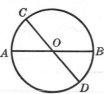

a. *Prove* that $\overarc{BC} = \overarc{AD}$.
b. *Prove* that COD is a diameter.

★ Proposition I. Theorem

267. *In a circle or in equal circles equal chords have equal arcs.*

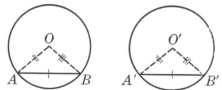

Given ⊙ O = ⊙ O' and chord AB = chord $A'B'$.

To prove that $\widehat{AB} = \widehat{A'B'}$.

Selection of Method: 1. Known methods of proving arcs =: §§ 262 *c* and 263.
2. Method to be used: § 263.

Proof: (The proof is left to the student.)

★ Proposition II. Theorem

268. *In a circle or in equal circles equal arcs have equal chords.*

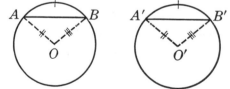

Given ⊙ O = ⊙ O' and $\widehat{AB} = \widehat{A'B'}$.

To prove that $AB = A'B'$.

Selection of Method: 1. Known methods of proving line segments =: §§ 86, 140, 202, and 262 *a*.
2. Method to be used: § 86 *a*.

Proof: (The proof is left to the student.)

269. Inscribed Polygon. A polygon is *inscribed in a circle* if its vertices lie on the circle. The circle is then said to be *circumscribed about the polygon*. *ABCDE* is an inscribed polygon.

EXERCISES. ANGLES AND ARCS

~ 0 = α
~ α = c

A

1. Name the methods you have had of proving arcs equal; of proving chords equal; of proving central angles equal. Have you located these methods on pages 547, 544, and 545?

2. If an equilateral polygon is inscribed in a circle, what is true of the arcs? Why? ~ chords have ~ ones

3. If a circle is divided into six equal arcs, and the points of division are joined in order, what can you say of the polygon thus formed? hexagon

4. Given $\widehat{AB} = \widehat{DC}$ and $\widehat{AD} = \widehat{BC}$.
Prove that *ABCD* is a $\square$.

5. If a circle contains 360°, how many degrees are in each arc of a circle circumscribed about an equilateral triangle? a square? a regular hexagon? a regular octagon?

6. If an arc is doubled, is its chord doubled? its central angle?

7. What is the difference between the "midpoint of an arc" and the "center of an arc"?

B

8. Given the diameter *AB* bisecting $\widehat{CD}$.
Prove that $AC = AD$.

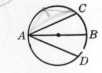

9. Given the diameter *AB* and $AC = AD$.
Prove that $\widehat{BC} = \widehat{BD}$.

10. The line joining the midpoints of the two arcs of a chord is the perpendicular bisector of the chord.

C

11. Given diameter *AB* of $\odot O$, chord *AC*, and radius $OD \parallel AC$.
Prove that $\widehat{BD} = \widehat{CD}$.

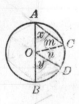

12. If the end points of two perpendicular diameters are joined in order, the figure formed is a square.

Art Collection of Randolph-Macon Woman's College

"Men of the Docks" by George Bellows

270. Geometry in the Arts. It has been known for years that nature has used geometric forms in the construction of crystals and in the framework of plant and animal life. Much of the beauty that is found in nature is due to some geometric pattern or to the use of numbers associated with geometry. It seems likely that as time passes, man will discover many more applications of geometry in nature.

Since the artist, sculptor, and architect often find their themes in nature, they too either deliberately or instinctively use geometric forms and proportions. Some of these applications of geometry to the arts are readily seen, while others are latent, being so hidden that they are not easily detected.

In paintings the geometric figures are usually latent and have to be discovered. Some of the early painters who deliberately based their works on geometric principles were Fra Bartolommeo, Raphael, Michelangelo, and Leonardo da Vinci.

Leonardo da Vinci obtained the "Mona Lisa" smile by tilting the lips so that the ends lie on a circle which touches the outer corners of the eyes. The outline of the top of the head is the arc of another circle exactly twice as large as the first. In the same artist's "Last Supper" the visible part of Christ conforms to sides of an equilateral triangle.

Today some artists use a style of design which is based upon the division of a rectangle into similar rectangles, a special case of which is given on page 446. It is the similarity of these rectangles which is supposed to give life to the picture. George Bellows used this principle, called *dynamic symmetry*, in painting the picture entitled "Men of the Docks," which is reproduced on page 255. He used the same principle in many of his other paintings, including the well-known "Eleanor, Jean, and Anna," which won first prize at the International Art Exhibition in Pittsburgh in 1922.

Sculpture, more than painting, is based on geometry. It makes more use of geometry when it is used with architecture than when it is used alone. The sculptor makes frequent use of the circle, the regular polygon, and the proportions of the human figure. As in paintings, the geometry is often latent in sculpture.

After making a most careful study of the "Apollo Belvedere," the great art critic Winckelmann said that even its seemingly careless beautiful lines show the action of the most exact mathematics. He found that the charm of the statue was due to its scientific proportions.

The geometry in architecture is both latent and visible. Almost any building of any consequence is a harmonious arrangement of geometric forms. The plane figures most commonly used in architecture are the circle, rectangle, square, and equilateral triangle.

The Romans used these figures in determining the proportions of triumphal arches and the Italians in constructing Gothic cathedrals. An excellent modern example of Gothic architecture is the National Cathedral at Washington, D. C., a picture of which is shown on page 284.

Leonardo da Vinci's Famous Painting of Mona Lisa Hangs in the Louvre Museum, Paris

★★ Proposition III. Theorem

271. *If a line through the center of a circle is perpendicular to a chord, it bisects the chord and its arc.*

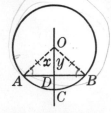

Given ⊙ *O* with the line *OC* ⊥ *AB*.

To prove that *AD = DB* and $\overparen{AC} = \overparen{CB}$.

Selection of Method: 1. Known methods of proving (*a*) line segments
=: §§ 86, 140, 202, 262 *a*, and 268; (*b*) arcs =:
§§ 262 *c*, 263, 267.
2. Methods to be used: (*a*) § 86 *a*; (*b*) § 263.

Proof:

STATEMENTS	REASONS
1. Draw *OA* and *OB*.	1. Why possible?
2. ∡ *ADO* and *BDO* are rt. ∡.	2. Why?
3. Rt. △ *AOD* ≅ rt. △ *BOD*.	3. Give full proof.
4. *AD = DB*.	4. Why?
5. ∠ *x* = ∠ *y*.	5. Why?
6. ∴ $\overparen{AC} = \overparen{CB}$.	6. Why?

Proposition IV. Theorem

272. *If a line through the center of a circle bisects a chord that is not a diameter, it is perpendicular to the chord.*

SUGGESTION. Draw radii to the end points of the chord and use § 142 *b*.

273. Corollary. *The perpendicular bisector of a chord passes through the center of the circle.*

SUGGESTIONS. *OA = OB*. Why? Use § 123.

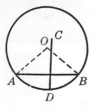

These Designs for Costume Jewelry Are Based on the Circle

EXERCISES

A

1. *Given an arc of a circle, find the center of the circle.*

SUGGESTION. Draw any two nonparallel chords and use § 273.

2. Are two arcs equal if they have equal lengths?

3. Name all the methods you have had of proving lines perpendicular.

4. The line joining the midpoints of a chord and its arc is perpendicular to the chord.

5. If a radius bisects an arc, it is the perpendicular bisector of the chord of the arc.

B

6. The line joining the midpoints of a chord and its arc passes through the center of the circle.

7. If two chords of a circle are drawn from a point of the circle and make equal angles with the radius drawn to the point, the chords are equal.

C

8. If a diameter bisects one of two parallel chords (which are not diameters), it bisects the other.

9. Two points of a circle each equidistant from two other points of the circle determine a diameter of the circle.

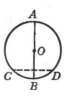

★★ Proposition V. Theorem

274. *In a circle or in equal circles equal chords are equidistant from the center.*

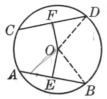

Given ⊙ *O* with *AB = CD*, *OE* ⊥ *AB*, and *OF* ⊥ *CD*.

To prove that *OE = OF*.

Selection of Method: 1. Known methods of proving line segments =:
§§ 86, 140, 202, 262 *a*, 268, and 271.
2. Method to be used: § 86 *a*.

Proof: *STATEMENTS*   *REASONS*

STATEMENTS	REASONS
1. Draw *OB* and *OD*.	1. Why possible?
2. *OE* ⊥ *AB* and *OF* ⊥ *CD*.	2. Why?
3. ∴ *EB* = $\frac{1}{2}$ *AB* and *FD* = $\frac{1}{2}$ *CD*.	3. § 271.
4. But *AB = CD*.	4. Why?
5. ∴ $\frac{1}{2}$ *AB* = $\frac{1}{2}$ *CD* and *EB = FD*.	5. Axs. 3, 5.
6. *OD = OB*.	6. Why?
7. Rt. △ *OEB* ≅ rt. △ *OFD*.	7. Why?
8. ∴ *OE = OF*.	8. Why?

EXERCISES [A]. CHORDS

1. In this circle equal chords are drawn. Are they equidistant from the center? Why?

2. The sides of an inscribed square are equidistant from the center.

3. If two equal chords which are not diameters intersect a diameter at the same point, they make equal angles with it.

4. The perpendicular bisectors of the sides of an inscribed polygon meet in a point.

★★Proposition VI. Theorem

275. *In a circle or in equal circles chords equidistant from the center are equal.*

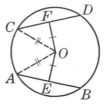

Given ⊙ *O*, the chords *AB* and *CD*, *OE* ⊥ *AB*, *OF* ⊥ *CD*, and *OE = OF*.

To prove that *AB = CD*.

Selection of Method: 1. Known methods of proving line segments =:
§§ 86, 140, 202, 262 *a*, 268, 271, and 274.
2. Method to be used: § 86 *a*.

Proof: *STATEMENTS*	*REASONS*
1. Draw *OA* and *OC*.	1. Why possible?
2. *OE* ⊥ *AB* and *OF* ⊥ *CD*.	2. Why?
3. Rt. △ *AEO* ≅ rt. △ *CFO*.	3. Give full proof.
4. ∴ *AE = CF*.	4. Why?
5. *AE* = ½ *AB* and *CF* = ½ *CD*.	5. § 271.
6. ∴ ½ *AB* = ½ *CD* and *AB = CD*.	6. Why?

EXERCISES [B]. CHORDS

1. What is the converse of Prop. VI? the inverse?

2. If two chords intersect a diameter at the same point and make equal angles with it, they are equal.

3. *Given* equal chords *AB* and *CD* extended to meet at *P*.
Prove that *PA = PC*.

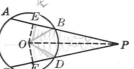

4. If two equal chords of a circle intersect, the segments of one are respectively equal to the segments of the other.

End Assign. #16

★Proposition VII. Theorem

276. *If a line is tangent to a circle, it is perpendicular to the radius drawn to the point of contact.*

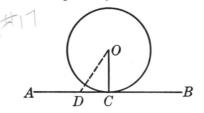

Given *AB* tangent to ⊙ *O* at *C* and *OC* a radius.

To prove that *AB* ⊥ *OC*.

Selection of Method: 1. Known methods of proving lines ⊥: §§ 51, 142, 205, and 272.
2. Method to be used: § 51 *b*.

Proof: STATEMENTS	REASONS
1. From *D*, any point on *AB* except *C*, draw *DO*.	1. Why possible?
2. *AB* is tangent to ⊙ *O* at *C*.	2. Why?
3. *D* is outside ⊙ *O*.	3. Def. of a tangent.
4. ∴ *OD* > *OC*, or *OC* is the shortest line segment from *O* to *AB*.	4. § 262 *b*.
5. ∴ *OC* ⊥ *AB* or *AB* ⊥ *OC*.	5. § 51 *b*.

277. Corollary I. *If a line is perpendicular to a tangent at the point of contact, it passes through the center of the circle.*

SUGGESTION. Draw a radius to the point of contact and show that it coincides with the given perpendicular.

278. Corollary II. *If two circles are tangent to the same line at the same point, the line of centers passes through the point of contact.*

SUGGESTION. Show by § 277 that a perpendicular to the tangent at the point of contact passes through the centers of both circles.

★ Proposition VIII. Theorem

279. *If a line is perpendicular to a radius at its point on a circle, the line is a tangent to the circle.*

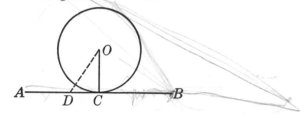

Given ⊙ *O* with *AB* ⊥ *OC* at *C*.

To prove that *AB* is tangent to ⊙ *O*.

Selection of Method: 1. Known methods of proving a line tangent to a ⊙: § 258 (Def. of a tangent).
2. Method to be used: § 258 (Def. of a tangent).

Proof: *STATEMENTS*   *REASONS*

STATEMENTS	REASONS
1. From *D*, any point in *AB* except *C*, draw *DO*.	1. Why possible?
2. *OC* ⊥ *AB*.	2. Given.
3. *OD* is not ⊥ *AB*.	3. § 83.
4. ∴ *OD* > *OC*.	4. Post. 11.
5. ∴ *D* lies outside ⊙ *O*.	5. § 262 *b*.
6. ∴ *AB* is tangent to ⊙ *O*.	6. § 258.

NOTE. Proving that any point *D* in *AB* except *C* lies outside the circle proves that every point in *AB* except *C* lies outside the circle. Why?

280. Tangent and Secant from an External Point. A *tangent from an external point* to a circle is the line segment between the external point and the point of contact. A *secant from an external point* to a circle is the line segment between the external point and the more remote point of intersection. In the figure of Prop. VIII, the line segment *AC* is the tangent from point *A* to the circle *O*.

★Proposition IX. Theorem

281. *The tangents to a circle from an external point are equal and make equal angles with the line joining the point to the center of the circle.*

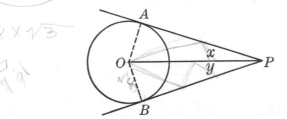

Given PA and PB tangents to $\odot$ O, and PO joining the external point to the center O.

To prove that $PA = PB$ and that $\angle x = \angle y$.

Selection of Method: 1. Known methods of proving (*a*) line segments
=: §§ 86, 140, 202, 262 *a*, 268, 271, 274, 275;
(*b*) ⪰ =: §§ 50, 87, 141, 204, 265.
2. Methods to be used: (*a*) § 86 *a*; (*b*) § 87 *b*.

Proof: (The proof is left to the student.)

Proposition X. Theorem

282. *If two circles intersect, the line joining their centers is the perpendicular bisector of the common chord.*

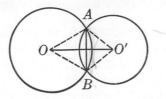

(The demonstration is left to the student.)

S GGESTION. Use § 124.

EXERCISES

A

1. PA is a tangent from point P to $\odot O$, and PO is a straight line segment.

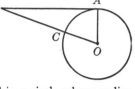

a. Find PA when AO is 5 and PO is 13.

b. Find AO when PA is 30 and PO is 34.

c. Find PO when AO is 4.2 and PA is 5.6.

d. Find PA when $AO = 8$ and $PC = 4$.

2. $ABCDEF$ is a regular polygon inscribed in a circle whose radius is 10 inches.

a. How large is $\angle B$?

b. How many degrees are there in $\angle AOB$?

c. How many degrees are there in $\angle ABO$?

d. How long is AB?

e. What is the length of the perimeter of $ABCDEF$?

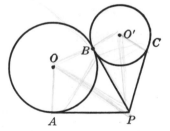

3. In a circle the distances from the center to two equal chords are represented by $x^2 + 5x$ and $2x + 10$. Find these distances.

4. AB is a 12-inch chord in a circle whose diameter is 20 inches. How far is the chord from the center of the circle?

5. A pentagon is circumscribed about a circle whose radius is 8 inches. Find the area of the polygon if its perimeter is 62 inches.

6. In this figure PA and PB are tangents to $\odot O$ and PB and PC are tangents to $\odot O'$. If $PA = 14''$, find PB and PC.

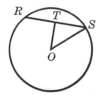

7. Rectangle $ABCD$ is inscribed in $\odot O$. Prove that the sides AB and CD are equidistant from O.

8. In the circle at the right $OT \perp RS$.

a. Find RS when $OT = 5$ and $SO = 7$.

b. Find OS when $OT = 12$ and $RS = 20$.

c. Find RS when $\angle TOS = 45°$ and $OT = 6$.

d. Find the area of $\triangle TOS$ if $TS = 8$ and $OS = 17$.

e. Find OS when $\angle O = 60°$ and $RS = 14$.

B

9. Two tangents to a circle meet at an angle of 60°. If the radius of the circle is 8 inches, find the length of the tangents.

10. AB is a chord perpendicular to the diameter CD at E. If AB is 16 inches and CD is 34 inches, find OE.

11. Find the area of △ ABC.

12. A chord 10 inches long is 1 inch from the midpoint of its arc. Find the radius of the circle.

13. In △ ABC, AB = 51″, AC = 24″, and BC = 45″. Find the length of the median CD.

Exs. 10–11

14. AB is tangent to ⊙ O and ⊙ O' at A and B respectively. OA is 6 inches, O'B is 16 inches, and OO' is 26 inches. Find the length of AB.

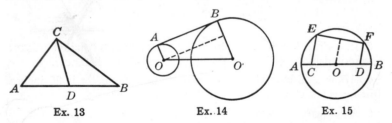

Ex. 13   Ex. 14   Ex. 15

15. In the circle O, AB is a diameter and EF is a chord. CE ⊥ EF and DF ⊥ EF. Prove that AC = DB.

C

16. The foreman in a street-railway shop discovers that a set of wheels has a flat surface 1 inch long. What makes the wheels flat? If the diameter of the wheels is 32 inches, how much of each wheel must be ground off to make the wheels round?

17. A quadrilateral ABCD is formed by the diameter CD of a circle, two tangents at C and D respectively, and another tangent which meets the other tangents at B and A respectively. Prove that the area of ABCD is equal to half the product of the opposite sides AB and CD.

18. The diameter AB of a circle is 24 inches. Chord BC of the circle forms an angle of 30° with AB. Find the distance of BC from the center of the circle.

Aqueduct Construction at Grand Coulee Dam, Washington

The engineers who planned this project mastered algebra and geometry as a preparation for their courses in engineering

19. In the figure $OABC$ is a rectangle with vertex O the center of a circle and vertex B on the circle. If $OC = 15$ and $OA = 20$, find the diameter of the circle.

20. A circle is circumscribed about triangle ABC. If AC is 60 inches long and 16 inches from the center of the circle, find the distances from the center to AB and BC when $AB = BC$.

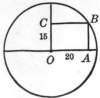

EXERCISES. PROOFS

A

1. *Given* chord AB and tangents PA and PB to $\odot O$ (Fig. 1). *Prove* that $\angle PAB = \angle PBA$.

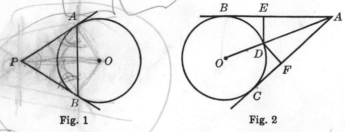

Fig. 1   Fig. 2

2. *Prove:* If a diameter of a circle bisects each of two chords, the chords are parallel.

3. *Given* tangents AB and AC to $\odot O$ and AO intersecting the circle in D (Fig. 2).
Prove that D is equidistant from AB and AC.

B

4. $\triangle ABC$ is inscribed in a circle; $\angle A = \angle C$. *Prove:* $\widehat{AB} = \widehat{BC}$.

5. *Prove:* If a point on a circle is equidistant from two radii, it bisects the arc included by the radii.

6. Tangents AB and AC are drawn to a circle O and BC is a chord. Prove that $\angle A = 2 \angle OBC$.

C

7. *Prove:* If two tangents are drawn to a circle from a point without, the triangle formed by these tangents and a tangent to the arc included by them has a perimeter equal to the sum of the tangents.

8. *Given* ⊙ *O,* tangents *PA* and *PB,* diameter *AC,* and line seg
ment *OP.* (See the diagram at the left below.)
Prove that *CB* ∥ *OP.*

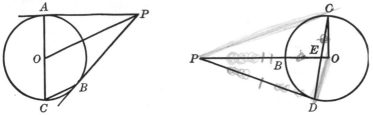

9. *Given* ⊙ *O,* tangent *PD,* line segment *PO, CO* ⊥ *PO,* and *CD*
intersecting *PO* in *E.* (See the diagram at the right above.)
Prove that *PE = PD.*

EXERCISES [B]. REFLECTION OF MIRRORS.

1. No matter where the light
from a point strikes a plane mirror,
it will, when reflected, be traveling
in a line which passes through a
point called its image. In the
figure at the right, *C* represents
an object, *C'* its image, and *E*
and *E'* positions of the eye. Where
is the image located in a plane
mirror? When one sees an object
in a plane mirror, how do the
size and shape of the object compare with the size and shape of the
image?

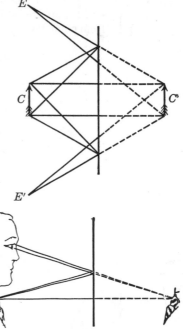

2. Study the diagram and explain why the image of the boy's
tie seems to be behind the
mirror. Explain why one can
judge distances better by using
both eyes instead of one.

3. Show that in order to see
your full-length image in a vertical mirror when you are
standing before it, the mirror must be at least half your height.

4. Look at your image in a mirror and raise your right hand. Which hand of the image appears to be lifted? Is the image direct or reversed?

5. The figure at the right shows a method of producing an optical illusion. *ABCD* is a vertical plate glass and *L* is a lighted candle placed in front of it. *EF* is a glass of water behind the plate. In darkness it is possible to move the glass of water to a position where the candle appears to be burning in the water. What are the relative positions of the glass of water and the candle in reference to the plate glass when this illusion is produced?

Name some other illusions which can be produced by reflections.

6. Concave mirrors are used to reflect light in a small beam. The diagram below represents a section of a concave spherical mirror, *O* being the center of the sphere and called the center of curvature. A ray of light *BC* from point *B* is reflected along *CB'* making equal angles

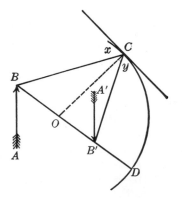

x and *y* with the tangent at *C*. A ray of light from *B* through *O* is reflected back through *DO*. Why? The two reflected rays meet at *B'*. Why do *BC* and *B'C* make equal angles with *OC*? *B'* is the image of *B*. The point *A'* is found in the same manner. Then *A'B'* is the image of *AB*.

Following the plan outlined above, construct the image produced by a concave mirror when the object is beyond the center of curvature.

7. At the left below is a longitudinal section of a spherical mirror. Copy the figure and show that the rays of the light F are reflected in a beam of nearly parallel rays.

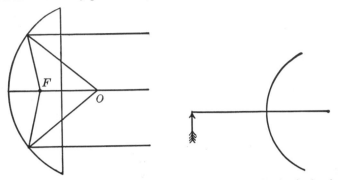

8. At the right above is the diagram of a convex spherical mirror. Construct the image of an object. Is the image upright or upside down?

9. Make a drawing showing whether or not a girl surrounded by three vertical mirrors can see the back of her head.

10. Why are the rear vision mirrors on trucks convex instead of plane?

283. Tangent Circles. Two circles are *tangent circles* when they are tangent to the same line at the same point. The circles are *tangent internally* when they lie on the same side of

the line, and *tangent externally* when they lie on opposite sides of the line. Circles C and C' are tangent internally, and circles O and O' are tangent externally.

284. Common Tangent. A *common internal tangent* of two circles is a tangent to both circles which cuts the line segment joining the centers of the circles. A *common external tangent* of two circles is a tangent to both circles which does not cut the line segment joining the centers of the circles.

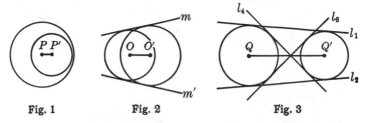

Fig. 1   Fig. 2   Fig. 3

In Fig. 1 the circles have no common tangents. In Fig. 2 m and m' are common external tangents. In Fig. 3, l_1 and l_2 are common external tangents and l_3 and l_4 are common internal tangents.

EXERCISES

A

1. Two circles may have from zero to four common tangents, de·pending upon their relative positions. How many common internal tangents and common external tangents do two circles have (*a*) if one circle is within the other? (*b*) if the circles are tangent internally? (*c*) if the circles intersect? (*d*) if the circles are tangent externally? (*e*) if one circle lies without the other?

2. How many tangents may be drawn to a circle through a point within the circle? through a point on the circle? through a point without the circle?

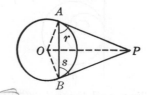

3. *Given AB* a diameter of ⊙ *O*, *AC* a chord, and *OC* a radius.
  a. Prove that $\angle m = 2 \angle x$.
  b. Prove that the bisector of $\angle BOC \parallel AC$.

4. *Given PA* and *PB* tangents to ⊙ *O*, and *AB* a chord joining the points of contact.
  a. Prove that $\angle r = \angle s$.
  b. Prove that *PO* is the ⊥ bisector of *AB*.

5. If two circles are tangent externally, tangents drawn to the circles from any point in their common internal tangent are equal.

6. The tangents to a circle at the extremities of a diameter are parallel.

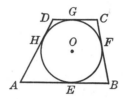

B

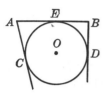

7. *Given AB, AC,* and *BD* tangents to ⊙ *O.*
Prove that $AB = AC + BD$.

8. *Given AB, BC, CD,* and *DA* tangents to ⊙ *O.*
Prove that $AB+DC=AD+BC$.

9. If two circles are tangent externally, their common internal tangent bisects either common external tangent.

C

10. If one circle is without another, their common internal tangents are equal.

11. If one circle is without another, their common external tangents are equal.

12. If the angle made by two tangents to a circle is 60°, the circle bisects the line segment joining the vertex of the angle and the center of the circle.

MISCELLANEOUS EXERCISES [B, C]

1. Two tangents, drawn from an external point to a circle, form an angle of 60°. The radius of the circle is 5 inches. Find the length of the line segments joining the external point to the center of the circle.

2. Prove that the perpendicular bisectors of the sides of an inscribed triangle pass through the same point.

3. If two tangents drawn from an external point to a circle form an angle of 120°, the segment joining the point to the center of the circle is equal to the sum of the tangents.

4. In this figure, AB represents the axis of the earth, O the center, and $CMDN$ the equator. AB is perpendicular to CD. If P is any point on the earth's surface, OG, a line through P, is vertical to the earth's surface, and PE, a perpendicular to OG, is horizontal to the earth's surface. The axis AB points to the North Star. Because of the great distance to the North Star, the line PF, pointing to the star, may be considered parallel to AB.

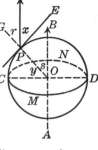

Prove that the angle of elevation of the North Star from P, or $\angle x$, is equal to the latitude of P, or $\angle y$.

5. This is a diagram of a piece of a broken circular saw. In order to purchase a new saw it is necessary to know the diameter of the original saw. Show how the diameter may be found.

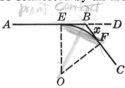

6. The arc AB of circle O and the arc BC of circle O' form a *compound curve*.

a. Are the circles O and O' tangent internally or externally?

b. What do you know concerning the points O, B, and O'? on line of ⊥ bisector

7. This figure shows the plan for laying out a simple railroad curve. The straight lines AB and BC are to be connected by an arc of a circle so that AB and BC are tangent to the circle. The lengths of BE and BF depend upon the surface of the ground and the speed at which trains are to be operated. What is the relation of EO to AD? of OF to BC? Does $BE = BF$? Prove that $\angle x = \angle O$. If trains are to be operated at a high speed, should the radius of the curve be large or small? Can $\angle ABC$ be acute?

8. This diagram shows two parallel railroad tracks connected by a switch from A to B. Construct a plan for laying out the switch in the form of a compound curve composed of arcs having equal radii.

SUGGESTIONS. Draw AB. Find C, the midpoint of AB. The center of arc AC is the intersection of the ⊥ bisector of AC and the ⊥ to the track at A.

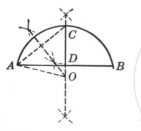

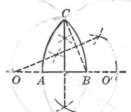

radius

diameter

9. $\overset{\frown}{ACB}$ represents a *circular arch*. *AB* is the *span* and *CD* is the altitude of the arch.

Draw the plan for a circular arch having a span of 60 feet and an altitude of 30 feet, using the scale of 1 inch = 12 feet.

10. *ACB* represents a *Gothic arch.*

Draw the plan for a Gothic arch having a span of 8 feet and an altitude of 12 feet, using a scale of 1 inch = 4 feet.

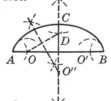

11. *ACB* represents a *basket-handle arch.*

Draw a plan for a basket-handle arch having a span of 20 feet and an altitude of 6 feet, using a scale of 1 inch = 6 feet. (Take *AO* a suitable length and make *CD* = *AO* = *O'B*.)

Tangents to C and make $= \angle s$ with a line joining to center of ⊙.

[Space geometry. Optional]

285. Right Circular Cylinder. The adjoining figure represents a *right circular cylinder*. The bases are circles lying in parallel planes. *AD*, a line segment joining the centers of the bases and perpendicular to them, is the axis of the cylinder.

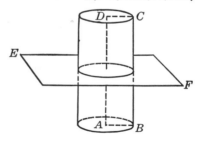

EXERCISES

1. In the above figure, if *EF* is a plane parallel to the base, what kind of figure is its intersection with the cylinder?

2. If plane *EF* is oblique to the base, what kind of figure is its intersection with the cylinder?

End Assign. #17

286. Right Circular Cone. The figure below represents **a** *right circular cone.* The base is a circle and the axis *SO* is perpendicular to the base at its center.

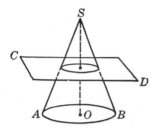

EXERCISES ·

1. If *CD* is a plane parallel to the base, what kind of figure is its intersection with the cone?

2. If plane *CD* is not parallel to the base, what kind of figure is its intersection with the cone?

287. Spheres. A sphere is a closed surface all points of which are equidistant from a fixed point within called the center. A *radius* of a sphere is a straight line segment joining the center to any point of the sphere. All radii of a sphere are equal.

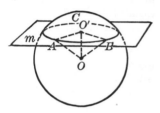

EXERCISES

1. Prove that the intersection of a plane and a sphere is a circle.

SUGGESTIONS. In the figure of § 287 take *A* and *B* any two points of the intersection and *O* the center of the sphere. Draw $OO' \perp m$. Draw *OA*, *OB*, *O'A*, and *O'B*. Then prove $O'A = O'B$.

2. In the figure of § 287, *ABC* is a *small circle* of the sphere. If a plane passes through the center of a sphere, its intersection with the sphere is called a *great circle* of the sphere. In the adjoining figure a small circle and a great circle are represented as passing through the same two points *A* and *B*. Is the arc *ACB* of the great circle or the arc *AEB* of the small circle the greater distance? Test your answer, using chalk and a baseball or a basketball.

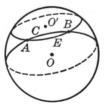

3. If a plane is perpendicular to a radius at its point on the sphere, is it tangent to the sphere? To what theorem in plane geometry does this question correspond?

4. In how many points can a line intersect a sphere?

5. Using the figure at the right, prove that if the radii of two small circles of a sphere are equal, their planes are equidistant from the center of the sphere.

6. How many lines may be tangent to a sphere at a point on the sphere?

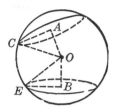

7. How many planes may be tangent to a sphere at a point on the sphere?

8. The meridians of the earth are great circles passing through the north and south poles. What kind of circle of the earth is the equator? What kind of circles are the other circles of latitude? *ACB* represents an airplane course between two places having a latitude of 30°. Why does the course not follow the circle of latitude through the places?

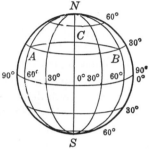

EXERCISES IN DEDUCTIVE REASONING (Optional)

Below are five household receipts:

1. Tar spots can be removed from cloth by rubbing the spots with another cloth saturated with turpentine.

2. Machine oil can be removed from cloth by using a mixture of water, ammonia, and soap.

3. To destroy roaches, sprinkle hellebore on the floor at night.

4. Ink can be taken out of linen by dipping the ink spot in melted tallow and then washing out the tallow.

5. To remove egg tarnish from silver, apply salt with a soft cloth.

The following exercises are based upon the five receipts given above:

1. Frank spilled some automobile oil on his overalls. How can he remove the oil?

2. Frances had a dark coloring on her finest handkerchief. She tried receipt number 4 without any effect. What is your conclusion?

3. Mrs. Wilcox had a bedspread that she prized very highly. Her grandfather raised the flax which her grandmother used to make the spread. Show whether or not ink can be removed from the spread by any of the receipts given on page 277.

4. Mrs. Jamison moved into an apartment on Tuesday. On Wednesday she discovered that the apartment contained a great number of roaches. By Thursday morning all the roaches were gone. No member of her family placed any powder to kill the roaches and no one except the janitor had a key to the apartment. Did the janitor sprinkle hellebore on the apartment floor?

5. After making a cake batter Faye discovered that a silver spoon was tarnished. She failed to remove the stain with salt and a soft cloth. What is your conclusion?

6. Dick removed a black spot from his trousers by rubbing them with another cloth dipped in turpentine. He said he knew that the spot was due to tar. Was he correct?

7. June removed the tarnish from the silverware with salt and a soft cloth. Can you tell what caused the tarnish?

REVIEW QUESTIONS

1. What lines form a central angle? an inscribed angle?

2. How many chords may be drawn from a point on a circle? How many diameters?

3. How many tangents may be drawn to a circle from an external point? How many secants?

4. What is the greatest chord in a circle?

5. An arc has how many chords? A chord has how many arcs?

6. Through what point does the perpendicular bisector of a chord pass?

7. What line segments in a circle are always equal? What line segments in a circle are not always equal?

8. What is the name of a line that has one point, and only one, in common with a circle? that has two points in common with the circle?

9. Where is the vertex of an inscribed angle?

W. M. Rittase

Notice how Circular Arches Are Used in the Construction of This Dam

10. What is the name of the point where a tangent touches the circle?

11. What is the distance from the center of a circle to one of its tangents?

12. How long is the chord which is perpendicular to a tangent to a circle having a radius equal to 6 inches?

13. If a chord were extended at either end or both ends, what would it become?

14. Are two circles equal if they have equal radii? equal diameters? equal chords?

15. If a diameter bisects a chord, is it perpendicular to the chord?

16. What is the difference between a common internal tangent and a common external tangent?

SUMMARY OF PRINCIPAL METHODS OF PROOF

288. *In a circle or in equal circles two line segments are equal*

a. If they are radii.

b. If they are chords with equal arcs.

c. If they are chords equidistant from the center.

d. If they are perpendiculars from the center to equal chords.

289. *Two line segments are equal*

a. If they are segments of a chord which are made by a line through the center of a circle perpendicular to the chord.

b. If they are tangents to a circle from an external point.

290. *Two angles of a circle or of equal circles are equal*

a. If they are central angles with equal arcs.

291. *Two lines are perpendicular*

a. If one is a chord that does not pass through the center of a circle and the other is a line through the center bisecting the chord.

b. If one is a tangent to a circle and the other is a radius drawn to the point of contact.

292. *In a circle or in equal circles two arcs are equal*

a. If they are arcs of equal central angles.

b. If they are arcs of equal chords.

293. *In a circle two arcs are equal*

a. If they are parts of an arc which are made by a line through the center of the circle perpendicular to the chord of the arc.

WORD LIST

Can you spell and use each of the following words?

alternate	decagon	interior	rectangle
altitude	demonstration	isosceles	regular
central	diagonal	median	rhombus
chord	diameter	minor	right
circumference	equiangular	octagon	secant
circumscribed	equilateral	parallel	semicircle
coincide	exterior	parallelogram	square
contact	external	pentagon	tangency
converse	hexagon	perimeter	tangent
convex	hypotenuse	polygon	transversal
corollary	inscribed	quadrant	trapezoid
corresponding	intercept	quadrilateral	

TEST 20

Completing Statements (*Seven Minutes*)

On your paper write one word, and only one, for each blank to make the following statements true:

1. If a line is perpendicular to a radius at its point on the circle, the line is __?__ to the circle.

2. A chord passing through the center of a circle is a __?__.

3. The perpendicular bisector of a chord passes through __?__ __?__ the circle.

4. If a chord bisects a circle, it is a __?__.

5. In a circle or in equal circles chords equidistant from the center are __?__.

6. Tangents to a circle from __?__ __?__ __?__ are equal.

7. If two circles intersect, the line of centers is the perpendicular bisector of the __?__ __?__.

8. Two unequal circles with the same center have __?__ common tangents.

9. Two circles are __?__ circles when they are tangent to the same line at the same point.

10. The common internal tangent of two circles intersects __?__ __?__ __?__ their centers.

TEST 21

Supplying Reasons (*Eighteen Minutes*)

Supply axioms, postulates, definitions, or theorems for the following statements:

1. *Given* two unequal ⊚ having the same center *O*, and the chord *AB* of the greater ⊙ intersecting the smaller ⊙ at *C* and *D*.
Prove that $AC = DB$.

    a. Draw $OE \perp AB$.
    b. $AE = EB$.
    c. $CE = ED$.
    d. $AC = DB$.

2. Given ⊙ *O* with diameter *AB*, and chord *AC* = chord *BD*.
Prove that *AC* ∥ *BD*.

a. $\overset{\frown}{ACB} = \overset{\frown}{ADB}$. *def diameter*

b. *AC* = *BD*. *Given*

c. $\overset{\frown}{AC} = \overset{\frown}{BD}$.

d. $\overset{\frown}{BC} = \overset{\frown}{AD}$.

e. *BC* = *AD*.

f. *AB* = *AB*.

g. △ *ABC* ≅ △ *ADB*.

h. ∠ *x* = ∠ *y*.

i. *AC* ∥ *BD*.

TEST 22

Multiple-Choice Statements (*Six Minutes*)

On your paper write the word or group of words in boldface type which makes each statement true:

1. The line segment joining any two points on a circle is a **diameter chord secant.**

2. The greatest number of common tangents two circles may have is **one two three four five.**

3. A central angle whose chord is equal to the radius contains **45° 60° 75° 90°.**

4. If tangents are drawn at the ends of a chord which has an arc of 100°, a **right obtuse isosceles equilateral** triangle is formed.

5. The sides of an inscribed angle are **two radii two diameters two chords a chord and a tangent.**

6. In a circle two equal chords are **perpendicular parallel equidistant from the center.**

TEST 23

Stating the Given and To Prove (*Ten Minutes*)

State the *Given* and *To prove* in the following:

1. The line joining the midpoints of a chord and its arc is perpendicular to the chord.

2. If perpendiculars are drawn to two radii from the midpoint of the arc intercepted by the radii, the perpendiculars are equal.

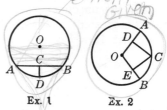

Ex. 1   Ex. 2

CHAPTER IX

Measurement of Angles and Arcs

In this chapter we shall study the numerical relations between the arcs of a circle and the angles associated with a circle.

294. The Central Angle and Its Arc. Any quantity can be measured by finding how many times it contains some unit of measurement. As you know, the degree is a unit for measuring angles and has been defined as one ninetieth of a right angle.

The arc which a central angle of one degree intercepts on a circle is called an *arc degree*. We shall use the arc degree as a unit for measuring arcs. Since the number of angle degrees about a point is 360, the number of arc degrees in a circle is 360. Do you think that any central angle, such as $\angle MON$, contains the same number of angle degrees as its intercepted arc, $\widehat{MN}$, contains arc degrees? We shall postulate the answer to this question.

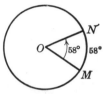

295. Post. 28. *A central angle is equal in degrees to (or has the same number of degrees as) its intercepted arc.*

This means that the number of angle degrees in $\angle O$ is equal to the number of arc degrees in $\widehat{AB}$. Thus if $\angle O$ contains 50°, $\widehat{AB}$ contains 50°. The relation between $\angle O$ and $\widehat{AB}$ may be written $\angle O =$ (in degrees) $\widehat{AB}$, or $\angle O \stackrel{\circ}{=} \widehat{AB}$. We sometimes say that $\angle O$ is measured by $\widehat{AB}$. In reading the expression $\angle O \stackrel{\circ}{=} \widehat{AB}$, we should be careful not to say "Angle O equals arc AB," because an angle does not equal an arc. The symbol $\stackrel{\circ}{=}$ never means "is congruent to."

The National Cathedral at Washington, D.C., Is a Fine Example of Gothic Architecture. Notice the Rose Window

296. Comparison of Arcs. In this figure the two circles are unequal and have the same center, O. Since each of the arcs AB and CD contains the same number of arc degrees as $\angle O$ contains angle degrees (§ 295), the two arcs have the same number of arc degrees $(\widehat{AB} \doteq \widehat{CD})$. But the two arcs are unequal. Thus two arcs in different circles may have the same number of arc degrees and be unequal Now consider the following theorem.

297. Theorem. *In a circle or in equal circles two arcs which have the same number of arc degrees are equal.*

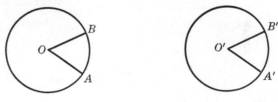

SUGGESTIONS. $\widehat{AB} \doteq \widehat{A'B'}$. Why? $\angle O \doteq \widehat{AB}$ and $\angle O' \doteq \widehat{A'B'}$. Then $\angle O$ $= \angle O'$ and $\widehat{AB} = \widehat{A'B'}$.

EXERCISES

A

1. If two arcs of a circle are equal, are their central angles equal?

2. If two arcs of unequal circles contain the same number of degrees, are their central angles equal?

3. Is it possible for two circles to have one point in common? two points in common? three points in common?

4. If a chord is equal to the radius of a circle, how many degrees are in its central angle?

5. Are the sides of an inscribed angle radii or chords?

6. As an arc of a circle increases in size, what change takes place in its central angle?

7. If an arc of a circle is halved, is its central angle halved?

8. If a chord of a circle is doubled, is its central angle doubled?

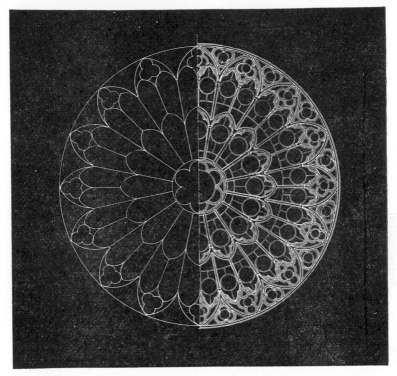

A Typical Design for a Rose Window

The left portion, which illustrates the mathematical layout of the window, shows clearly how circles and arcs are used in the design. The right portion represents the material of stone and leaded glass built up over the layout

9. In the figure, what arc contains the same number of degrees as ∠ *BOC*?

10. What is the exterior angle of △ *AOC*?

11. Does ∠ *A* = ∠ *C*? Does ∠ *A* = ½ ∠ *BOC*?

12. Does ∠ *BOC* ≟ $\widehat{BC}$? Does ∠ *A* ≟ ½ $\widehat{BC}$?

B

13. Construct a quilt pattern using the circle as the basis of design.

14. Construct a decorative design for the back of a chair.

★★ Proposition I. Theorem

298. *An inscribed angle is equal in degrees to one half its intercepted arc.*

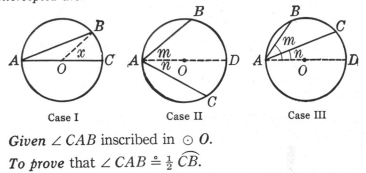

Case I   Case II   Case III

Given $\angle CAB$ inscribed in $\odot O$.

To prove that $\angle CAB \stackrel{\circ}{=} \frac{1}{2} \widehat{CB}$.

Selection of Method: 1. Known methods of comparing ⊿ and their arcs: § 295.

2. Method to be used: § 295.

Case I. If one side of the angle is a diameter.

Proof:

STATEMENTS	REASONS
1. Draw OB.	1. Why possible?
2. $OB = OA$.	2. Why?
3. ∴ $\angle A = \angle B$.	3. Why?
4. $\angle A + \angle B = \angle x$.	4. § 110.
5. $2 \angle A = \angle x$.	5. Why?
6. $\angle x \stackrel{\circ}{=} \widehat{CB}$.	6. Why?
7. ∴ $2 \angle A \stackrel{\circ}{=} \widehat{CB}$.	7. Why?
8. ∴ $\angle A \stackrel{\circ}{=} \frac{1}{2} \widehat{CB}$.	8. Why?

Case II. If the center of the circle lies within the angle.

SUGGESTIONS. Draw the diameter AD. Apply Case I to $\angle m$ and to $\angle n$. Use the addition axiom.

Case III. If the center of the circle lies without the angle.

SUGGESTIONS. Draw the diameter AD. Apply Case I to $\angle m$ and to $\angle n$. Use the subtraction axiom.

299. Corollary I. *An angle inscribed in a semicircle is a right angle.*

NOTE. This fact is said to have been discovered by Thales.

Given ∠ *B* inscribed in semicircle *ABC*.
To prove that ∠ *B* is a rt. ∠.

300. Corollary II. *Inscribed angles which intercept the same arc are equal.*

SUGGESTION. Draw two or more inscribed angles which intercept the same arc, and use § 298.

301. Corollary III. *If a quadrilateral is inscribed in a circle, the opposite angles are supplementary.*

SUGGESTIONS. ∠ *A* ≐ ½ which arc? ∠ *C* ≐ ½ which arc?
∠ *A* + ∠ *C* ≐ ½ which arcs?

EXERCISES

A

1. In the figure of Case I of Prop. I, how many degrees are there in ∠ *A* if $\widehat{BC}$ = 70°? if ∠ *x* = 45°? if $\widehat{AB}$ = 120°?

2. In the figure of Case II, how many degrees are there in ∠ *A* if $\widehat{BD}$ = 40° and $\widehat{DC}$ = 30°? if $\widehat{AB}$ = 120° and $\widehat{AC}$ = 132°?

3. In the figure of Case III, how many degrees are there in ∠ *CAB* if $\widehat{BD}$ = 90° and $\widehat{CD}$ = 38°? if $\widehat{ADC}$ = 200° and $\widehat{AB}$ = 88°?

4. In the figure of § 301, if $\widehat{AB}$ = 100°, $\widehat{BC}$ = 126°, and $\widehat{CD}$ = 54°, find the number of degrees in each angle of the quadrilateral.

5. A parallelogram inscribed in a circle is a rectangle.

6. Two sides of an inscribed triangle have arcs of 134° and 148°. How many degrees are there in each angle of the triangle?

B

7. The diameter *AB* of ⊙ *O* is 18 inches. *AC* and *BC* are chords of the circle. Find *AC* and *BC* if ∠ *BOC* is 60°.

8. Find the area of a parallelogram inscribed in a 34-inch circle if one of its sides is $\frac{8}{15}$ of another.

9. Prove that a right angle can be inscribed in a semicircle.

★Proposition II. Theorem

302. *An angle formed by a tangent and a chord drawn from the point of contact is equal in degrees to one half its intercepted arc.*

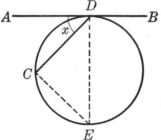

Given AB tangent to $\odot$ O at D and DC a chord.

To prove that $\angle x \overset{\circ}{=} \frac{1}{2} \widehat{DC}$.

Selection of Method: 1. Known methods of comparing ⩘ and their arcs: §§ 295, 298.
2. Method to be used: § 298.

Proof:

STATEMENTS	REASONS
1. Draw diameter DE and line CE.	1. Why possible?
2. $AB \perp DE$.	2. Why?
3. $\angle C$ is a rt. $\angle$.	3. Why?
4. $\therefore CE \perp CD$.	4. Why?
5. $\angle E = \angle x$.	5. § 113.
6. $\angle E \overset{\circ}{=} \frac{1}{2} \widehat{CD}$.	6. Why?
7. $\therefore \angle x \overset{\circ}{=} \frac{1}{2} \widehat{CD}$.	7. Why?

EXERCISES

A

1. Using the figure above, find the number of degrees in $\angle x$ when $\widehat{CD} = 68°$; when $\widehat{CE} = 44°$.

2. Using the same figure, find the number of degrees in $\widehat{CD}$ when $\angle x = 24°$; when $\angle E = 31°$.

3. *Given AB* a tangent to ⊙ *O* and *AD* a secant to ⊙ *O*.
Prove that ∠ *ABC* = ∠ *D*.

4. In the figure at the right, find $\overset{\frown}{BC}$ if
∠ *A* = 33° and $\overset{\frown}{BCD}$ = 220°.

5. A tangent to a circle at the midpoint of
an arc is parallel to the chord of the arc.

6. *Given* the isosceles △ *ABC*
inscribed in a circle with *AC* = *BC*
and $\overset{\frown}{BC}$ = 144°.

Find the number of degrees in
∡ *A*, *B*, and *C*.

7. *Given* ⊚ *O* and *O'* tangent
internally at *B*, and *BD* a chord
of ⊙ *O*.

Prove that $\overset{\frown}{BD}$ and $\overset{\frown}{BC}$ contain
the same number of degrees.

8. If two angles of a triangle inscribed in a circle are 37° and 75°
respectively, find the number of degrees in the three arcs of the circle.

B

9. If two tangents drawn from a point to a circle form an angle of
60°, the tangents and the chord joining the points of contact form an
equilateral triangle.

10. A quadrilateral *ABCD* is inscribed in a circle. $\overset{\frown}{AB}$ = 80°,
$\overset{\frown}{BC}$ = 114°, and ∠ *C* = 95°. Find the number of degrees in the remaining angles and arcs.

C

11. If two circles are tangent externally and two lines are drawn
through the point of contact and terminated by the
circles, the chords joining the end points of these
lines are parallel.

12. *Given* two circles tangent internally at *B*, and
BE and *BD* chords of the larger circle.
Prove that *DE* ∥ *FG*.

13. In the inscribed quadrilateral *ABCD*, *AB* = *AD* and *CB* = *CD*.
Prove that *AC* is a diameter of the circle.

★Proposition III. Theorem

303. *An angle formed by two chords intersecting within a circle is equal in degrees to one half the sum of the arcs intercepted by it and its vertical angle.*

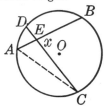

Given ∠ x formed by the chords AB and CD of ⊙ O.

To prove that $\angle x \stackrel{\circ}{=} \frac{1}{2}(\widehat{BC} + \widehat{AD})$.

Selection of Method: 1. Known methods of comparing ⊿ and their arcs: §§ 295, 298, 302.
2. Method to be used: § 298.

Proof: *STATEMENTS*	*REASONS*
1. Draw AC.	1. Why possible?
2. $\angle x = \angle A + \angle C$.	2. Why?
3. $\angle A \stackrel{\circ}{=} \frac{1}{2} \widehat{BC}$.	3. Why?
4. $\angle C \stackrel{\circ}{=} \frac{1}{2} \widehat{AD}$.	4. Why?
5. $\angle A + \angle C \stackrel{\circ}{=} \frac{1}{2}(\widehat{BC} + \widehat{AD})$.	5. Why?
6. ∴ $\angle x \stackrel{\circ}{=} \frac{1}{2}(\widehat{BC} + \widehat{AD})$.	6. Why?

EXERCISES. ANGLES AND ARCS

A

Example. In the above figure, if $\angle x = 75°$ and $\widehat{AD} = 20°$, find $\widehat{BC}$.

Solution: From § 303, $\angle x \stackrel{\circ}{=} \frac{1}{2}(\widehat{BC} + \widehat{AD})$.

Substituting, $75° = \frac{1}{2}(\widehat{BC} + 20°)$;

whence $150° = \widehat{BC} + 20°$,

and $\widehat{BC} = 130°$.

1. In the figure for Prop. III, how many degrees are there in ∠ *x* if $\widehat{BC} = 150°$ and $\widehat{AD} = 64°$? if $\widehat{AD} = 79°$ and $\widehat{BC} = 141°$?

2. In the figure for Prop. III, if $\angle x = 110°$ and $\overset{\frown}{BC} = 145°$, how many degrees are there in $\overset{\frown}{AD}$?

3. In the figure for Prop. III, if $\overset{\frown}{AC} = 62°$ and $\overset{\frown}{DB} = 55°$, how many degrees are there in $\angle x$?

4. *Given* AB and CD chords of $\odot O$ intersecting at E.

Prove that $\angle C = \angle B$ and that $\angle A = \angle D$.

5. If two chords of a circle are perpendicular to each other and two adjacent arcs contain 12° and 62° respectively, find the number of degrees in the other arcs.

6. *Given* $\odot CBD$, tangent AC, secant AD, $\overset{\frown}{BD} = 102°$, and $\angle D = 44°$.

Find $\angle A$; $\angle BCD$; $\angle ACB$.

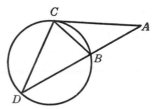

7. The two diagonals drawn from one vertex of an inscribed regular pentagon trisect the angle from whose vertex they are drawn.

B

8. If a point is inside a circle, the lines joining it to the ends of a diameter form an obtuse angle.

9. A central angle and an inscribed angle intercept the same arc of the circle. Find the angles if their sum is 135°.

10. A rhombus inscribed in a circle is a square.

11. If one angle of an inscribed triangle formed by two chords and a diameter contains 30°, prove that the side opposite this angle is equal to a radius.

C

12. An exterior angle of an inscribed quadrilateral is equal to its opposite interior angle.

13. *Given* ⊛ O and O' tangent externally at C, AB a common external tangent, and chords AC and BC.

Prove that $\angle ACB$ is a rt. $\angle$.

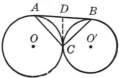

SUGGESTION. Draw DC, the common internal tangent.

★Proposition IV.   Theorem

304. *An angle formed by two tangents, or a tangent and a secant, or two secants, intersecting outside a circle, is equal in degrees to one half the difference of the intercepted arcs.*

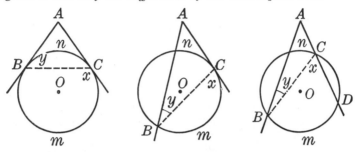

Given the two lines AB and AC intercepting the two arcs m and n on $\odot O$.

To prove that $\angle A \doteq \frac{1}{2}(\widehat{m} - \widehat{n})$.

Selection of Method: 1. Known methods of comparing △ and their arcs: §§ 295, 298, 302, 303.
  2. Method to be used: §§ 302 and 298.

Proof: *STATEMENTS*	*REASONS*
1. Draw BC.	1. Why possible?
2. $\angle A + \angle y = \angle x$.	2. Why?
3. $\therefore \angle A = \angle x - \angle y$.	3. Why?
4. $\angle x \doteq \frac{1}{2}\widehat{m}$ and $\angle y \doteq \frac{1}{2}\widehat{n}$.	4. §§ 302, 298.
5. $\therefore \angle x - \angle y \doteq \frac{1}{2}(\widehat{m} - \widehat{n})$.	5. Why?
6. $\therefore \angle A \doteq \frac{1}{2}(\widehat{m} - \widehat{n})$.	6. Why?

305.* **Circumscribed Polygon.** A polygon is *circumscribed about a circle* if its sides are tangents to the circle. The circle is then said to be *inscribed in the polygon*. *ABCDE* is a circumscribed polygon.

*If desired, pages 477–480 inclusive may be studied at this time.

EXERCISES. ANGLES AND ARCS

A

Example. In the figure for Prop. IV, if $\angle A = 30°$ and $\widehat{n} = 25°$, find the number of degrees in $\widehat{m}$.

Solution. From § 304, $\qquad \angle A \overset{\circ}{=} \frac{1}{2}(\widehat{m} - \widehat{n})$.
Substituting, $\qquad\qquad\qquad 30° = \frac{1}{2}(\widehat{m} - 25°)$;
whence $\qquad\qquad\qquad\quad 60° = \widehat{m} - 25°$, and $\widehat{m} = 85°$.

1. Two secants are drawn to a circle from an external point and intercept on the circle arcs of 112° and 54° respectively. How many degrees are there in the angle?

2. If a tangent and a secant to a circle form an angle of 63° and intercept one arc of 230°, find the number of degrees in the other intercepted arc.

3. In this figure, if $\widehat{AB} = 42°$, $\widehat{BC} = 47°$, and $\widehat{CD} = 103°$, find the number of degrees in each angle of the figure.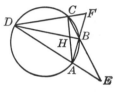

4. If a tangent to a circle forms equal angles with two chords drawn to the point of contact, the chords are equal.

B

5. Find the number of degrees in the arcs intercepted by two perpendicular tangents.

6. The bisector of the angle formed by a tangent and a chord drawn to the point of contact bisects the intercepted arc.

7. If AB is the common chord of two intersecting circles and BC and BD are two diameters, prove that CAD is a straight line.

C

8. If two circles are tangent internally and the smaller circle passes through the center of the larger circle, any chord of the larger circle drawn to the point of tangency is bisected by the smaller circle.

9. If one leg of a right triangle is a diameter of a circle, the tangent at the point where the circle cuts the hypotenuse bisects the other leg.

10. The vertex of an angle of 25° is without a circle and its sides intercept on the circle arcs whose sum is 152°. How many degrees are there in each arc?

306. Principle of Continuity. We can combine the theorems of §§ 298, 302, 303, and 304 into one general theorem as follows:

General Theorem. The angle formed by two intersecting lines, each of which intersects or is tangent to a circle, is equal in degrees to one half the sum of the intercepted arcs.

In diagram (1) below, the lines intersect within the circle and §303 applies. Now notice, in diagrams (2) and (3), how the intersecting lines change their position so that one of the arcs becomes zero. Then as the point of intersection moves outside the circle, we may think of the minor arc, *n*, as becoming negative. Keeping these conditions in mind, see how the general theorem applies in all cases.

The reasoning involved in combining several related theorems into one general statement is known as reasoning by the Principle of Continuity.

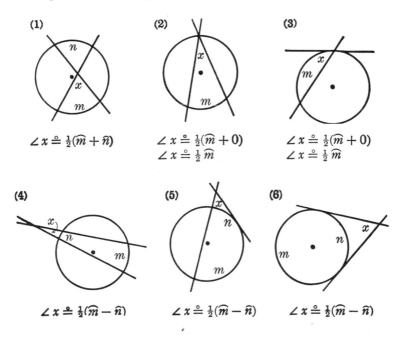

(1)　　　　　　　(2)　　　　　　　(3)

$\angle x \stackrel{\circ}{=} \frac{1}{2}(\widehat{m} + \widehat{n})$　$\angle x \stackrel{\circ}{=} \frac{1}{2}(\widehat{m} + 0)$　$\angle x \stackrel{\circ}{=} \frac{1}{2}(\widehat{m} + 0)$

$\angle x \stackrel{\circ}{=} \frac{1}{2}\widehat{m}$　$\angle x \stackrel{\circ}{=} \frac{1}{2}\widehat{m}$

(4)　　　　　　　(5)　　　　　　　(6)

$\angle x \stackrel{\circ}{=} \frac{1}{2}(\widehat{m} - \widehat{n})$　$\angle x \stackrel{\circ}{=} \frac{1}{2}(\widehat{m} - \widehat{n})$　$\angle x \stackrel{\circ}{=} \frac{1}{2}(\widehat{m} - \widehat{n})$

Proposition V. Theorem

307. *Parallel lines intercept equal arcs on a circle.*

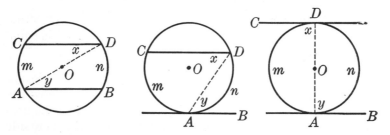

Given ⊙ *O* and arcs *m* and *n* intercepted on the circle by the parallel lines *AB* and *CD*.

To prove $\widehat{m} = \widehat{n}$.

Selection of Method: 1. Known methods of proving arcs =: § 292, 293, 297.
2. Method to be used: § 297.

Proof: *STATEMENTS*   *REASONS*

1. *AB* ∥ *CD*.	1. Why?
2. Draw *AD*.	2. Why possible?
3. $\angle x \stackrel{\circ}{=} \frac{1}{2}\widehat{m}$ and $\angle y \stackrel{\circ}{=} \frac{1}{2}\widehat{n}$.	3. Why?
4. $\angle x = \angle y$.	4. Why?
5. ∴ $\frac{1}{2}\widehat{m} \stackrel{\circ}{=} \frac{1}{2}\widehat{n}$.	5. Why?
6. $\widehat{m} = \widehat{n}$.	6. Ax. 3; § 297.

EXERCISES

1. *Prove:* A trapezoid inscribed in a circle is isosceles.

2. *Prove:* The base angles of an inscribed trapezoid are equal.

3. A rectangle is inscribed in a circle. One of the small arcs contains 82°. Draw the diagonals of the rectangle and find the number of degrees in each angle of the figure.

Proposition VI. Problem

308. *To bisect a given arc of a circle.*

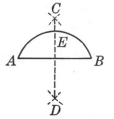

Given $\overset{\frown}{AB}$ of a ⊙.

To bisect $\overset{\frown}{AB}$.

Construction:

STATEMENTS	REASONS
1. Draw *AB*.	1. Why possible?
2. Construct *CD*, the ⊥ bisector of *AB*, intersecting $\overset{\frown}{AB}$ at *E*.	2. Why possible?

Then $\overset{\frown}{AE} = \overset{\frown}{EB}$.

Proof: (The proof is left to the student. Use §§ 273 and 271.)

★★ Proposition VII. Problem

309. *To construct the tangent to a given circle at a given point on the circle.*

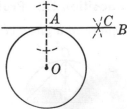

Given ⊙ *O* with point *A* on the circle.

To construct a tangent to ⊙ *O* at point *A*.

(The construction and proof are left to the student.)

★★Proposition VIII. Problem

310. *To construct the tangents to a given circle from a given external point.*

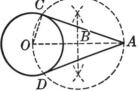

Given ⊙ *O* and external point *A*.

To construct the tangents to ⊙ *O* from point *A*.

Construction:

STATEMENTS	REASONS
1. Draw *OA*.	1. Why possible?
2. Bisect line segment *OA*, calling the point of intersection *B*.	2. Why possible?
3. With *B* as a center and *BO* as a radius draw a ⊙ intersecting ⊙ *O* at *C* and *D*.	3. Why possible?
4. Draw *AC* and *AD*.	4. Why possible?

Then AC and AD are the required tangents.

Proof: (The proof is left to the student. See §§ 299 and 279.)

Discussion. How many tangents can be drawn to ⊙ *O* from point *A*?

★★Proposition IX. Problem

311. *To inscribe a square in a given circle.*

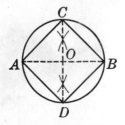

(The solution is left to the student.)

★★Proposition X. Problem

312. *To inscribe a regular hexagon in a given circle.*

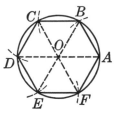

Given ⊙ *O.*

To inscribe a regular hexagon in ⊙ *O.*

Construction: *STATEMENTS*   *REASONS*

1. Draw any radius *OA*.	1. Why possible?
2. With *A* as a center and *OA* as a radius draw an arc intersecting ⊙ *O* at *B*.	2. Why possible?
3. With *B* as a center and *OA* as a radius draw an arc intersecting ⊙ *O* at *C*.	3. Why possible?
4. In like manner draw arcs intersecting ⊙ *O* at *D*, *E*, and *F*.	4. Why possible?
5. Draw *AB*, *BC*, *CD*, *DE*, *EF*, and *FA*.	5. Why possible?

Then ABCDEF is the required hexagon.

Proof:

'1. Connect *O* to each vertex of the hexagon.	1. Why possible?
2. △ *AOB* is equilateral.	2. Why?
3. ∴ △ *AOB* is equiangular.	3. Why?
4. ∠ *AOB* = 60°.	4. Why?
5. ∡ *BOC, COD, DOE*, and *EOF* = 60°.	5. Reasons 2–4.
6. Then ∠ *FOA* = 60°.	6. Give full proof.
7. ∴ $\widehat{AB} = \widehat{BC} = \widehat{CD} = \widehat{DE} = \widehat{EF} = \widehat{FA}$.	7. Why?
8. ∴ *AB* = *BC* = *CD* = *DE* = *EF* = *FA*.	8. Why?
9. Each ∠ of the hexagon = 120°.	9. Give full proof.
10. ∴ *ABCDEF* is a regular hexagon.	10. Why?

EXERCISES

A

1. Construct two parallel tangents to a given circle.

2. Construct the following designs:

3. Circumscribe a square about a given circle.

4. Inscribe an equilateral triangle in a given circle.

5. Construct four circles within a given square, so that each circle is tangent to two sides of the square and to two of the other circles.

B

6. Inscribe an equilateral octagon in a given circle.

7. Inscribe an equilateral polygon of twelve sides in a given circle.

8. The space enclosed by a circle may be divided into three equal parts by the method shown here. The diameter AB is trisected at C and D. Make this construction for a circle with a radius of 2 inches.

9. Construct an original design for a linoleum pattern.

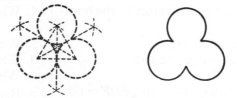

10. A *trefoil* and its basis of construction are shown above. Construct a similar trefoil in which the radii of the circles are 1 inch.

11. *Prove:* If the bisector of an inscribed angle is extended until it intersects the circle, and through this point of intersection a chord is drawn parallel to one side of the angle, it is equal to the other side.

EXERCISES. APPLICATIONS

1. Show how it is possible to find the center and the radius of a circle by using a carpenter's square.

2. Given a circle and the midpoint of a chord, construct the chord.

3. Prove that an inscribed angle is greater than an angle formed by two secants which intercept the same arc.

4. When sailing near rocky coast lines, captains often steer their ships by the aid of two lighthouses and the "horizontal danger angle." In the figure, A and B represent two lighthouses, and $\angle ACB$ is the "horizontal danger angle." Show that if the angle formed by the lines drawn from the ship to the two lighthouses is less than $\angle C$, the ship is out of danger.

5. Mr. Woods has a corner lot $ABCD$ with sidewalks along AD and AB. He wishes to round the corner at A by the use of a circular arc. Show how he can construct the arc, which is to be tangent to AB at E and tangent to AD.

6. A coach laid off a football field, using only a steel tape and some stakes. To construct $BF \perp AB$ at B, he set stakes at B and C 50 feet apart. Then he found the point D, 50 feet from B and C. He then set a stake at E in line with stakes at C and D and 50 feet from D. He said that EB was $\perp AB$. Can you prove it '

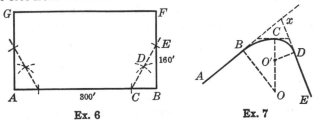

Ex. 6   Ex. 7

7. $ABCDE$ is a portion of a street-car track. It consists of two straight pieces joined by a compound curve BCD. Explain how the compound curve BCD is constructed. Prove that $\angle x = \angle O + \angle CO'D$.

EXERCISES IN REASONING (*Optional*)

Which of the following conclusions are valid?

1. The Pyramid Theater always has good pictures. I know that *The Man Gone Wild* is good because the Pyramid showed it last week.

2. Olive has a good voice and she should have a leading role in *Naughty Marietta*.

3. Our basketball team won from Walton 52 to 36 and Walton beat Rochelle 49 to 44. From the results of these two games, I believe that we can win from Rochelle.

4. Miss Best is a good teacher because all her pupils pass.

5. I do not try hard in geometry because I do not care for my geometry teacher.

6. The morning paper stated that our school janitor was arrested yesterday for driving a truck while intoxicated. He should lose his job as janitor.

7. Our next-door neighbor has an automobile that uses a lot of oil. The car is only one year old, too. I would not want that make of car.

8. Mrs. Franklin is very particular about her appearance and is always immaculate. I am sure that she keeps her home clean and tidy.

9. Mary went to college and Priscilla became a stenographer. So Mary is better educated than Priscilla.

10. Mr. Wertz is not an educated man. He never went to high school.

11. Our tax rate is lower this year than it was last year. Because of the decreased tax rate, our taxes will be lowered.

12. Most of the colleges require plane geometry for entrance. I cannot go to college because I am not studying geometry.

REVIEW QUESTIONS

1. What is the difference between an arc degree and an angle degree?

2. $\overset{\frown}{AB}$ and $\overset{\frown}{CD}$ contain 13° each. If the radius of $\overset{\frown}{AB}$ is 10 inches and the radius of $\overset{\frown}{CD}$ is 8 inches, which arc is the longer?

3. How many degrees are there in an angle that is inscribed in a semicircle?

4. What is the name of the point where a tangent touches the circle?

5. Name the order of sequence of the following theorems:

a. An angle formed by a tangent and a chord · · ·.

b. An angle formed by two tangents, or a tangent and a secant · · ·.

c. An inscribed angle is equal in degrees · · ·.

d. An angle formed by two chords · · ·.

6. An angle is inscribed in a minor arc. Is the angle acute?

7. Can a square be inscribed in any circle?

8. Define: arc; chord; tangent; secant; inscribed angle.

9. How many arcs does a chord have?

10. If one arc of a chord contains 80°, what kind of arc is it?

11. How many chords may be drawn from a point on a circle?

In the figure at the right, AC is a diameter, $\overset{\frown}{BC} = 50°$, and $\angle AOD = 110°$.

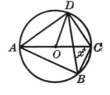

12. Find the number of degrees in $\overset{\frown}{CD}$; in $\angle CAD$; in $\angle ADB$; in $\angle x$.

13. If $AC = 29$ inches and $CD = 20$ inches, how long is AD?

In this figure AB is tangent to $\odot O$ at B, and AE is tangent to the circle at E.

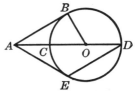

14. If $\angle OAB = 30°$, find $\overset{\frown}{CB}$; $\overset{\frown}{BD}$; $\overset{\frown}{CE}$; $\angle COB$; $\angle ADE$.

15. If $\angle BOA = 60°$ and $BO = 8$ inches, find CO; AO; AC; AB; AE.

16. What do you know about the angles of a quadrilateral if the quadrilateral can be inscribed in a circle?

17. Is it true that the line which bisects two chords of a circle passes through the center of the circle?

18. AB is a diameter of circle O, and BC and AC are chords. Diameter AB is 10 inches and $\overset{\frown}{BC}$ is 60°. How long is chord BC?

19. The side DE of $\triangle DEF$ is a diameter of a circle, and F is a point on the circle. DF is 36 inches and EF is 15 inches. How long is DE?

20. *ABC* is a triangle inscribed in a circle, and tangents to the circle at *B* and *C* meet in a point *D*. If the angle at *A* is 50°, what is the angle at *D*?

SUMMARY OF PRINCIPAL METHODS OF PROOF

313. *Comparison of angles and their arcs*

a. A central angle is equal in degrees to its intercepted arc.

b. An inscribed angle is equal in degrees to one half its intercepted arc.

c. An angle formed by a tangent and a chord drawn from the point of contact is equal in degrees to one half its intercepted arc.

d. An angle formed by two chords intersecting within a circle is equal in degrees to one half the sum of the arcs intercepted by it and its vertical angle.

e. An angle formed by two tangents, or a tangent and a secant, or two secants, intersecting outside a circle, is equal in degrees to one half the difference of the intercepted arcs.

314. *Two angles are equal*

If they are inscribed angles intercepting the same arc.

315. *Two lines are perpendicular*

If they are sides of an angle inscribed in a semicircle.

316. *Constructions*

a. To bisect a given arc of a circle.

b. To construct the tangent to a given circle at a given point on the circle.

c. To construct the tangents to a given circle from a given external point.

d. To inscribe a square in a given circle.

e. To inscribe a regular hexagon in a given circle.

317. *Two arcs are equal*

a. If they are arcs of the same circle or of equal circles and have the same number of degrees.

b. If they are arcs of a circle intercepted by parallel lines.

TEST 24

Multiple-Choice Statements (*Eight Minutes*)

On your paper write the word or group of words in boldface type which makes each statement true:

1. An angle inscribed in a semicircle is **an acute angle** **a right angle** **an obtuse angle.**

2. A central angle is equal in degrees to **its intercepted arc** **one half its intercepted arc** **twice its intercepted arc.**

3. If a central angle is doubled, its arc **is doubled** **remains the same** **is tripled.**

4. An inscribed angle is equal in degrees to **its intercepted arc** **one half its intercepted arc** **twice its intercepted arc.**

5. An inscribed angle intercepting an arc of 90° is **acute** **right** **obtuse.**

6. If a quadrilateral is inscribed in a circle, the opposite angles are **equal** **complementary** **supplementary.**

7. Inscribed angles which intercept the same arc are **equal** **complementary** **supplementary.**

8. An angle formed by two secants is equal in degrees to **one half the sum of its intercepted arcs** **one half the difference of its intercepted arcs** **the difference of its intercepted arcs.**

9. An angle formed by two intersecting chords is equal in degrees to **the sum** **the difference** **one half the sum** **one half the difference** of the arcs intercepted by it and its vertical angle.

10. A polygon is inscribed in a circle if its sides are **tangents** **secants** **chords** of the circle.

TEST 25

Constructions (*Seventeen Minutes*)

Make the following geometric constructions:

1. In a given circle inscribe an angle of 60°.
2. Given the arc of a circle, locate its center.
3. Construct a tangent to a given circle at a given point on the circle.
4. Inscribe a square in a given circle.

TEST 26

Applications (*Thirty Minutes*)

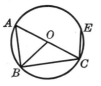

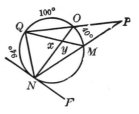

1. AC is a diameter, $\overset{\frown}{AB}$ contains 70° and $\overset{\frown}{CE}$ contains 46°. How many degrees are there in $\angle BCA$? in $\angle BOC$? in $\overset{\frown}{BC}$? in $\angle ACE$? in $\angle ABC$?

2. How many degrees are there in $\angle MQO$? in $\angle QON$? in $\angle P$? in $\angle x$? in $\angle FNM$? in $\angle y$? in $\angle QNO$? in $\angle QNM$? in $\angle ONM$?

3. Two tangents to a circle are perpendicular to each other. How many degrees are there in the minor arc?

4. Two tangents to a circle form an angle of 60°. How many degrees are there in the major arc of the circle?

5. How many degrees are there in each of the arcs formed by the sides of a regular pentagon inscribed in a circle?

6. A circle is divided into six equal arcs. If the diameter of the circle is 14 inches, how many inches are there in a chord joining any two successive points of division?

7. If $KT \parallel RS$ and $\overset{\frown}{KR} = 40°$, how many degrees are there in $\overset{\frown}{TS}$?

8. If $KT \parallel RS$, $\overset{\frown}{ST} = 30°$, and $\overset{\frown}{KT} = 80°$, how many degrees are there in $\overset{\frown}{RPS}$? how many degrees in $\angle RKT$?

9. AB is a diameter and AC is a chord of a circle. If AC is equal to a radius of the circle, how many degrees are there in $\overset{\frown}{BC}$?

10. In the figure, if $\angle A = 32°$ and $\overset{\frown}{BD} = 24°$, how many degrees are there in $\overset{\frown}{CE}$?

11. If the hypotenuse of a right triangle is 10 inches, what is the length of the median on the hypotenuse?

CHAPTER X

Loci

We are already familiar with the location of points from our study of pages 138–139. In this chapter we shall make a more thorough study of locus and its application to theorems and construction problems.

318. Locus of Points. A *locus of points* is a geometric figure containing **all the points, and only those points**, that satisfy a given condition or set of conditions. A locus may consist of one or more points, lines, surfaces, or any combination of them.

The word *locus*, the plural of which is *loci* (pronounced (lō′sī), is the Latin word meaning "place" or "location." "Locus" may also be defined as the path of a moving point satisfying a given condition.

Locus lines will be indicated by long-dash lines to distinguish them from given lines and construction lines.

There are four important steps in determining a locus, the first three of which will be illustrated in the following examples:

Example 1. What is the locus of points $\frac{3}{8}$ inch from a given point O?

The given condition is that the points shall be $\frac{3}{8}$ inch from O.

Step 1. We first locate several points that are $\frac{3}{8}$ inch from O. We know that there is an infinite number of them.

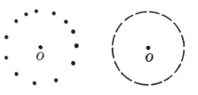

Step 2. We draw a broken smooth curve through these points.

Step 3. We describe the geometric figure which the locus appears to be. The locus of points $\frac{3}{8}$ inch from the given point O is a circle with center O and a radius of $\frac{3}{8}$ inch.

Example 2. What is the locus of points equidistant from two given parallel lines l and l'?

The given condition is that the points shall be the same distance from l and l'.

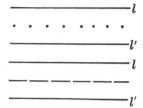

Step 1. We locate several points that are equidistant from l and l'. We know that there is an infinite number of such points.

Step 2. The points appear to lie on a straight line; so we draw a broken straight line through the points.

Step 3. Now we describe the geometric locus which the figure appears to be. The locus of points equidistant from two given parallel lines l and l' is the line parallel to l and l' and midway between them.

Example 3. Find the locus of points $\frac{1}{2}$ inch from a given line l.

The given condition is that the points shall be $\frac{1}{2}$ inch from l.

Step 1. Draw a given line l. Locate several points on both sides of l and $\frac{1}{2}$ inch from l.

Step 2. Draw a broken line through the points on one side of l. Draw another broken line through the points on the other side of l.

Step 3. The locus of points $\frac{1}{2}$ inch from a given line l is two lines parallel to l and $\frac{1}{2}$ inch from it.

319. Directions for Determining a Locus:

1. Locate several points which satisfy the given conditions.

2. Draw a smooth line* or lines through these points.

3. Describe accurately the geometric figure you think is the locus.

4. Prove that this figure is the locus.

320. Distance from a Point to a Circle. The distance from a point to a circle is measured on the line joining the point to the center of the circle and is the length of the line segment between the point and the circle. AC is the distance of point A from $\odot O$, and BC is the distance of point B from $\odot O$. Show that AC is less than any other line segment drawn from A to the circle.

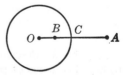

*A line may be a straight line or a curve.

EXERCISES [A]

Making use of the directions given in § 319 for determining a locus, draw a figure and describe the locus for each of the following exercises. No proof is required.

1. The locus of points which are 3 inches from a given point.

2. The locus of the center of a ball as it rolls on a straight line over a level floor.

3. The locus of the center of a circle that rolls around the outside of another circle.

4. The locus of points on this page 3 inches from the top.

5. The locus of all cities that are 5 miles from a given railroad.

6. The locus of points 5 inches from a circle whose radius is 5 inches.

7. The locus of points equidistant from the top and bottom of this page.

8. The locus of points less than 5 inches from a given point.

9. The locus of points equidistant from two given points.

10. The locus of points within an angle equidistant from the sides of the angle.

11. The locus of the vertex of a right triangle with a given hypotenuse as a base.

12. The locus of the centers of all circles tangent to a given line at a given point.

13. The locus of points equidistant from the points of intersection of two given intersecting circles.

14. The locus of the midpoints of parallel chords of a given circle.

15. The locus of the midpoints of all equal chords of a given circle.

16. The locus of the midpoints of the radii of a given circle.

17. What is the locus of a point that is inside a 4-inch square and 1 inch from a side?

18. What is the locus of points inside a circle whose radius is 3 inches?

19. What is the locus inside a circle of a point whose distance from the circle is equal to a radius?

20. What is the locus of the center of a circle that rolls around the inside of a larger circle and is always tangent to the larger circle?

321. Postulates on Loci. From the examples of § 318, and previous definitions, we may state the following postulates on loci:

a. **Post. 29.** *The locus of points at a given distance from a given point is a circle with the given point as the center and the given distance as the radius.*

b. **Post. 30.** *The locus of points at a given distance from a given line is a pair of lines parallel to the given line and at the given distance from it.* (In the figure, l is the given line and d the given distance.)

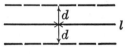

c. **Post. 31.** *The locus of points equidistant from two given parallel lines is the line parallel to each of the given lines and midway between them.* (In the figure, l_1 and l_2 are the given lines.)

322. Proving a Locus Theorem. Any geometric figure, such as a straight line or a circle, consists of an infinite number of points. To prove that two geometric figures coincide, it is only necessary to show that all points of the first are points of the second and that all points of the second are points of the first.

For example, consider the portion of planes bounded by the squares $ABCD$ and $A'B'C'D'$. In Fig. 1, no point in either square lies in the other square. In Fig. 2, there are points (but not all) in either square that lie in the other square. In Fig. 3, all the points in $A'B'C'D'$ lie in $ABCD$ but not all the

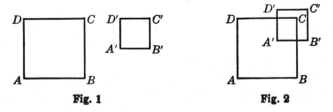

Fig. 1   **Fig. 2**

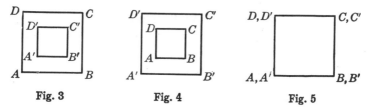

Fig. 3 Fig. 4 Fig. 5

points in *ABCD* lie in *A'B'C'D'*. In Fig. 4, the converse is true. In Fig. 5, all the points in *ABCD* lie in *A'B'C'D'* and all the points in *A'B'C'D'* lie in *ABCD*. In this case the portions of planes bounded by the squares coincide.

When we say that a locus of points is a circle, we mean that the locus of points and the circle coincide. When we say that a line is a locus of points, we mean that the line and the locus coincide. In general, when we say that a locus is a certain geometric figure, we mean that all points of the locus are points of the geometric figure and that all points of the geometric figure are points of the locus.

From this discussion the following directions can be stated.

To prove that a geometric figure is a locus:

1. Prove that every point of the figure is a point of the locus.
2. Prove that (a) every point of the locus is a point of the figure, or (b) every point outside the figure is not a point of the locus.

Step 1 is needed to show that all the geometric figure is a part of the locus. Either step 2 (a) or 2 (b) is needed to show that all the locus is part of the figure. If step 2 (a) is true, we know that step 2 (b) is true; and if step 2 (b) is true, we know that step 2 (a) is true (§ 118).

When studying Prop. I on the next page, note carefully the two parts of the demonstration. Part I proves that every point of the figure is a point of the locus and Part II proves that every point of the locus is a point of the figure.

★Proposition I. Theorem

323. *The locus of points within an angle equidistant from the sides is the bisector of the angle.*

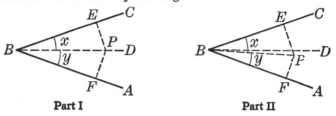

Part I   **Part II**

Part I

Any point on the bisector of the angle is equidistant from the sides of the angle.

Given BD the bisector of $\angle ABC$, and P any point in BD.

To prove that P is equidistant from BC and BA.

Selection of Method: 1. Known methods of proving line segments $=$:
§§ 86, 140, 202, 288, 289.
2. Method to be used: § 86 *a*.

Proof: *STATEMENTS*	*REASONS*
1. Draw $PF \perp BA$ and $PE \perp BC$.	1. Why possible?
2. ⊿ PEB and PFB are rt. ⊿.	2. Why?
3. $\angle x = \angle y$.	3. Why?
4. $BP = BP$.	4. Why?
5. Rt. $\triangle\ PEB \cong$ rt. $\triangle\ PFB$.	5. Why?
6. ∴ $PE = PF$; i.e., any point on BD is equidistant from BA and BC.	6. Why?

In Part I above it is proved that every point of BD is equidistant from BC and BA. This is done by selecting any point P at random to represent every point of BD, and then proving that this one point P is equidistant from BC and BA.

In Part II the coincidence method of indirect proof is used.

Part II

Any point equidistant from the sides of an angle is on the bisector of the angle.

Given BD the bisector of ∠ *ABC*, and any point *P* which is equidistant from *BC* and *BA*.

To prove that *P* is on *BD*.

Selection of Method: 1. Known methods of proving ⩋ =: §§ 50, 87, 141, 204, 290, 314.
2. Method to be used: § 87 *b*.

Proof: STATEMENTS	REASONS
1. Draw *PF* ⊥ *BA* and *PE* ⊥ *BC*.	1. Why possible?
2. Draw *PB*.	2. Why possible?
3. ⩋ *BPE* and *BPF* are rt. ⩋.	3. Why?
4. *PE* = *PF*.	4. Why?
5. *BP* = *BP*.	5. Why?
6. ∴ rt. △ *BPE* ≅ rt. △ *BPF*.	6. Why?
7. ∴ ∠ *x* = ∠ *y*.	7. Why?
8. ∴ *BP* bisects ∠ *ABC* and *P* lies on *BD*.	8. Why?

★**324. Corollary.** *The locus of points equidistant from two given intersecting lines is the pair of lines bisecting the angles formed by the given lines.*

EXERCISES [A].   LOCI

To decide on these loci use steps 1 and 2 of § 319. Then construct each locus with straightedge and compasses. Do not prove.

1. Determine the locus of the midpoints of the radii of a given circle.

2. Determine the locus of the midpoints of all chords of a given length in a given circle.

3. Determine the locus of the vertices of all triangles having a given base and a given altitude.

4. Determine the locus of points equidistant from two circles having the same center.

★★ Proposition II. Theorem

325. *The locus of points equidistant from two given points is the perpendicular bisector of the line segment joining the two points.*

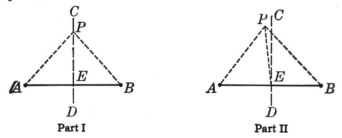

Part I   Part II

Part I

Any point on the perpendicular bisector of a line segment is equidistant from the end points of the segment.

Given points A and B, the line segment AB, CD the ⊥ bisector of AB, and P any point on CD.

To prove that P is equidistant from A and B.

Selection of Method: 1. Known methods of proving line segments =:
§§ 86, 140, 202, 288, 289, 323.
2. Method to be used: § 86 *a*.

Proof: STATEMENTS	REASONS
1. Draw PA and PB.	1. Why possible?
2. ∡ PEA and PEB are rt. ∡.	2. Why?
3. $AE = EB$.	3. Why?
4. $PE = PE$.	4. Why?
5. Rt. $\triangle PEA \cong$ rt. $\triangle PEB$.	5. Why?
6. ∴ $PA = PB$; i.e., any point on CD is equidistant from A and B.	6. Why?

(The proof of Part II is left to the student. See § 123.)

Proposition III. Theorem

326. *The locus of the vertex of a right triangle with a given hypotenuse as the base is a circle upon the hypotenuse as a diameter.*

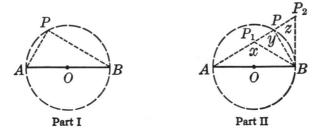

Part I   Part II

(The demonstration is left to the student. In the proof of Part II, prove 2 (*b*) of § 322, using § 82.)

Proposition IV. Theorem

327. *The locus of the centers of all circles tangent to a given line at a given point is the perpendicular to the line at that point.*

(The demonstration is left to the student.)

NOTE. The loci developed in Posts. 29–31 and Theorems I–IV should be thoroughly understood, as most loci problems are applications of them.

328. Concentric Circles. *Concentric circles* are circles having the same center.

EXERCISES

A

1. Determine the locus of the centers of all circles passing through two given points.

2. Determine the locus of the center of a circle tangent to the sides of a given angle.

3. Determine the locus of points within a given circle which are equidistant from the ends of a given chord.

4. Determine the locus of the center of a circle which has a given radius and is tangent to a given line.

5. Determine the locus of the centers of all circles (*a*) tangent to two given parallel lines; (*b*) tangent to two given intersecting lines.

B

6. Determine the locus of the centers of all circles tangent to a given circle at a given point on the circle.

7. Determine the locus of points at a given distance from a given circle (three different loci, depending on the relative length of the radius and the given distance).

8. Determine the locus of the midpoints of all chords which can be drawn from a given point on a given circle.

9. Determine the locus of the centers of all circles with a given radius and passing through a given point.

C

10. Determine the locus of the midpoints of all chords formed by secants drawn to a circle from a given external point.

11. In a rectangle *ABCD*, *AB* equals 2 inches and *BC* equals 1 inch. A line *EB* is drawn from *E*, the midpoint of *CD*, to *B*. Draw the locus of the midpoints of lines parallel to *EB* and terminated by the sides of the rectangle.

12. If the range of a field artillery gun is between 1000 yards and 5000 yards, and the gun can be turned through an angle of 135°, draw the locus of points where the projectiles may fall.

13. See if you can plot and give the names of the following two loci, which are curves but not circles: (*a*) the locus of points equidistant from a given line and a given point; (*b*) the locus of points the sum of whose distances from two given points is a given length.

329. Compound Locus. Sometimes points are required to satisfy two separate conditions. In such cases the points will be the intersections of the separate loci determined by each condition. A *compound locus* is determined by the intersection of two or more loci.

In solving a locus problem place the given parts in the most general positions in order to determine the most general locus, and then in a discussion state the locus for all special conditions.

Example. Find all the points equidistant from two given points and also equidistant from two given parallel lines.

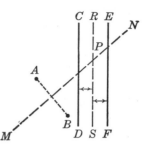

Given the points *A* and *B* and the two ∥s *CD* and *EF*.

To find all points equidistant from *A* and *B* and also equidistant from *CD* and *EF*.

Solution: *STATEMENTS*   *REASONS*

1. *MN*, the ⊥ bisector of *AB*, the line segment joining *A* and *B*, is the locus of points equidistant from *A* and *B*.	1. § 325.
2. *RS*, the line ∥ *CD* and *EF* and midway between them, is the locus of points equidistant from *CD* and *EF*.	2. § 321 *c*.
3. The required point is *P*, the intersection of *MN* and *RS*.	3. § 329.

Discussion.

1. If *RS* ∥ *MN*, there are no points.
2. If *RS* coincides with *MN*, every point of *MN* is a required point.
3. In all other positions there is only one point.

EXERCISES

A

1. Find all the points equidistant from three given points. (Find the locus for two points at a time.)

2. Find all the points $1\frac{1}{2}$ inches from a given point and equidistant from two given parallels which are 1 inch apart.

3. Find all the points equidistant from two given intersecting lines and at a distance of 1 inch from the point of intersection of the two lines.

4. Find all the points at a distance of 2 inches from each of two given points which are 3 inches apart.

5. Find all the points equidistant from two given parallel lines and at a given distance from a third given line.

6. Find all the points equidistant from two given points and at a given distance from a third given point.

7. Find all the points equidistant from two given points and at a given distance from a given line.

8. Find all the points at a given distance from a given line and at a given distance from a given point.

B

9. Find all the points equidistant from two given parallels and also equidistant from two given intersecting lines.

10. Find all the points equidistant from two given intersecting lines and at a given distance from a third given line.

11. Find all the points at a given distance from a given circle and equidistant from two given points.

12. Find all the points at a distance of the radius of a given circle from the given circle and at the same distance from a given tangent to the given circle.

C

13. Find all the points equidistant from two given concentric circles and also equidistant from two given parallels intersecting the circles.

14. Find all the points at a given distance from a given circle and also equidistant from two given lines that intersect at the center of the given circle.

15. Find all the points equidistant from two given equal intersecting circles and at the distance of their common chord from their line of centers.

16. *AB* is a line segment 3 inches long. Locate all the points which are 1 inch from *AB* and are vertices of right angles whose sides pass through the end points *A* and *B*. What would be the distance of the vertices of the right angles from *AB* if the locus consisted of only two points?

330. Concurrent Lines. *Concurrent lines* are three or more lines passing through the same point.

331. Loci in Algebra (*Optional*). In geometry the condition for a locus is stated in the form of a theorem. In algebra the condition for a locus is stated in the form of a conditional equation. To every conditional equation in one or two unknowns there corresponds a geometric figure. For example, the geometric figure corresponding to the equation $x = 4$ is the line l parallel to the y-axis and 4 units to the right of it. The line l satisfies the condition that every point on l has a value of $x = 4$ and every point in the plane for which $x = 4$ lies on l. Then the locus of the equation $x = 4$ is l. In like manner, the locus of the equation $y + 3 = 0$ is the line l' parallel to the x-axis and three units below it.

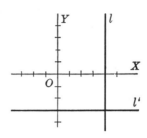

As a review, an explanation of the rectangular co-ordinate system and the definitions of the terms used are given below.

332. Cartesian, or Rectangular, Co-ordinates (*Optional*). In the figure two perpendicular lines $X'X$ and $Y'Y$ are chosen as reference lines. Their intersection O is called the origin.

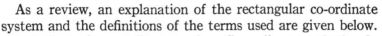

Values to the right of the origin on the horizontal axis, or x-axis, are positive, and to the left of the origin are negative; values above the origin on the vertical axis, or y-axis, are positive and below the origin are negative. PA, the distance of a point from the y-axis, is called the *abscissa* of P; PB, the distance of P from the x-axis, is called the *ordinate* of P. Together the values of the abscissa and the ordinate are called the co-ordinates of P. The point P is called the point $(4, 3)$. In like manner, point Q is the point $(-3, 1)$.

EXERCISES [A]

1. Plot each group of points, using separate co-ordinate axes:
a. $(3, 4)$, $(-2, 3)$, $(5, -1)$, $(-2, -4)$.   *b.* $(-3, 5)$, $(0, 2)$, $(-3, 0)$.
       c. $(5, 0)$, $(0, -3)$, $(7, -4)$, $(-1, -1)$.

2. What geometric figure is the locus for each of these conditions?
a. $x + 3 = 0$.   *b.* $y + 5 = 0$.   *c.* $x - 2 = 0$.   *d.* $y - 4 = 0$.

3. What is the locus of points with ordinate 6? with abscissa -3?

333. Linear Loci (*Optional*). From your study of graphs in algebra you know that the graph of the equation $x - y = 3$ is a straight line. In the figure at the right, every point on the line AB satisfies the condition $x - y = 3$. Also, every point that satisfies the condition $x - y = 3$ is on the line AB. Therefore we can say that AB is the locus of points satisfying the condition $x - y = 3$. In like manner, CD is the locus of points satisfying the condition $x + y = 1$. AB and CD intersect at P. $P(2, -1)$ is the locus of points satisfying the two conditions $x - y = 3$ and $x + y = 1$.

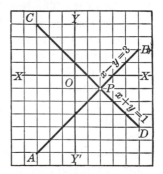

In drawing graphs of first-degree equations in two unknowns, we usually plot three points, two in order to determine the line and one as a check.

Example. Find the locus of points satisfying the conditions [1] $x + y = 0$ and [2] $x - 3y = -2$.

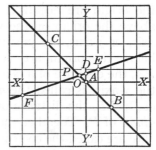

Solution. In [1]: if $x = 0$, $y = 0$; if $x = 2$, $y = -2$; if $x = -3$, $y = 3$. These points are A, B, and C in the figure, and CB is the locus of points satisfying the condition $x + y = 0$.

In [2]: if $x = 0$, $y = \frac{2}{3}$; if $x = 1$, $y = 1$; if $x = -5$, $y = -1$. These points are D, E, and F in the figure, and FE is the locus of points satisfying the condition $x - 3y = -2$.

The intersection of lines CB and FE, namely, $P(-\frac{1}{2}, \frac{1}{2})$, is the required locus.

Algebraic Solution.	$x + y = 0$	[1]
	$x - 3y = -2$	[2]
Subtracting,	$4y = 2$	
	$y = \frac{1}{2}$	
Substituting in [1],	$x = -\frac{1}{2}.$	

EXERCISES

Find the locus of points satisfying the following sets of conditions and check by algebraic solutions (see page 42):

1. $x + y = 10$,
   $x - y = 6$.

2. $x - y = 4$,
   $x + y = 6$.

3. $4x + y = 5$,
   $4x - y = 3$.

4. $y = 2x$,
   $x - 2y = -6$.

5. $x = 3y$,
   $x + 2y = 5$.

6. $2x + y = 10$,
   $3x - y = 10$

334. Other Algebraic Loci (*Optional*). *a.* The locus of points satisfying the condition $x^2 + y^2 = 16$ is a circle with its center at the origin and a radius of $\sqrt{16}$, or 4. (See Post. 29, p. 310.) The circle can be drawn with compasses.

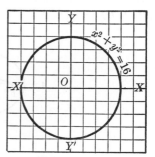

b. The locus of points satisfying the condition $y^2 = 4x$ is a parabola. In graphing the parabola in the figure at the right, the following points were used:

x	4	1	0	1	4
y	4	2	0	-2	-4

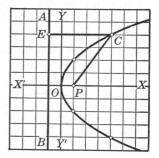

A parabola is the locus of points equidistant from a given point and a given line. In the figure, P is the given point and AB the given line. $CP = CE$. A ball thrown or batted into the air follows the path of a parabola.

EXERCISES

Find loci satisfying the following conditions:

1. $x^2 + y^2 = 25$.

2. $x^2 + y^2 = 9$.

3. $x^2 = 4y$.

4. $y = x^2 + 2$.

5. $y = x^3$.

6. $y^2 = x^3$.

7. $x^2 + y^2 = 4$,
   $x = y$.

8. $x^2 = 2y$,
   $y = 3$.

c. The locus of points satisfying the condition $9\,x^2 + 25\,y^2 = 225$ is an ellipse. In graphing the ellipse in the figure below, the following points were used:

x	-5	-4	-2	0	$+2$	$+4$	$+5$
y	0	± 1.8	± 2.8	3	± 2.8	± 1.8	0

An ellipse is the locus of points the sum of whose distances from two given points (the foci) is constant. In the figure, $PF + PF' = AB.$

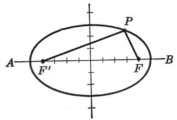

Some automobile springs, gears in machines, and arches in bridges are applications of the ellipse. The orbits of the planets as they move around the sun are ellipses.

d. The locus of a given point on a circle as it rolls along a straight line is a cycloid.

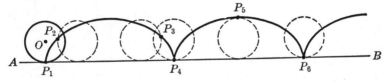

The curve $P_1P_2P_3P_4$ is one arch of a cycloid made by point P on circle O as the circle rolls along AB.

In the figure at the right, CE is half an arch of a cycloid. If an object is released at C it will travel to E in less time than if it followed any other path from C to E. For

this reason the cycloid is called "the curve of quickest descent."

★Proposition V. Theorem

335. *The perpendicular bisectors of the sides of a triangle are concurrent in a point equidistant from the vertices.*

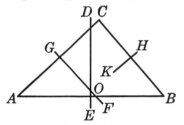

Given △ *ABC* with *DE*, *FG*, and *HK* the ⊥ bisectors of the sides *AB*, *AC*, and *BC* respectively.

To prove that *DE*, *FG*, and *HK* are concurrent in a point equidistant from *A*, *B*, and *C*.

Selection of Method. 1. Known methods of proving a point equidistant from other points: §§ 257, 325.
2. Method to be used: § 325.

Proof:

STATEMENTS	REASONS
1. *DE* and *FG* will intersect in some point, as *O*.	1. § 102.
2. *DE* is the locus of points equidistant from *A* and *B*.	2. § 325.
3. *FG* is the locus of points equidistant from *A* and *C*.	3. Why?
4. ∴ *O* is equidistant from *A*, *B*, and *C*.	4. Ax. 5.
5. ∴ *O* is on *HK*, the ⊥ bisector of *BC*.	5. Why?
6. ∴ *DE*, *GF*, and *HK* are concurrent in a point equidistant from *A*, *B*, and *C*.	6. Sts. 1, 4, 5.

336. Circumcenter. The point where the perpendicular bisectors of the sides of a triangle are concurrent is called the *circumcenter* of the triangle.

EXERCISE

In the figure of Prop. V, if the distance *OA* equals 5, find the distances *OB* and *OC*.

★Proposition VI. Theorem

337. *The bisectors of the angles of a triangle are concurrent in a point equidistant from the sides.*

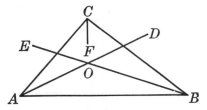

Given △ *ABC* with *AD, BE,* and *CF* bisecting ∡ *A, B,* and *C* respectively.

To prove that *AD, BE,* and *CF* are concurrent in a point equidistant from *AB, BC,* and *AC.*

Selection of Method: 1. Known methods of proving a point equidistant from lines: §§ 321 *c*, 323, 324.
2. Method to be used: § 323.

Proof: STATEMENTS	REASONS
1. *AD* and *BE* will intersect in some point *O*.	1. Give full proof.*
2. *AD* is the locus of points equidistant from *AB* and *AC*.	2. Why?
3. *BE* is the locus of points equidistant from *AB* and *BC*.	3. Why?
4. ∴ *O* is equidistant from *AB*, *AC*, and *BC*.	4. Why?
5. ∴ *O* is on *CF*, the bisector of ∠ *C*.	5. § 323.
6. ∴ *AD*, *BE*, and *CF* are concurrent in a point equidistant from the sides *AB*, *BC*, and *AC*.	6. Statements 1, 4, and 5.

338. Incenter. The point where the bisectors of the angles of a triangle are concurrent is called the *incenter* of the triangle.

*If *AD* and *BE* do not intersect, *AD* ∥ *BE*. Why? Then ∠ *DAB* + ∠ *EBA* = 1 st. ∠ (§ 145). This is impossible (§ 107).

Proposition VII. Theorem

339. *The altitudes of a triangle are concurrent.*

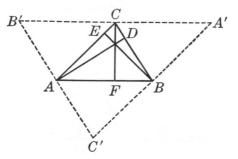

Given △ *ABC* with the altitudes *AD*, *BE*, and *CF*.

To prove that *AD*, *BE*, and *CF* are concurrent.

Selection of Method: 1. Known methods of proving lines concurrent: §§ 335, 337.
            2. Method to be used: § 335.

Proof: *STATEMENTS*	*REASONS*
1. Draw *B'A'* through *C* ∥ *AB*; *C'A'* through *B* ∥ *AC*; and *C'B'* through *A* ∥ *BC*.	1. § 96.
2. *ABCB'* and *ABA'C* are ▱.	2. Why?
3. ∴ *B'C* = *AB* and *CA'* = *AB*.	3. Why?
4. ∴ *B'C* = *CA'*.	4. Why?
5. *CF* ⊥ *AB*.	5. Why?
6. *CF* ⊥ *B'A'*.	6. Why?
7. ∴ *CF* is the ⊥ bisector of *B'A'*.	7. Statements 4 and 6.
8. In like manner, *BE* and *AD* are the ⊥ bisectors of *C'A'* and *B'C'* respectively.	8. Reasons 2–7.
9. ∴ *AD*, *BE*, and *CF* are concurrent.	9. § 335.

340. Orthocenter. The point where the altitudes of a triangle are concurrent is called the *orthocenter* of the triangle. "Ortho" is from the Greek word *orthos*, meaning "straight."

★★Proposition VIII. Theorem

341. *The medians of a triangle are concurrent in a point which lies two thirds of the distance from each vertex to the midpoint of the opposite side.*

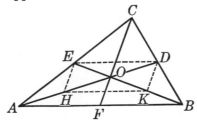

Given △ *ABC* with the medians *AD, BE,* and *CF.*

To prove that *AD, BE,* and *CF* are concurrent in a point which lies two thirds of the distance from each vertex to the midpoint of the opposite side.

Selection of Method: 1. Known methods of proving line segments =:
§§ 86, 140, 202, 288, 289, 323, 325.
2. Method to be used: § 202 *c.*

Proof: *STATEMENTS*	*REASONS*
1. *AD* and *BE* will meet in some point, such as *O.*	1. Give indirect proof.
2. Draw *HK* joining the midpoints, *H* and *K,* of the line segments *AO* and *BO* respectively.	2. Why possible?
3. Draw *EH, ED,* and *DK.*	3. Why possible?
4. In △ *AOB, HK* ∥ *AB* and *HK* = ½ *AB.*	4. §§ 206 *b,* 203 *a.*
5. In △ *ABC, ED* ∥ *AB* and *ED* = ½ *AB.*	5. Why?
6. ∴ *HK* = *ED* and *HK* ∥ *ED.*	6. Why?
7. ∴ *HKDE* is a ▱.	7. Why?
8. ∴ *HO* = *OD* and *EO* = *OK.*	8. § 202 *c.*

(*Proof continued on opposite page.*)

9. ∴ $AH = HO = OD$ and $EO = OK = KB$.	9. Why?
10. ∴ AD and BE intersect in a point which lies $\frac{2}{3}$ the distance from A to D and B to E respectively.	10. Why?
11. In like manner, AD and CF intersect in a point which lies $\frac{2}{3}$ the distance from A to D and C to F respectively.	11. Reasons 2–10.
12. ∴ CF passes through O.	12. Why?
13. ∴ AD, BE, and CF are concurrent in a point which lies two thirds of the distance from each vertex to the midpoint of the opposite side.	13. Why?

342. Centroid. The point where the medians of a triangle are concurrent is called the *centroid* of the triangle. It is the center of gravity of the triangle. If a triangular piece of board of uniform thickness and material is suspended from any vertex, the centroid of the triangle will lie on a plumb line through the vertex.

★★Proposition IX. Problem

343. *To circumscribe a circle about a given triangle.*

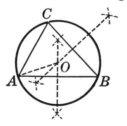

(The solution is left to the student. See § 335.)

344. Circumcircle. The radius of the circle circumscribed about a triangle is called the *circumradius* of the triangle and the circle the *circumcircle* of the triangle. In the figure for § 343, OA is the circumradius, and the circle with center at O the circumcircle, of triangle ABC. O is the circumcenter of triangle ABC. (See § 336.)

★**345. Corollary I.** *Through three points not in a straight line one circle, and only one, can be drawn.* (The three points can be considered as the vertices of a triangle.)

346. Corollary II. *Two circles cannot intersect in more than two points.*

347. Corollary III. *A straight line cannot intersect a circle in more than two points.* (This corollary is the same as Post. 17.)

★★ Proposition X. Problem

348. *To inscribe a circle in a given triangle.*

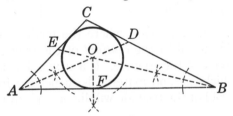

(The solution is left to the student. See § 337.)

349. Incircle. The radius of the circle inscribed in a triangle is called the *inradius* of the triangle, and the circle the *incircle* of the triangle. In the figure for § 348, *OF* is the inradius, and the circle with its center at *O* the incircle, of triangle *ABC*. *O* is the incenter of triangle *ABC*. (See § 338.)

350. Segment of a Circle. A *segment of a circle* is the figure formed by an arc of a circle and its chord. Notice that the definitions for the segment of a circle and the segment of a line do not correspond. A part of a line is called a line segment; a part of a circle is called an arc. A segment of a circle is a figure composed of both a part of a circle and a part of a line.

EXERCISES [A]. CONSTRUCTIONS

1. Given a side, construct an equilateral triangle and circumscribe a circle about it.

2. Construct a 30°-60° right triangle and inscribe a circle in it. Circumscribe a circle about the triangle.

Proposition XI. Problem

351. *Upon a given line segment as a chord to construct an arc of a circle in which a given angle can be inscribed.*

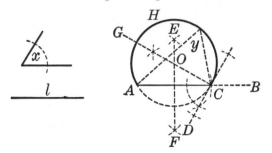

Given line segment *l* and ∠ *x*.

To construct on *l* as a chord an arc of a circle in which ∠ *x* can be inscribed.

Construction: *STATEMENTS*   *REASONS*

STATEMENTS	REASONS
1. On any line *AB* construct *AC = l*.	1. Why possible?
2. At *C* construct ∠ *ACD* = ∠ *x*.	2. Why possible?
3. Construct *EF*, the ⊥ bisector of *AC*.	3. Why possible?
4. Construct *CG* ⊥ *CD* at *C*.	4. Why possible?
5. *CG* will intersect *EF* at some point, such as *O*.	5. § 102.
6. With *O* as center and *OC* as radius draw a ⊙.	6. Why?

Then AHC is the required arc of a ⊙.

Proof:

STATEMENTS	REASONS
1. Inscribe any ∠ as ∠ *y* in the arc *AHC*.	1. Why possible?
2. ∠ *ACD* ≐ ½ $\widehat{AC}$.	2. Why?
3. ∠ *y* ≐ ½ $\widehat{AC}$.	3. Why?
4. ∴ ∠ *y* = ∠ *ACD*.	4. Why?
5. But ∠ *x* = ∠ *ACD*.	5. Why?
6. ∴ ∠ *x* = ∠ *y*.	6. Why?

352. Notation in a Triangle. It is convenient to denote certain points and lines connected with the triangle by definite letters. In a △ ABC, the sides opposite ∡ A, B, and C are denoted by a, b, and c respectively; the altitudes by h_a, h_b, h_c; the medians by m_a, m_b, m_c; the bisectors of the angles by t_a, t_b, t_c; and the radii of the circumcircle and incircle by R and r respectively. In a right triangle, ∠ C denotes the right angle and c the hypotenuse.

353. Analysis of a Problem. The *analysis* of a problem consists in an assumption that the problem is solved, the drawing of a figure approximately satisfying the given conditions, and an investigation of the relation among the given and the unknown parts.

354. Loci in Construction. In many cases the solution of a construction problem depends on the finding of a point which satisfies certain conditions. A thorough knowledge of the theorems on loci often makes it possible to discover immediately where the required point is to be located.

Example. Construct a right triangle, given the hypotenuse and the altitude on the hypotenuse.

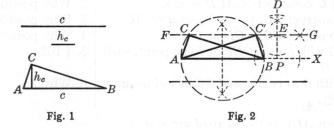

Fig. 1   Fig. 2

Given the hypotenuse c and the altitude h_c.

To construct the rt. △.

Analysis. 1. The drawing when completed will appear as in Fig. 1.

2. Since h_c is given and we know it is ⊥ AB, the vertex of the rt. ∠ must lie on a line ∥ AB at the distance h_c from it. (§ 321 b.)

3. We know that the locus of the vertex of a rt. △ with a given hypotenuse as the base is a ⊙ upon the hypotenuse as a diameter. (§ 326.)

4. ∴ C will lie on the intersection of two loci.

Construction: *STATEMENTS*   *REASONS*

1. On any line AX construct $AB = c$.	1. Why possible?
2. Construct a $\odot$ on AB as a diameter.	2. Why possible?
3. At any point on AX, as P, construct $PD \perp AX$.	3. Why possible?
4. On PD construct $PE = h_c$.	4. Why possible?
5. Through E construct $FG \parallel AX$.	5. Why possible?
6. Let C and C' be the points where the $\odot$ and FG intersect.	6. § 347.
7. Join C to A and B, and C' to A and B.	7. Why possible?

Then either $\triangle ABC$ or $\triangle ABC'$ is the required $\triangle$.

Proof:

In $\triangle ABC$ or $\triangle ABC'$,	
1. AB is the required hypotenuse.	1. Const.
2. PE is the required altitude.	2. Const.
3. $\angle ACB$ or $\angle AC'B$ is a rt. $\angle$.	3. § 299.

Discussion.

1. The construction shows two right triangles having $h_c < \frac{1}{2} c$.

2. If the complete locus of step 2 in the analysis had been drawn in the construction, two other right triangles fulfilling the given conditions could have been drawn.

3. If $h_c = \frac{1}{2} c$, there would be two right triangles, one above AB and one below AB.

4. If $h_c > \frac{1}{2} c$, there would be no solution. Why?

CONSTRUCTION EXERCISES

A

Construct a right triangle, given

1. The altitude on the hypotenuse and one acute angle.

2. An acute angle and the radius of the circumcircle.

3. A leg and the altitude on the hypotenuse.

4. A leg and the radius of the circumcircle.

Construct an isosceles triangle, given

5. The altitude on the base and a base angle.

6. One of the equal sides and the altitude on it.

Construct an isosceles triangle, given

7. The base and the radius of the circumcircle.
8. The base and the radius of the incircle.

Construct a triangle, given

9. The base, altitude, and an angle at the base.
10. The base, altitude, and one of the other sides.
11. One side and the altitude and median on it.
12. Two sides and the altitude on the third side.
13. The base, the median on the base, and one of the other sides.

Construct a parallelogram, given

14. One angle, one side, and the altitude on that side.

Construct an isosceles trapezoid, given

15. One base, the diagonal, and the angle included by them.

Construct a circle that

16. Has a given radius and is tangent to a given circle at a given point.

17. Is tangent to a given line at a given point and has its center on another given line.

18. Is tangent to two given intersecting lines, to one of them at a given point.

B

Construct a right triangle, given

19. Both the altitude and the median on the hypotenuse.
20. A leg and the radius of the incircle.

Construct an isosceles triangle, given

21. The vertex angle and the radius of the circumcircle.

22. The base and the altitude on one of the equal sides.

23. The perimeter and the altitude on the base. (See the figure at the right.)

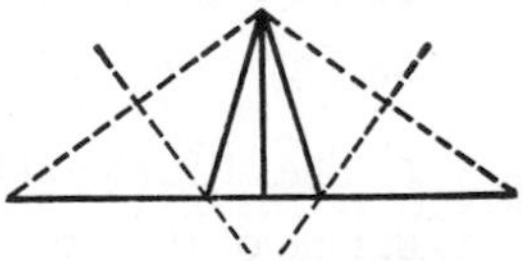

24. The vertex angle and the radius of the incircle.

Construct an equilateral triangle, given

25. The radius of the incircle.   **26.** The radius of the circumcircle.

Construct a triangle, given

27. Two angles and the altitude on the side included by the angles.

28. One side, an adjacent angle, and the radius of the circumcircle.

29. An angle, the bisector of the angle, and the altitude on a side adjacent to the angle.

30. The midpoints of the three sides.
SUGGESTION. Join the three points and see § 187.

31. Two angles and the radius of the incircle.
SUGGESTION. ∠ A + ∠ a = 180°.

Ex. 31

32. The three medians.

33. One side, an adjacent angle, and the radius of the incircle.

34. Construct an isosceles trapezoid, given the bases and diagonal.

35. Construct a circle that is tangent to two given intersecting lines and has a given radius.

C

Construct a right triangle, given

36. The segments of the hypotenuse made by the bisector of the right angle.

37. An acute angle and the radius of the incircle.

38. The sum of the legs and an acute angle.

Construct a triangle, given

39. The base, the median on the base, and the vertex angle.

40. The base, the angle at the vertex, and one of the other sides.

41. Two angles and the perimeter. (See the figure at the right.)

42. The base, altitude, and vertex angle.

43. One side and the two medians on the other two sides.

44. One side, an adjacent angle, and the sum of the other two sides. (See the figure at the right.)

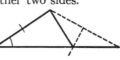

Construct a triangle, given

45. One side, an adjacent angle, and the difference of the other two sides.

46. Two sides and the median on the third side.

SUGGESTION. The diagonals of a ▱ bisect each other.

Construct a circle that

47. Has a given radius and is tangent to two given unequal circles.

48. Is tangent to two given parallel lines and passes through a given point between the parallels.

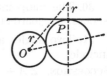

49. Is tangent to a given circle and also is tangent to a given line at a given point. (In the figure, O is the given circle.)

50. Is tangent to a given circle at a given point and passes through a given external point.

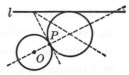

51. Is tangent to a given line and is also tangent to a given circle at a given point. (In the figure, O is the given circle.)

52. Is tangent to two equal circles and has a given radius.

MISCELLANEOUS CONSTRUCTIONS AND LOCI [C]

53. Construct a line tangent to a given circle and perpendicular to a given line.

54. Construct a line tangent to a given circle and parallel to a given line.

55. Construct a line passing through a given point and making equal angles with two given lines.

56. Given the three radii, construct three circles, each tangent externally to the other two.

57. Construct four equal circles inside a square, each tangent to one side of the square and to two of the circles.

58. Through one vertex of a triangle draw two lines, each of which is equidistant from the other two vertices.

59. Construct the bisector of the angle between two given nonparallel lines without extending them to their point of intersection.

60. Construct a right triangle, given the radii of the incircle and the circumcircle

61. Construct a common external tangent to two given circles. (See the figure at the right.)

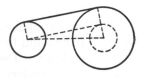

62. Construct a common internal tangent to two given circles.

63. Three lines are concurrent. Construct a line segment terminating in the outer two and bisected by the inner one.

64. Inscribe in a given circle a rectangle with one side equal to a given line segment.

65. Inscribe a circle in a given square.

66. Inscribe a circle in a given rhombus.

67. In a given sector of a circle inscribe another circle.

68. In a given circle inscribe three equal circles each tangent to two others and to the given circle.

69. Construct a tangent to a given circle without using any points or lines within the circle.

70. Determine the locus of the orthocenters of acute triangles with a given base and a given vertex angle.

71. Determine the locus of the centroids of triangles with a given base and a given vertex angle.

72. Determine the locus of points of contact of tangents drawn from a given point to a series of concentric circles.

73. Determine the locus of the center of a circle as it rolls around the sides of a given square.

74. Perform the following construction without proof:

Draw a large scalene triangle RST. Construct the perpendicular bisectors of the sides and call the circumcenter C. Construct the altitudes RA, SB, and TE, and call the orthocenter O. Draw CO. Find by construction G, H, I, and N, the midpoints of RO, SO, TO, and CO respectively. With N as a center and $\frac{1}{2}$ the circumradius as a radius, draw a circle. This circle, called the *nine-point circle* of the triangle, will pass through points E, G, B, I, A, H, and the midpoints of the sides of the triangle. The circumcenter, orthocenter, nine-point center, and the centroid of the triangle lie on a line known as *Euler's line*.

355. Loci in Space. The loci we have studied have consisted of points and lines in a plane. In space a locus may also include surfaces. The more common surfaces are planes, spheres, and cylinders. In space geometry we cannot actually construct points fulfilling a given condition but must visualize where they lie.

Example. What is the locus of points in space equidistant from two parallel planes m and n?

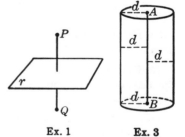

Solution. If we think of the top of a desk and the ceiling, and then visualize several points midway between the two, we reach the conclusion that the locus is a plane r parallel to m and n and midway between them.

EXERCISES. SPACE LOCI

State without proof the following loci:

1. The locus of points in space equidistant from two given points P and Q.

2. The locus of points in space at a given distance from a given point.

3. The locus of points in space at a given distance d from a given line AB.

4. The locus of points in space at a given distance from a given plane.

Ex. 1   **Ex. 3**

5. The locus of points in space equidistant from all points on a circle.

6. The locus of points in space equidistant from the vertices of a triangle.

7. The locus of points in space at the distances d and d' respectively from two given points O and O'.

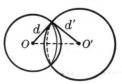

Official U. S. Navy Photograph

A Navigator at Work in a Large Navy Plane

356. Mathematics in Aviation.* The average person usually
does not appreciate the large part mathematics has taken in
air navigation.

The flying of small aircraft on short flights does not require
the use of much mathematics. For this kind of flying a good
course in arithmetic is sufficient. The pilot should know how
to read the panel instruments and to use charts and maps,
and should be able to make mental computations quickly.

For transcontinental and ocean flights much more training
in mathematics is needed. Both pilot and navigator should be
good in mathematics. They should have had one and one half
years of algebra, plane and solid geometry, and trigonometry.

Geometry is used in plotting a course; in finding the drift
angle, the bearing of a point, and the radius of action; in
establishing a fix (finding one's position); and in the interception of another moving body.

Spherical trigonometry is required for celestial navigation,
which is done by observing the position of the sun, moon, stars,
and planets.

* Pages 495–503 on aeronautics may be studied at this time.

EXERCISES IN INDIRECT REASONING (Optional)

1. On a certain passenger train three passengers and the conductor engaged in a conversation. The following facts were given:

a. The names of the passengers were Smith, Jones, and Robinson.

b. The conductor said that these names were the names of his crew, which consisted of engineer, fireman, and brakeman.

c. Mr. Robinson said that he lived in Detroit.

d. The conductor said that his engineer lived halfway between Chicago and Detroit.

e. Mr. Jones said that he earned $8000 a year.

f. The conductor said that his fireman always lost at billiards to Smith, one of the crew members.

g. One of the three passengers lived next door to the engineer and received exactly three times as much salary as the brakeman.

h. The engineer had the same name as the passenger living in Chicago.

What is the brakeman's name? Give proof.

2. Three boys, *A*, *B*, and *C*, of above average thinking ability applied to Mr. X for a position. The boys' qualifications were apparently equal; so Mr. X placed the boys in a circle facing the center. He blindfolded them and said, "I will place either a black or a white cross on each of your heads. As soon as anyone sees a black cross he is to sit down." He removed the blindfolds and all three boys sat down. Then Mr. X said, "If you know the color of the cross on your head, stand up and explain why you know." After a few minutes *A* stood up and said he had a black cross on his forehead. How did *A* know that he had a black cross?

REVIEW QUESTIONS

1. What is the definition of a locus of points?

2. Name the steps in determining a locus.

3. State the three postulates on loci.

4. What is the locus of points equidistant from the sides of an angle?

5. What is the locus of points equidistant from two given points?

6. What is the locus of the vertex of a right triangle having a fixed hypotenuse as a base?

7. What is the locus of the centers of all circles tangent to a given line at a given point?

8. What are the two steps necessary in proving that a geometric figure is a locus?

9. What is a compound locus?

10. In this chapter you have studied four centers of a triangle. Name and define each.

11. How many circles can be drawn through three points not in a straight line?

12. In how many points may two circles intersect?

13. Define incircle and circumcircle.

14. What figure is formed by the arc of a circle and its chord?

15. Into what ratio does the centroid of a triangle divide a median?

16. What are concentric circles?

17. On what line is the distance from a point to a circle measured?

18. What is the locus of points equidistant from two equal circles that are tangent externally?

19. What is the locus of the midpoint of the leg BC of a right triangle ABC whose hypotenuse is AC?

20. Find the inradius of equilateral $\triangle ABC$ if $AB = 8$ inches.

SUMMARY OF PRINCIPAL METHODS OF PROOF

357. *Loci*

a. The locus of points within an angle equidistant from the sides is the bisector of the angle.

b. The locus of points equidistant from two given intersecting lines is the pair of lines bisecting the angles formed by the given lines.

c. The locus of points equidistant from two given points is the perpendicular bisector of the line segment joining the two points.

d. The locus of the vertex of a right triangle with a given hypotenuse as the base is the circle upon the hypotenuse as a diameter.

e. The locus of the centers of all circles tangent to a given line at a given point is the perpendicular to the line at that point.

358. *Concurrent line theorems*

a. The perpendicular bisectors of the sides of a triangle are concurrent in a point equidistant from the vertices.

b. The bisectors of the angles of a triangle are concurrent in a point equidistant from the sides.

c. The altitudes of a triangle are concurrent.

d. The medians of a triangle are concurrent in a point which lies two thirds of the distance from each vertex to the midpoint of the opposite side.

359. *Constructions*

a. To circumscribe a circle about a given triangle.

b. To inscribe a circle in a given triangle.

c. Upon a given line segment as a chord to construct an arc of a circle in which a given angle can be inscribed.

WORD LIST

Can you spell and use each of the following words?

centroid	circumradius	incenter	loci
circumcenter	concentric	incircle	locus
circumcircle	concurrent	inradius	orthocenter

TEST 27

True-False Statements (*Twelve Minutes*)

Copy the numbers of these statements on your paper. Then if a statement is *always* true, write T after its number. If a statement is *not always* true, write F after its number.

1. The locus of points 3 inches from a given point *P* is a circle with the given point as center and a radius of 3 inches.

2. The locus of points 5 inches from a given line is two lines each parallel to the given line and 5 inches from the given line.

3. The locus of points equidistant from two given parallel lines is a line perpendicular to each of the given lines.

4. The locus of points equidistant from two given points is two circles whose centers are the given points and whose radii are equal to one half the line segment joining the given points.

5. The locus of the centers of all circles tangent to both sides of an angle is the bisector of the angle.

6. The locus of the vertex of the right angle of all right triangles constructed on the same hypotenuse is a line parallel to the hypotenuse.

7. The locus of the midpoints of all chords of a given circle *O* passing through a given point *P* within the circle is a circle whose diameter is *PO*.

8. The locus of the centers of all circles tangent to a given line at a given point is the perpendicular to the line at that point.

9. The medians of a triangle are concurrent in a point that is equidistant from the three vertices of the triangle.

10. The altitudes of a triangle are concurrent in a point equidistant from the sides of the triangle.

11. Only one circle may be drawn through three points not in a straight line.

12. Two circles are concentric if one lies within the other.

TEST 28

Constructions (*Twenty-five Minutes*)

Make the following geometric constructions as accurately as you can:

1. Construct the medians of a given triangle.

2. Construct a circle through three given points not in a straight line.

3. Construct the locus of points equidistant from two given points.

4. Construct a circle tangent to the sides of a given triangle.

5. With a given radius, construct a circle tangent to two given unequal circles which are tangent externally.

State Capitol at Lincoln, Nebraska. This Beautiful Building Is an Excellent Example of the Use of Proportional Lines

CHAPTER XI

Proportion and Proportional Line Segments

360. Ratios. In Chapter VII you learned that the ratio of one number to another is the quotient obtained by dividing the first by the second.

For example, the ratio of 3 to 4 is $\frac{3}{4}$, or 3 : 4. In this book the ratio is usually written in the form of a fraction.

361. Proportion. A *proportion* is an equation whose two members are ratios. Thus $\frac{x}{3} = \frac{5}{9}$ is a proportion. The proportion $\frac{x}{3} = \frac{5}{9}$ may be read "x divided by 3 equals 5 divided by 9" or "x is to 3 as 5 is to 9." The word "as" in this case means "equals."

362. Terms of a Proportion. The four quantities which form a proportion are called its terms. Since the proportion $\frac{a}{b} = \frac{c}{d}$ may be written $a : b = c : d$, a is called the *first term*, b the *second term*, c the *third term*, and d the *fourth term*. The second and third terms, being in the middle, are called the *means*, and the first and fourth terms are called the *extremes*.

363. Fourth Proportional. The *fourth proportional* to three given quantities is the fourth term of the proportion whose first three terms are the three quantities taken in order. Thus in the proportion $\frac{a}{b} = \frac{c}{d}$, d is the fourth proportional to a, b, and c.

364. Mean Proportional and Third Proportional. When the means of a proportion are equal, either mean is said to be the *mean proportional* between the first and fourth terms of the proportion. Also, the fourth term is said to be the *third proportional* to the first and second terms.

Thus in the proportion $\frac{a}{b} = \frac{b}{c}$, b is the mean proportional between a and c, and c is the third proportional to a and b.

EXERCISES [A]

Express each of the following ratios in lowest terms:

1. $\frac{8}{12}$.

2. $\frac{10}{25}$.

3. $\frac{m^2}{2\,m}$.

4. $\frac{3\,xy}{12\,x^2y}$.

5. $15\,abc : 18\,b^2$.

6. $\frac{x^2 - 7\,x + 12}{4\,x^2 - 12\,x}$.

Which of the following are proportions?

7. $\frac{4}{5} = \frac{12}{15}$.

8. $\frac{5}{7} = \frac{25}{35}$.

9. $\frac{3}{4} = \frac{9}{16}$

10. $\frac{11}{12} = \frac{10}{11}$.

11. $\frac{ab}{b^2} = \frac{a}{b}$.

12. $\frac{x}{1} = \frac{6\,x}{6}$.

13. Is 6 a ratio? Is $\frac{6}{1}$ a ratio?

Find the value of x in each of the following proportions:

14. $\frac{x}{12} = \frac{4}{3}$.

15. $\frac{8}{x} = \frac{24}{9}$.

16. $\frac{x+3}{4} = \frac{7}{5}$.

17. $\frac{x}{5-x} = \frac{7}{8}$.

18. $\frac{2\,x - 1}{3} = \frac{3}{1}$.

19. $\frac{3\,x + 2}{5} = \frac{x - 4}{4}$.

20. $\frac{x}{a} = \frac{b}{c}$.

21. $\frac{x}{4} = \frac{4}{x}$.

22. $\frac{bx}{3} = \frac{b}{6}$.

23. Tell what are the first, second, third, and fourth terms of the proportion $\frac{3}{4} = \frac{6}{8}$; of the proportion $(a + b) : (c + d) = m : n$; of the proportion $(a^2 + 1) : a = (a - 1) : 5$.

24. Tell what terms are the means and what terms are the extremes in $\frac{5}{6} = \frac{15}{18}$; in $\frac{4\,x}{5} = \frac{7}{8}$; in $\frac{a^2}{b} = \frac{c}{d}$.

25. Write a proportion stating that x is the mean proportional between 4 and 9.

26. Write the proportion stating that 32 is the third proportional to 2 and 8.

27. Solve for x:

a. $1 : 7 = 4 : x$. c. $5 : (x - 3) = 2 : (2x + 1)$.

b. $7 : 21 = x : 6$. d. $12.5 : x = x : 2$.

[Fundamental theorems on proportion]

365.* *In a proportion the product of the extremes is equal to the product of the means.*

Given $\dfrac{a}{b} = \dfrac{c}{d}$.

To prove that $ad = bc$.

Proof:

STATEMENTS	REASONS
1. $\dfrac{a}{b} = \dfrac{c}{d}$.	1. Given.
2. $bd \times \dfrac{a}{b} = bd \times \dfrac{c}{d}$, or $ad = bc$.	2. Ax. 3.

366. *If the product of two quantities is equal to the product of two other quantities, either pair may be made the means of a proportion and the other pair the extremes.*

Given $ad = bc$.

To prove that $\dfrac{a}{b} = \dfrac{c}{d}$.

SUGGESTION. By what must you divide both members of $ad = bc$ to obtain $\dfrac{a}{b} = \dfrac{c}{d}$?

367. *If the numerators of a proportion are equal, the denominators are equal; and conversely.*

Given $\dfrac{a}{x} = \dfrac{b}{y}$ and $a = b$.

To prove that $x = y$.

SUGGESTION. Use § 365. The converse is left to the student.

*If desired, the proofs of these theorems on proportion may be omitted.

368. *If three terms of one proportion are equal respectively to the corresponding terms of another proportion, the remaining terms are equal.*

Given $\dfrac{a}{b} = \dfrac{c}{d}$, $\dfrac{w}{x} = \dfrac{y}{z}$, $a = w$, $b = x$, and $c = y$.

To prove that $d = z$.

369. *In a series of equal ratios, the sum of the numerators is to the sum of the denominators as any numerator is to its denominator.*

Given $\dfrac{a}{b} = \dfrac{c}{d} = \dfrac{e}{f}$.   *To prove* that $\dfrac{a+c+e}{b+d+f} = \dfrac{a}{b}$.

Proof: *STATEMENTS*   *REASONS*

STATEMENTS	REASONS
1. Let $\dfrac{a}{b} = r$. Then $\dfrac{c}{d} = r$, and $\dfrac{e}{f} = r$.	1. Why?
2. Then $a = br$, $c = dr$, and $e = fr$.	2. Why?
3. $a + c + e = (b + d + f)r$.	3. Why?
4. $\therefore \dfrac{a+c+e}{b+d+f} = r$.	4. Why?
5. Then $\dfrac{a+c+e}{b+d+f} = \dfrac{a}{b}$.	5. Why?

370.* *In a proportion the means may be interchanged; or in a proportion the terms are in proportion by alternation.*

Given $\dfrac{a}{b} = \dfrac{c}{d}$.   *To prove* $\dfrac{a}{c} = \dfrac{b}{d}$.

SUGGESTION. First use § 365, and second, § 366.

371. *In a proportion the ratios may be inverted;* that is, the second term is to the first term as the fourth term is to the third term.

Given $\dfrac{a}{b} = \dfrac{c}{d}$.   *To prove* that $\dfrac{b}{a} = \dfrac{d}{c}$.

*Also, the extremes of a proportion can be interchanged.

372. *In a proportion the terms are in proportion by addition or subtraction*; that is, the sum (or difference) of the first and second terms is to the second term as the sum (or difference) of the third and fourth terms is to the fourth term.

Given $\dfrac{a}{b} = \dfrac{c}{d}$.

To prove that $\dfrac{a+b}{b} = \dfrac{c+d}{d}$ and $\dfrac{a-b}{b} = \dfrac{c-d}{d}$.

SUGGESTIONS. $\dfrac{a}{b} + 1 = \dfrac{c}{d} + 1$. Why? Then $\dfrac{a+b}{b} = \dfrac{c+d}{d}$. Why?

EXERCISES [A]. PROPORTIONS

1. If the second and third terms of a proportion are alike, what is each of these terms called?

2. Name the extremes and the means in the proportion $m : n = s : t$.

3. Can you suggest any way of remembering which terms of a proportion form the means? the extremes?

4. Solve the following proportions for x:

a. $\dfrac{4}{x} = \dfrac{5}{7}$.

c. $\dfrac{x-5}{x+3} = \dfrac{1}{5}$.

e. $\dfrac{x^2-6}{x^2} = \dfrac{1}{x}$.

b. $\dfrac{2x}{3} = \dfrac{7}{8}$.

d. $\dfrac{4}{x} = \dfrac{x}{16}$.

f. $\dfrac{a+b}{b} = \dfrac{a+x}{x}$.

5. If $\dfrac{m}{n} = \dfrac{r}{s}$ and $\dfrac{m}{n} = \dfrac{r}{t}$, why does $s = t$?

6. Find the mean proportional between 9 and 16; 7 and 63.

7. Find the fourth proportional to

a. 2, 3, and 4.   b. 4, 6, and 10.   c. $\frac{1}{2}$, $\frac{1}{3}$, and $\frac{1}{4}$.   d. m, n, and p.

8. From each of the following proportions, form another proportion by inversion:

a. $\dfrac{2}{5} = \dfrac{14}{35}$.

c. $\dfrac{14}{9} = \dfrac{35}{22.5}$.

e. $\dfrac{a+b}{b} = \dfrac{c+d}{d}$.

b. $\dfrac{8}{3} = \dfrac{24}{9}$.

d. $\dfrac{m}{n} = \dfrac{s}{t}$.

f. $x : 3 = y : 5$.

9. From each of the proportions in Ex. 8, form another proportion (a) by interchanging the means; (b) by addition; (c) by subtraction.

EXERCISES [A]. RATIOS

1. Using § 366, find the ratio of x to y in each of the following:

a. $2x = 3y$ *c.* $4x = y$ *e.* $\frac{3}{5}x = \frac{7}{8}y$ *g.* $x(a+b) = y(c+d)$

b. $5x = 7y$ *d.* $x = \frac{1}{5}y$ *f.* $ax = by$ *h.* $mx + ny = rx + sy$

2. Find the ratio of x to y if

a. $3x = 4y$.   *b.* $mx = 5y$.   *c.* $x = 4y$.   *d.* $y = 7x$.

373. Commensurable and Incommensurable Quantities.

Two quantities of the same kind are *commensurable* if there is a common unit of measure that is contained in each of them an integral number of times. Thus 2 feet and 3 feet 7 inches are commensurable, since 1 inch is contained in each of them an integral number of times; 5 inches and $2\frac{7}{8}$ inches are commensurable, since $\frac{1}{8}$ inch is contained 40 times in 5 inches and 23 times in $2\frac{7}{8}$ inches.

Two quantities of the same kind are *incommensurable* when there is no common unit of measure which is contained in each of them an integral number of times. Thus 4 and $\sqrt{3}$ are incommensurable, since there is no number, however small, which is contained in each of them an integral number of times. 4 and $\sqrt{3}$ have no common divisor.

NOTE. In this text we prove theorems for the commensurable case only, and assume that the theorems are true for the incommensurable case.

374. Ratio of Geometric Quantities.

The *ratio of two geometric quantities* of the same kind is equal to the ratio of their numerical measures. In the figure the unit of measure d is exactly contained 3 times in AB and 5 times in CD. Therefore the ratio $\dfrac{AB}{CD} = \dfrac{3}{5}$.

375. Line Segments in Proportion.

Two line segments are *divided proportionally* when the segments of one have the same ratio as the corresponding segments of the other. Thus in the figure of Ex. 6 on page 349, CA and CB are divided proportionally if $\dfrac{CD}{DA} = \dfrac{CE}{EB}$; or $\dfrac{DA}{DC} = \dfrac{EB}{EC}$.

EXERCISES [A]. RATIOS

1. Name three common units of measure which are contained an integral number of times in each of the following:

   a. 4 feet and 12 feet.   *c.* $\frac{1}{2}$ foot and $\frac{1}{3}$ foot.

   b. 8 centimeters and 6 centimeters.   *d.* 4.3 inches and 5.4 inches.

2. Find a common unit of measure of

   a. 1 inch and 1.4 inches.   *c.* 1 inch and 1.414 inches.

   b. 1 inch and 1.41 inches.   *d.* 1 inch and 1.4142 inches.

3. The diagonal of a square 1 inch on a side is $\sqrt{2}$ inches. Are the side and diagonal of a square commensurable?

4. Are $\sqrt{2}$ and $\sqrt{3}$ commensurable?

5. Are $\sqrt{4}$ and 3 commensurable?

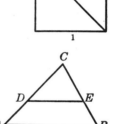

6. In $\triangle ABC$ at the right, $\dfrac{CD}{DA} = \dfrac{CE}{EB}$. Transform this proportion by alternation; by inversion. Transform it by addition and then substitute single line segments in the numerators.

7. In $\triangle ABC$, MN is drawn parallel to AB; d is contained four times in MC and three times in AM. To what numerical ratio is $\dfrac{MC}{AM}$ equal? The dash lines are parallel to AB. Are they parallel to each other? Why? Are the seven segments of BC equal to each other? Why? To what numerical ratio is $\dfrac{NC}{BN}$ equal? Is $\dfrac{MC}{AM} = \dfrac{NC}{BN}$? Why? Are the segments of BC equal to the segments of AC?

8. In the figure of Ex. 7, what is the ratio of $\dfrac{CM}{CA}$? of $\dfrac{CN}{CB}$? of $\dfrac{AM}{AC}$? of $\dfrac{BN}{BC}$?

9. In the figure of Ex. 7, show that $\dfrac{CM}{CA} = \dfrac{CN}{CB}$.

10. If $\dfrac{x-3}{4} = \dfrac{c}{2}$, then $\dfrac{x+1}{4} = \dfrac{c+2}{2}$. Why?

★★Proposition I. Theorem

376. *If a line is parallel to one side of a triangle and intersects the other two sides, it divides these sides proportionally.*

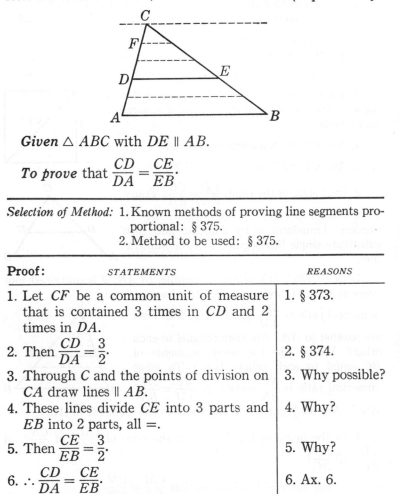

Given △ ABC with DE ∥ AB.

To prove that $\dfrac{CD}{DA} = \dfrac{CE}{EB}$.

Selection of Method: 1. Known methods of proving line segments proportional: § 375.
2. Method to be used: § 375.

Proof: STATEMENTS   REASONS

1. Let *CF* be a common unit of measure that is contained 3 times in *CD* and 2 times in *DA*.	1. § 373.
2. Then $\dfrac{CD}{DA} = \dfrac{3}{2}$.	2. § 374.
3. Through *C* and the points of division on *CA* draw lines ∥ *AB*.	3. Why possible?
4. These lines divide *CE* into 3 parts and *EB* into 2 parts, all =.	4. Why?
5. Then $\dfrac{CE}{EB} = \dfrac{3}{2}$.	5. Why?
6. ∴ $\dfrac{CD}{DA} = \dfrac{CE}{EB}$.	6. Ax. 6.
7. ∴ *AC* and *BC* are divided proportionally.	7. § 375.

NOTE. The proof is the same if any numbers other than 3 and 2 are used.

377. Corollary I. *If a line is parallel to one side of a triangle and intersects the other two sides, it divides these sides so that either side is to one of its segments as the other side is to its corresponding segment.*

SUGGESTION. Use §§ 376 and 372.

378. Corollary II. *Parallel lines intercept proportional segments on two transversals.*

SUGGESTIONS. Draw *BE*.

Does $\dfrac{m}{n} = \dfrac{x}{y}$?   Does $\dfrac{r}{s} = \dfrac{x}{y}$?   Does $\dfrac{m}{n} = \dfrac{r}{s}$?

EXERCISES

A

1. In § 376, if *CD* is twice *DA*, what is true of *CE* and *EB*?

2. In § 376, if *CD* is two thirds of *CA*, what is true of *CE* and *CB*?

3. In § 376, if $CD = 6$ inches, $DA = 3$ inches, and $CE = 8$ inches, find *EB*.

4. In § 376, if $CA = 10$ feet, $CD = 6$ feet, and $CE = 7\frac{1}{2}$ feet, find *CB*.

5. In § 376, if $CE = 12$, $EB = 8$, and $CA = 15$, find *CD* and *DA*.

6. In § 378, if $AC = 5$, $CE = 8$, and $BD = 12$, find *DF*.

B

7. Determine the locus of the midpoints of line segments drawn from a given point to a given line.

8. The nonparallel sides of a trapezoid are 10 inches and 15 inches respectively. A line parallel to the bases divides the 10-inch side in the ratio of 1 to 4. Find the segments of the 15-inch side.

C

9. A line drawn through the centroid of a triangle and parallel to one side divides each of the other two sides into segments having the ratio of 2 to 1.

10. The nonparallel sides of a trapezoid are 6 inches and 9 inches respectively. A line parallel to the bases divides the longer diagonal in the ratio of 3 to 4. Find the segments of the nonparallel sides.

★★Proposition II. Problem

379. *To construct the fourth proportional to three given line segments.*

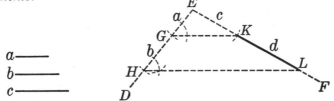

a——

b——

c——

Given the line segments a, b, and c.

To construct a line segment d so that $\dfrac{a}{b} = \dfrac{c}{d}$.

Construction: STATEMENTS	REASONS
1. Draw any $\angle DEF$; on ED construct $EG = a$ and $GH = b$; and on EF construct $EK = c$.	1. Why possible?
2. Draw GK.	2. Why possible?
3. Through H construct $HL \parallel GK$.	3. Why possible?

Then $\dfrac{a}{b} = \dfrac{c}{d}$.

Proof:

1. $GK \parallel HL$.	1. Why?
2. $\dfrac{EG}{GH} = \dfrac{EK}{KL}$.	2. Why?
3. $\therefore \dfrac{a}{b} = \dfrac{c}{d}$.	3. Why?

EXERCISES [A]. CONSTRUCTIONS

1. Construct the fourth proportional to three given line segments which are 2, 5, and 3 inches in length respectively. Measure the resulting segment and check by solving the proportion $\dfrac{2}{5} = \dfrac{3}{x}$ by algebra.

2. Given $\dfrac{2}{x} = \dfrac{3}{4}$. Find x by construction; by algebra.

★Proposition III. Problem

380. *To divide a given line segment into two parts which are proportional to two given line segments.*

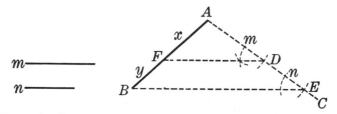

Given the line segment AB and the line segments m and n.

To divide AB into segments, x and y, so that $\dfrac{x}{y} = \dfrac{m}{n}$.

Construction:

STATEMENTS	REASONS
1. Through A draw any line AC.	1. Why possible?
2. On AC construct $AD = m$ and $DE = n$.	2. Why possible?
3. Draw BE.	3. Why possible?
4. Through D construct $DF \parallel BE$.	4. Why possible?

Then $\dfrac{x}{y} = \dfrac{m}{n}$.

Proof:

1. $FD \parallel BE$.	1. Why?
2. $\therefore \dfrac{AF}{FB} = \dfrac{AD}{DE}$.	2. Why?
3. $\therefore \dfrac{x}{y} = \dfrac{m}{n}$.	3. Why?

EXERCISES [B]. CONSTRUCTIONS

1. Divide a line segment 3 inches long into segments having the ratio of 2 to 5.

2. Construct x, given $\dfrac{2}{3} = \dfrac{3}{x}$. What proportional is 3 to 2 and x? What proportional is x to 2 and 3?

★★Proposition IV. Problem

381. *To divide a given line segment into n parts which are proportional to n given line segments.*

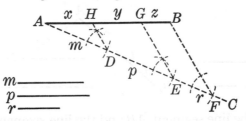

Given the line segment AB and line segments m, p, and r.

To divide AB into segments x, y, and z so that $\dfrac{x}{m} = \dfrac{y}{p} = \dfrac{z}{r}$.

Construction: STATEMENTS   REASONS

1. Through A draw any line AC.	1. Why possible?
2. On AC construct $AD = m$, $DE = p$, and $EF = r$.	2. Why possible?
3. Draw FB.	3. Why possible?
4. Through E construct $EG \parallel FB$.	4. Why possible?
5. Through D construct $DH \parallel FB$.	5. Why possible?

Then $\dfrac{x}{m} = \dfrac{y}{p} = \dfrac{z}{r}$.

(The proof is left to the student. See § 378.)

NOTE. In the construction above, $n = 3$. The same method is used when n has other values.

EXERCISES [B]

1. Construct the third proportional to two given line segments, a and b.

2. Divide a given line segment into parts proportional to 1, 2, and 3.

3. Divide the base of a triangle into segments proportional to the other two sides.

4. Trisect a given line segment.

★★Proposition V. Theorem

382. *If a line divides two sides of a triangle proportionally it is parallel to the third side.*

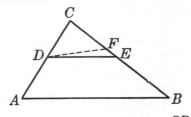

Given △ *ABC* with *DE* drawn so that $\dfrac{CD}{DA} = \dfrac{CE}{EB}$.

To prove that *DE* ‖ *AB*.

Selection of Method: 1. Known methods of proving lines ‖: §§ 143, 206.

2. Method to be used: Prove that *DE* coincides with a line ‖ *AB*.

Proof: STATEMENTS   REASONS

1. Through *D* draw *DF* ‖ *AB*, meeting *CB* at *F*.	1. Why possible?
2. Then $\dfrac{CA}{DA} = \dfrac{CB}{FB}$.	2. § 377.
3. But $\dfrac{CD}{DA} = \dfrac{CE}{EB}$.	3. Given.
4. Then $\dfrac{CA}{DA} = \dfrac{CB}{EB}$.	4. § 372.
5. From (2) and (4), *FB* = *EB*.	5. § 368.
6. ∴ *F* falls on *E* and *DF* coincides with *DE*.	6. Why?
7. ∴ *DE* ‖ *AB*.	7. Why?

★**383. Corollary.** *If a line divides two sides of a triangle so that either side is to one of its segments as the other side is to its corresponding segment, the line is parallel to the third side.* (Use subtraction, § 372, and then § 382.)

384. Internal and External Division of a Line Segment.
A line segment is *divided internally* into two segments if the point of division lies on the line segment. In the figure below, P divides the line segment AB internally into two segments, AP and PB, whose ratio is 2 to 3.

A line segment is *divided externally* into two segments if the point of division lies on the line segment extended. In this figure, P divides the line segment AB externally into segments AP and PB, whose ratio is 3 to 7.

If P is between A and B, it divides AB internally; if P is not between A and B, it divides AB externally. In either case, AP is one segment of AB and PB is the other. When a line segment is divided internally, the sum of the segments is equal to the line segment. When the line segment is divided externally, the difference of the segments is equal to the line segment.

EXERCISES

A

1. A line segment AB is divided internally into segments AP and PB. If $AP : PB = 2 : 3$, AP is what part of AB? PB is what part of AB? If $2x$ represents AP, what will represent PB?

2. With compasses and straightedge divide a given line segment internally into two segments whose ratio is 3 to 4. (See § 195.)

3. A line segment 16 inches long is divided internally into two segments which have the ratio $3 : 5$. Compute the lengths of the two segments. (Represent the segments by $3x$ and $5x$.)

B

4. A line segment AB is divided externally at P into segments AP and PB so that $AP : PB = 2 : 5$. AP is what part of AB? PB is what part of AB? If $2x$ represents AP, what will represent PB? AB?

5. A 14-inch line segment is divided externally into two segments whose ratio is $\frac{7}{9}$. Compute the lengths of the segments. (What does $9x - 7x$ equal?)

Proposition VI. Theorem

385. *The bisector of an interior angle of a triangle divides the opposite side internally into segments which are proportional to the adjacent sides.*

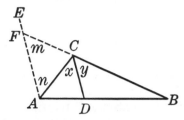

Given △ *ABC* with *CD* bisecting ∠ *ACB*.

To prove that $\dfrac{AD}{DB} = \dfrac{AC}{CB}$.

Selection of Method: 1. Known methods of proving line segments proportional: §§ 375, 376, 377, 378.
2. Method to be used: § 376.

Proof: *STATEMENTS*	*REASONS*
1. Through *A* draw *AE* ∥ *DC*.	1. Why possible?
2. Extend *BC* to meet *AE* at *F*.	2. Posts. 3, 19, 21.
3. In △ *FAB*, $\dfrac{AD}{DB} = \dfrac{FC}{CB}$.	3. Why?
4. ∠ *x* = ∠ *y*.	4. Why?
5. But ∠ *x* = ∠ *n* and ∠ *y* = ∠ *m*.	5. Two reasons.
6. ∴ ∠ *m* = ∠ *n*.	6. Why?
7. ∴ *FC* = *AC*.	7. Why?
8. From (3) and (7), $\dfrac{AD}{DB} = \dfrac{AC}{CB}$.	8. Why?

EXERCISES [A]

1. In § 385, find *AD* if *DB* = 6, *AC* = 8, and *CB* = 10.

2. In § 385, find *AC* if *CB* = 12, *AD* = 4, and *DB* = 6.

3. State and prove the converse of Prop. VI.

Proposition VII. Theorem

386. *The bisector of an exterior angle of a triangle divides the opposite side externally into segments which are proportional to the adjacent sides.*

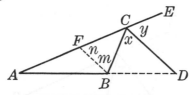

Given △ *ABC*, *AC* extended to *E*, and *CD* bisecting ∠ *BCE*.

To prove that $\dfrac{AD}{DB} = \dfrac{AC}{CB}$.

Selection of Method: 1. Known methods of proving line segments proportional: §§ 375, 376, 377, 378, 385.
2. Method to be used: § 377.

Proof: *STATEMENTS* | *REASONS*

1. Through *B* draw *BF* ∥ *DC*.	1. Why possible?
2. In △ *ADC*, $\dfrac{AD}{DB} = \dfrac{AC}{CF}$.	2. § 377.
3. ∠ *x* = ∠ *y*.	3. Why?
4. But ∠ *m* = ∠ *x* and ∠ *n* = ∠ *y*.	4. Why?
5. ∴ ∠ *m* = ∠ *n*.	5. Why?
6. ∴ *CF* = *CB*.	6. Why?
7. From (2) and (6), $\dfrac{AD}{DB} = \dfrac{AC}{CB}$.	7. Why?

387. Harmonic Division of a Line. A line segment is divided *harmonically* when it is divided internally and externally in the same ratio.

In this figure *P* and *P'* divide *AB* harmonically since $\dfrac{AP}{PB} = \dfrac{2}{1} = \dfrac{AP'}{P'B}$.

EXERCISES

B

1. In what kind of triangle is the bisector of an exterior angle parallel to one side of the triangle? Prove your answer.

2. In § 386, find AD if $DB = 12, AC = 14$, and $CB = 7$.

3. The sides of a triangle are 9, 12, and 14 inches respectively. Find the lengths of the segments into which the longest side is divided by the bisector of the opposite angle.

4. The sides of a triangle are 8, 12, and 15 inches respectively. Find the segments into which each side is divided by the bisector of the opposite angle. (Draw a figure for each computation.)

5. In $\triangle ABC$, $AB = 12$, $BC = 7$, and $AC = 10$. If the exterior angle at C is bisected, will the bisector meet the opposite side extended through B or extended through A? Find the segments of AB made by the bisector of the exterior angle at C.

6. The sides of a triangle are 4, 6, and 8. The smallest exterior angle is bisected. Find the segments into which the bisector divides the opposite side.

7. The sides of a triangle are 12, 24, and 28. Find the lengths of the segments of the side 28 made by the bisector of the opposite angle.

8. The sides of a triangle are 20, 30, and 40. Find the lengths of the segments of the longest side made by the bisector of the opposite angle.

9. By the use of Prop. VI divide a given line segment into segments having the ratio 2 : 3.

10. Construct a 30°-60° right triangle. Show that the bisector of the 60° angle divides the opposite side into segments having the ratio 2 : 1.

C

11. If two circles are tangent internally at A and a chord BC of the larger circle is tangent to the smaller circle at D, then AD bisects $\angle CAB$.

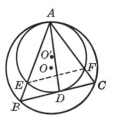

SUGGESTIONS. Prove that $EF \parallel BC$. (See Ex. 12, p. 290.) Then show that $\widehat{ED} = \widehat{DF}$.

12. *Given* $\triangle ABC$ with CP bisecting $\angle ACB$ and CP' bisecting $\angle BCE$.

Prove that AB is divided harmonically.

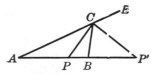

388. The Use of Analysis in Algebraic Proofs. The theorems on proportion, which were given at the beginning of this chapter, deal with principles of algebra. Although the proofs of some of them are easily forgotten, they may be easily discovered by analysis. Since the converses of these theorems are usually true, the proofs of the theorems can usually be made by first proving the converses and then reversing the order of the statements. This method is useful when the statement to be proved is more complex than the given statement.

Example. In a proportion the terms are in proportion by addition.

Given $\dfrac{a}{b} = \dfrac{c}{d}$.

To prove that $\dfrac{a+b}{b} = \dfrac{c+d}{d}$.

Proof of Converse:

STATEMENTS	REASONS
1. $\dfrac{a+b}{b} = \dfrac{c+d}{d}$.	1. Given
2. $b(c+d) = d(a+b)$.	2. § 365.
3. $bc + bd = ad + bd$.	3. Ax. 5.
4. $bc = ad$.	4. Ax. 2.
5. $\dfrac{a}{b} = \dfrac{c}{d}$.	5. § 366.

Proof of Theorem:

STATEMENTS	REASONS
1. $\dfrac{a}{b} = \dfrac{c}{d}$.	1. Given.
2. $bc = ad$.	2. § 365.
3. $bc + bd = ad + bd$.	3. Ax. 1.
4. $b(c+d) = d(a+b)$.	4. Ax. 5.
5. $\dfrac{a+b}{b} = \dfrac{c+d}{d}$.	5. § 366.

EXERCISES [B]. ALGEBRAIC PROOFS

Given $\dfrac{a}{b} = \dfrac{c}{d}$, prove:

1. $\dfrac{a-1}{b} = \dfrac{bc-d}{bd}$.

2. $\dfrac{a+1}{1} = \dfrac{bc+d}{d}$.

3. $\dfrac{a}{b} = \dfrac{c-a}{d-b}$.

4. $\dfrac{a-b}{b_{_4}} = \dfrac{c-d}{d}$.

5. $\dfrac{a+b}{a-b} = \dfrac{c+d}{c-d}$.

6. $\dfrac{a^2-b}{ac-d} = \dfrac{a}{c}$.

REVIEW EXERCISES

1. What is a ratio? a proportion?

2. Can two quantities be in proportion?

3. What are commensurable quantities? Give an example.

4. What are incommensurable quantities? Give an example.

5. Which of the following are true?

   a. $\dfrac{3}{7} = \dfrac{9}{21}$.   *b.* $\dfrac{3}{5} = \dfrac{12}{20}$.   *c.* $\dfrac{10}{3} = \dfrac{15}{6}$.   *d.* $\dfrac{7x}{5} = \dfrac{35x}{25}$.

6. State six fundamental theorems on proportion.

7. Transform $\dfrac{x}{y} = \dfrac{m}{n}$ by

   a. Alternation.   *b.* Inversion.   *c.* Addition.   *d.* Subtraction.

8. Write two proportions from $ab = cd$.

9. State the methods you have had in this chapter of proving

   a. Lines parallel.   *b.* Line segments in proportion.

10. State the propositions you have had on constructions in this chapter.

11. In the proportion $\dfrac{x}{y} = \dfrac{y}{z}$, what is y called? what is z called?

12. What is the mean proportional between 4 and 9?

13. Find the fourth proportional to 10, 15, and 18.

14. Find the third proportional to 10 and 12.

15. The sides of a triangle are 24, 36, and 40. Find the segments of the longest side made by the bisector of the opposite angle.

In △ *ACE*, *BD* ∥ *CE*.

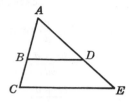

16. Find *DE* if *AB* = 6, *BC* = 4, and *AD* = 10.

17. Find *AB* if *AD* = 16, *DE* = 12, and *BC* = 8.

18. Find *AE* if *AC* = 21, *BC* = 6, and *AD* = 18.

19. A line segment 27 inches long is divided internally into two segments having the ratio 4 : 5. How long is each segment?

SUMMARY OF PRINCIPAL METHODS OF PROOF

389. *Line segments in proportion*

a. If a line is parallel to one side of a triangle and intersects the other two sides, it divides these sides proportionally.

b. If a line is parallel to one side of a triangle and intersects the other two sides, it divides these sides so that either side is to one of its segments as the other side is to its corresponding segment.

c. Parallel lines intercept proportional segments on two transversals.

d. The bisector of an interior (or exterior) angle of a triangle divides the opposite side internally (or externally) into segments which are proportional to the adjacent sides.

390. *Lines parallel*

a. If a line divides two sides of a triangle proportionally, it is parallel to the third side.

b. If a line divides two sides of a triangle so that either side is to one of its segments as the other side is to its corresponding segment, the line is parallel to the third side.

391. *Constructions*

a. To construct the fourth proportional to three given line segments.

b. To divide a line segment into parts which are proportional to two given line segments.

c. To divide a given line segment into *n* parts which are proportional to *n* given line segments.

WORD LIST

alternation	decagon	intercept	parallel
central	denominator	internal	perimeter
circumscribed	equiangular	inversion	proportion
coincide	exterior	isosceles	proportional
commensurable	hexagon	numerator	ratio
corollary	hypotenuse	octagon	series

TEST 29

True-False Statements (*Fifteen Minutes*)

Copy the numbers of these statements on your paper. Then if a statement is *always* true, place a T after its number. If a statement is *not always* true, place an F after its number. Do not guess.

1. The fraction $\frac{2}{3}$ is a proportion.

2. A ratio is an equation.

3. If $\frac{x}{y} = \frac{m}{n}$, then $xm = yn$.

4. $\frac{2}{3} = \frac{10}{15}$ is a proportion.

5. If $\frac{x}{12} = \frac{4}{3}$, then $x = 9$.

6. If $ab = cd$, then $\frac{a}{d} = \frac{c}{b}$.

7. 6 is a mean proportional between 4 and 9.

8. In the proportion $\frac{x}{y} = \frac{z}{w}$, w is the fourth proportional to x, y, and z.

9. The extremes of the proportion $\frac{7}{8} = \frac{x}{6}$ are 8 and 6.

10. If $\frac{a}{b} = \frac{c}{d}$, then $\frac{a}{c} = \frac{b}{d}$ by alternation.

11. If $\frac{x}{y} = \frac{z}{w}$, then $\frac{x}{w} = \frac{z}{y}$ by inversion.

12. If $\frac{m}{n} = \frac{r}{s}$, then $\frac{m+n}{n} = \frac{r+s}{s}$ by addition.

13. If the second and third terms of a proportion are equal, either term is a mean proportional between the first and fourth terms.

14. If the first and fourth terms of a proportion are equal, the second and third terms are equal.

15. If the first and third terms of a proportion are equal, the second and fourth terms are equal.

16. A proportion always contains two equal ratios.

17. In $\triangle ABC$, if $AC = 75$, $DC = 30$, $CE = 36$, and $BC = 90$, then $DE \parallel AB$.

18. In $\triangle ABC$, if $CD = 12$, $AD = 40$, $BE = 70$, and $EC = 21$, then $DE \parallel AB$.

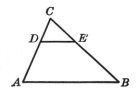

TEST 30

Applications (*Twenty Minutes*)

1. Find the fourth proportional to 2, 3, and 4.

2. Solve for x in the equation $\dfrac{2x}{5} = \dfrac{12}{10}$.

3. Transform $\dfrac{m}{6} = \dfrac{2n}{5}$ by inversion.

4. Name a measure common to 6 inches and 9 inches.

5. In the figure, $DE \parallel AB$. If $AD = 10$, $DC = 15$, and $EC = 18$, find EB.

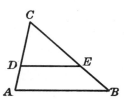

6. In the figure of Ex. 5, if $AC = 24$, $AD = 9$, and $BC = 40$, find BE.

7. In the figure of Ex. 5, if $CD = 14$, $AD = 7$, and $CB = 18$, find BE.

8. Find two complementary angles whose ratio is 2 to 3.

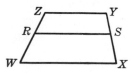

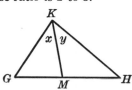

9. $WXYZ$ is a trapezoid with $RS \parallel$ base WX. If $ZR = 10$, $WR = 12$, and $YS = 8$, find SX.

10. In the figure of Ex. 9, if $YX = 27$, $ZR = 12$, and $RW = 18$, find YS.

11. In the figure, $\angle x = \angle y$. If $GK = 9$, $GM = 6$, and $KH = 12$, find MH.

12. In the figure of Ex. 11, if $GM = 10$, $GH = 25$, and $KH = 16$, find GK.

13. What is the largest common measure of one yard and one half inch?

14. If $a : b = c : d$ then $ad =$ __?__.

CHAPTER XII

Similar Polygons

392. Corresponding Angles and Corresponding Sides. So far in our study of geometry the term "corresponding angles" has been applied to the pairs of equal angles of congruent polygons and to the four pairs of angles formed by two lines and their transversal. We shall now extend the meaning of these words.

If two polygons have the same number of angles and the angles of one are equal respectively to the angles of the other, each pair of equal angles is called *corresponding angles* and the polygons are said to be *mutually equiangular*.

Likewise we shall extend the meaning of "corresponding sides." If two polygons are mutually equiangular, the sides included by corresponding angles are called *corresponding sides* of the polygons. Do you see that "corresponding" means having the same relative position?

393. Similar Polygons. *Similar polygons* are polygons which have their corresponding angles equal and their corresponding sides proportional.

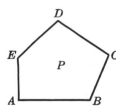

The polygons P and P' above are similar ($\sim$) if

(1) $\angle A = \angle A'$, $\angle B = \angle B'$, $\angle C = \angle C'$, $\angle D = \angle D'$, $\angle E = \angle E'$;

(2) $\dfrac{AB}{A'B'} = \dfrac{BC}{B'C'} = \dfrac{CD}{C'D'} = \dfrac{DE}{D'E'} = \dfrac{EA}{E'A'}.$

Two polygons may have their corresponding sides proportional and not be similar, or they may have their corresponding angles equal and not be similar. Thus in the figures below, P and R have their sides proportional but are not similar,

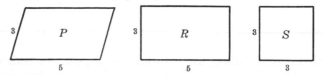

since their corresponding angles are not equal; R and S have their corresponding angles equal but are not similar, since their corresponding sides are not proportional.

394. Conditions of Similarity. From the definition of similar polygons (§ 393), it follows that for two polygons to be similar, two distinct conditions must be fulfilled:

1. The corresponding angles must be equal.

2. The corresponding sides must be proportional.

Also, since a definition is reversible, if two polygons are known to be similar, their corresponding angles are equal and their corresponding sides are proportional.

395. Ratio of Similitude. If two polygons are similar, the ratio of any two corresponding sides is called the *ratio of similitude.*

EXERCISES. SIMILAR POLYGONS

A

1. The legs of a right triangle are 5 inches and 7 inches respectively. If the shorter leg of a similar triangle is 15 inches, find the other leg.

2. The sides of a triangle are 3, 6, and 8 inches respectively. If the longest side of a similar triangle is 12 feet, find the other two sides.

3. Polygons $ABCD$ and $A'B'C'D'$ are similar. If $A'D' = 6$, find $A'B'$, $B'C'$, and $C'D'$.

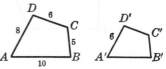

4. The sides of a pentagon are 4, 5, 6, 8, and 12 respectively. If the longest side of a similar polygon is 18, find the lengths of the remaining sides. What is the ratio of similitude of the two polygons?

5. If each side of one square is 8 inches and a side of another square is 12 inches, show that their corresponding sides are proportional. Are their corresponding angles equal? Are the two squares similar? Are all squares similar?

6. Are two congruent polygons similar? Why? Are two similar polygons congruent? Why? What is the ratio of similitude of two congruent triangles?

7. If two polygons are similar, do they have the same shape? Illustrate your answer with figures.

8. Can a pentagon be similar to a triangle? to a quadrilateral? to another pentagon?

9. If the angles of one polygon are equal respectively to the angles of another polygon, do the polygons necessarily have the same shape?

10. $\triangle ACD \sim \triangle BCD$ and the corresponding angles are indicated by like marks.

Complete:

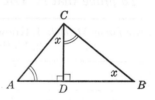

a. $AD : \_\_?\_\_ = AC : \_\_?\_\_.$
b. $AD : \_\_?\_\_ = \_\_?\_\_ : BD.$
c. $AC : \_\_?\_\_ = CD : \_\_?\_\_.$

11. *Given* $\triangle DEC \sim \triangle ABC.$

a. If $AD = 9$ inches, $DC = 15$ inches, $CE = 18$ inches, and $DE = 21$ inches, find the length of AB; of CB; of EB.

b. If $AC = 28$ feet, $AB = 35$ feet, $BC = 21$ feet, and $EC = 6$ feet, find the length of DC; of DE; of AD.

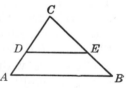

B

12. Prove that two equilateral triangles are similar.

13. Prove that two equiangular triangles are similar.

14. $ABCD$ is a square 15 inches on a side. The diagonal is 21.21 inches long. If $BE = 6$ inches and $FE \parallel AB$, what is the length of AF?

C

15. Prove that two regular polygons of the same number of sides are similar.

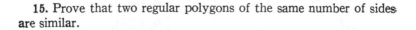

★★Proposition I. Theorem

396. *If two triangles have two angles of one equal respectively to two angles of the other, the triangles are similar.*

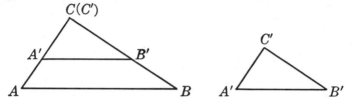

Given △ *ABC* and *A'B'C'* with ∠ *A* = ∠ *A'* and ∠ *B* = ∠ *B'*.

To prove that △ *ABC* ∼ △ *A'B'C'*.

Selection of Method: 1. Known methods of proving △ ∼: § 394.
2. Method to be used: § 394.

Proof: STATEMENTS	REASONS
1. ∠ *A* = ∠ *A'* and ∠ *B* = ∠ *B'*.	1. Given.
2. Then ∠ *C* = ∠ *C'*.	2. § 141 *c*.
3. ∴ △ *ABC* and *A'B'C'* have their corresponding angles =.	3. Statements 1 and 2.
4. Place △ *A'B'C'* on △ *ABC* so that ∠ *C'* coincides with ∠ *C*, △ *A'B'C'* taking the position *A'B'C*.	4. Why?
5. *A'B'* ∥ *AB*.	5. § 143 *b* (2).
6. ∴ $\dfrac{AC}{A'C} = \dfrac{BC}{B'C}$, or $\dfrac{AC}{A'C'} = \dfrac{BC}{B'C'}$.	6. Why?
7. In the same manner, by placing △ *A'B'C'* on △ *ABC* so that ∠ *B'* coincides with its equal ∠ *B*, it may be proved that $\dfrac{AB}{A'B'} = \dfrac{BC}{B'C'}$.	7. Reasons 4–6.
8. ∴ $\dfrac{AC}{A'C'} = \dfrac{AB}{A'B'} = \dfrac{BC}{B'C'}$.	8. Ax. 5.
9. ∴ △ *ABC* ∼ △ *A'B'C'*.	9. § 394.

397. Corollary I. *If two right triangles have an acute angle of one equal to an acute angle of the other, the triangles are similar.*

398. Corollary II. *The corresponding altitudes of two similar triangles have the same ratio as any two corresponding sides.*

SUGGESTION. Base proof on § 397.

399. Corollary III. *If two triangles are similar to a third triangle, they are similar to each other.*

400. How to Determine the Corresponding Sides of Similar Triangles. If the corresponding angles of two similar triangles are known, the corresponding sides are those which lie opposite the equal angles. Thus in the figure, if △ I ∼ △ II, ∠ m = ∠ n, and ∠ x = ∠ y, then the side *DO* being opposite ∠ m in △ I corresponds to the side *BO*, which is opposite ∠ n in △ II; also the side *AO* being opposite ∠ x in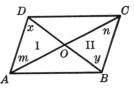
△ I corresponds to the side *CO*, which is opposite ∠ y in △ II. Why does *AD* correspond to *BC*?

Also, if the corresponding sides of two similar triangles are known, the equal angles are those which lie opposite the corresponding sides.

401. Methods of Proving Line Segments Proportional. So far we have had six principal methods of proving line segments proportional, §§ 376, 377, 378, 385, 386, and 393. Of these, the last is very essential in this chapter and the remaining chapters. It is the first of the three methods given below.

a. To prove that four line segments are proportional, show that the line segments are corresponding sides of similar triangles.

The steps in applying this method are:

1. Find two triangles each of which has two of the four segments as sides.
2. Prove that these triangles are similar.
3. Form a proportion using the fact that these line segments are corresponding sides of the similar triangles.
4. If necessary, transform the proportion.

Example 1. *Given AB and CD intersecting at E, and AC ∥ BD.*

To prove that $\dfrac{AE}{BE} = \dfrac{AC}{BD}$.

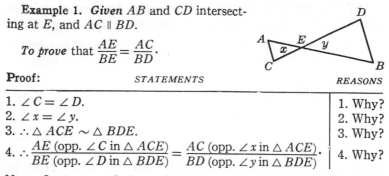

Proof:

STATEMENTS	REASONS
1. ∠ C = ∠ D.	1. Why?
2. ∠ x = ∠ y.	2. Why?
3. ∴ △ ACE ∼ △ BDE.	3. Why?
4. ∴ $\dfrac{AE \text{ (opp. } \angle C \text{ in } \triangle ACE)}{BE \text{ (opp. } \angle D \text{ in } \triangle BDE)} = \dfrac{AC \text{ (opp. } \angle x \text{ in } \triangle ACE)}{BD \text{ (opp. } \angle y \text{ in } \triangle BDE)}$.	4. Why?

NOTE. In statement 3 above, the vertices of the corresponding angles are paired, *A* with *B*, *C* with *D*, and *E* with *E*. This arrangement makes it easy to check for corresponding sides. For example, side *AC* corresponds to side *BD*. In statement 4 note that the numerators in the proportion are obtained from one triangle and the denominators from another triangle. (The expressions in parentheses are to help the student in selecting the corresponding sides. They may be omitted in written proofs.)

b. To prove that four line segments which are not sides of similar triangles are proportional, show that each of the two given ratios is equal to a third ratio.

c. To prove that a line segment is the mean proportional between two other line segments, prove that two triangles which have the first line segment as a common side are similar.

Example 2. *Given ∠ ACB a rt. ∠ and CD ⊥ AB.*

To prove that $\dfrac{AD}{AC} = \dfrac{AC}{AB}$.

Since *AC* is to be proved the mean proportional between *AD* and *AB*, we try to prove it a side common to two similar triangles.

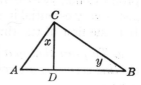

Proof:

STATEMENTS	REASONS
In △ ADC and ACB,	
1. ∠ A = ∠ A.	1. Why?
2. ∠ ADC = ∠ ACB.	2. Why?
3. ∴ △ ADC ∼ △ ACB.	3. Why?
4. ∴ $\dfrac{AD \text{ (opp. } \angle x \text{ in } \triangle ADC)}{AC \text{ (opp. } \angle y \text{ in } \triangle ACB)} = \dfrac{AC \text{ (opp. rt. } \angle \text{ in } \triangle ADC)}{AB \text{ (opp. rt. } \angle \text{ in } \triangle ACB)}$.	4. Why?

402. Methods of Proving Products of Line Segments Equal.

a. To prove that the product of two line segments is equal to the product of two other line segments, show that the segments are proportional (§ 401 *a*) *and apply* § 365.

For example, from statement 4 in Example 1 on the opposite page we know that $AE \times BD = BE \times AC$.

b. To prove that the square of one line segment is equal to the product of two others, prove that the first segment is the mean proportional between the two others (§ 401 *c*) *and then use* § 365.

For example, from statement 4 in Example 2 on the opposite site page $\overline{AC}^2 = AD \times AB$.

EXERCISES. SIMILAR TRIANGLES

A

1. In the figure, $AC = 18$, $DC = 6$, $BC = 24$, and $EC = 8$. Is $DE \parallel AB$? Does $\angle CDE = \angle A$? Does $\angle CED = \angle B$? Is $\triangle CDE \sim \triangle CAB$? CD is what part of CA? DE is what part of AB?

2. From §§ 389 and 401 state six methods of proving line segments in proportion.

3. A tower casts a shadow 120 feet long when a 20-foot telephone pole casts a shadow 15 feet long. How high is the tower?

4. *Given* $AC \perp AB$ and $BD \perp AB$.

Prove that $\dfrac{AC}{CO} = \dfrac{BD}{DO}$.

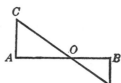

5. Triangle ABC is inscribed in a circle, AB being a diameter of the circle. ED is a perpendicular drawn from any point E on AC to AB. Prove that triangle ABC is similar to triangle ADE.

6. *Given* $\odot O$ with two chords, AB and CD, intersecting at E.

   a. Prove that $\triangle AEC \sim \triangle BED$.

   b. Prove that $\dfrac{CE}{EB} = \dfrac{AE}{ED}$.

B

7. *Given* AB tangent to a $\odot$ at B and AC a secant to the $\odot$.

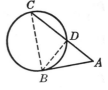

   a. *Prove that* $\triangle ABD \sim \triangle ABC$.

   b. *Prove that* $\dfrac{AC}{AB} = \dfrac{AB}{AD}$.

   c. *Prove that* $\overline{AB}^2 = AC \times AD$.

8. *Given* rt. $\triangle ABC$, in which $\angle ACB$ is the rt. $\angle$, and $CD \perp AB$.

   a. *Prove that* $\triangle ADC \sim \triangle ABC$.

   b. *Prove that* $\triangle BCD \sim \triangle ABC$.

   c. *Prove that* $\triangle ADC \sim \triangle BCD$.

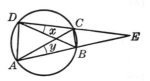

   d. *Prove that* $\dfrac{AD}{DC} = \dfrac{DC}{DB}$.

   e. *Prove that* $\overline{DC}^2 = AD \times DB$.

9. The lines joining the midpoints of the sides of a triangle form a triangle that is similar to the given triangle.

10. *Given* the inscribed quadrilateral $ABCD$ with the diagonals AC and BD, and the sides AB and DC produced to meet at E.

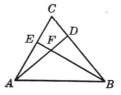

   a. *Prove that* $\triangle BDE \sim \triangle ACE$.

   b. *Prove that* $\dfrac{BD}{CA} = \dfrac{DE}{AE}$.

C

11. The bisectors of two corresponding angles of two similar triangles have the same ratio as a pair of corresponding sides.

12. The diagonals of a trapezoid divide each other so that the corresponding segments are proportional.

13. *Given* $\triangle ABC$ with two altitudes, AD and BE, intersecting at F.

   a. *Prove that* $\dfrac{AF}{BF} = \dfrac{EF}{FD}$.

   b. *Prove that* $\dfrac{AD}{BE} = \dfrac{AC}{BC}$.

★★ Proposition II. Theorem

403. *If two triangles have an angle of one equal to an angle of the other and the including sides proportional, the triangles are similar.*

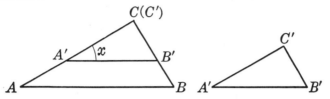

Given ⚓ *ABC* and *A'B'C'* having ∠ *C* = ∠ *C'* and $\dfrac{AC}{A'C'} = \dfrac{BC}{B'C'}$.

To prove that △ *ABC* ∼ △ *A'B'C'*.

Selection of Method: 1. Known methods of proving ⚓ ∼: §§ 394, 396, 397, 399.
2. Method to be used: § 396.

Proof: STATEMENTS	REASONS
1. Place △ *A'B'C'* on △ *ABC* so that ∠ *C'* coincides with its equal ∠ *C*, △ *A'B'C'* taking the position *A'B'C*.	1. Why?
2. $\dfrac{AC}{A'C} = \dfrac{BC}{B'C}$, or $\dfrac{AC}{A'C'} = \dfrac{BC}{B'C'}$.	2. Why?
3. ∴ *A'B'* ∥ *AB*.	3. § 390 *b*.
4. ∴ ∠ *A* = ∠ *x*, or ∠ *A'*.	4. Why?
5. ∴ △ *ABC* ∼ △ *A'B'C'*.	5. Why?

EXERCISES [A]

1. In a △ *DEF*, *DF* = 20, *DE* = 16, *EF* = 24. Between *H*, a point in *DF*, and *K*, a point in *EF*, *HK* is drawn so that *FH* = 15 and *FK* = 18. Show that △ *HKF* ∼ △ *DEF*. How long is *HK*?

2. Two isosceles triangles are similar if a base angle of one equals a base angle of the other.

★Proposition III.   Theorem

404. *If two triangles have their sides respectively propor-*
tional, they are similar.

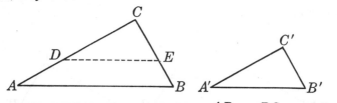

Given ⬟ *ABC* and *A'B'C'* having $\dfrac{AB}{A'B'} = \dfrac{BC}{B'C'} = \dfrac{AC}{A'C'}$.

To prove that $\triangle ABC \sim \triangle A'B'C'$.

Selection of Method: 1. Known methods of proving ⬟ ~: §§ 394, 396,
397, 399, 403.
2. Method to be used: § 399.

Proof: *STATEMENTS*   *REASONS*

1. On *CA* construct $CD = C'A'$ and on *CB* construct $CE = C'B'$.	1. Why possible?
2. Draw *DE*.	2. Why possible?
3. $\dfrac{AC}{A'C'} = \dfrac{BC}{B'C'}$.	3. Why?
4. $\therefore \dfrac{AC}{DC} = \dfrac{BC}{EC}$.	4. Why?
5. $\angle C = \angle C$.	5. Why?
6. $\triangle ABC \sim \triangle DEC$.	6. Why?
7. $\therefore \dfrac{AB}{DE} = \dfrac{AC}{DC}$, or $\dfrac{AB}{DE} = \dfrac{AC}{A'C'}$.	7. Why?
8. But $\dfrac{AB}{A'B'} = \dfrac{AC}{A'C'}$.	8. Why?
9. $\therefore A'B' = DE$.	9. § 368.
10. $\therefore \triangle A'B'C' \cong \triangle DEC$.	10. Why?
11. $\therefore \triangle A'B'C' \sim \triangle DEC$.	11. § 396.
12. $\therefore \triangle ABC \sim \triangle A'B'C'$.	12. § 399.

EXERCISES. SIMILAR TRIANGLES

A

1. What methods have you had of proving two triangles similar? Find these methods on page 550. Are two polygons necessarily similar if their corresponding sides are proportional? What kind of polygons are similar if their corresponding sides are proportional? Why?

2. A line intersects two sides of a triangle so that the segments of one side are 8 and 22 and the corresponding segments of the other side are 12 and 33. Is the line parallel to the third side?

3. *Given* polygon $ABCDE \sim$ polygon $A'B'C'D'E'$.

Prove that $\triangle BCD \sim \triangle B'C'D'$.

SUGGESTION. Use § 403.

4. Prove that two isosceles triangles are similar if the vertex angle of one equals the vertex angle of the other.

B

5. In $\triangle ABC$, $\angle C$ is acute, AD is perpendicular to BC, and BE is perpendicular to AC. Find a pair of similar triangles. Prove that the triangles are similar. Prove that $\dfrac{AD}{BE} = \dfrac{AC}{BC}$. State this proportion as a theorem.

6. The corresponding medians of two similar triangles have the same ratio as any two corresponding sides. (Use § 403.)

7. Two corresponding medians of two similar triangles have the same ratio as the bisectors of the angles from whose vertices the medians are drawn.

C

8. *Given* quadrilateral $ABCD$ inscribed in a $\odot$. BD bisects $\angle ABC$ and intersects AC at E.

 a. *Prove* that $\triangle BEC \sim \triangle BDA$.

 b. *Prove* that $\triangle BEA \sim \triangle BDC$.

9. A and B are two points on opposite sides of a pond. Show how to find the distance between them without using congruent triangles.

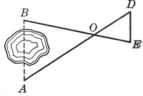

★★Proposition IV. Theorem

405. *The altitude on the hypotenuse of a right triangle forms two right triangles which are similar to the given triangle and to each other.*

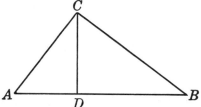

Given rt. △ *ABC* having *CD* ⊥ hypotenuse *AB*.

To prove that △ *ADC* ∼ △ *ACB* ∼ △ *CDB*.

Selection of Method: 1. Known methods of proving ▲ ∼: §§ 394, 396, 397, 399, 403, 404.

2. Method to be used: §§ 397, 399.

Proof: STATEMENTS   REASONS

1. ▲ *ADC* and *ACB* are rt. ▲.	1. Why?
2. ∠ *A* = ∠ *A*.	2. Why?
3. ∴ △ *ADC* ∼ △ *ACB*.	3. Why?
4. ▲ *CDB* and *ACB* are rt. ▲.	4. Why?
5. ∠ *B* = ∠ *B*.	5. Why?
6. ∴ △ *CDB* ∼ △ *ACB*.	6. Why?
7. ∴ △ *ADC* ∼ △ *CDB*.	7. § 399.

★★406. Corollary I. *The altitude on the hypotenuse of a right triangle is the mean proportional between the segments of the hypotenuse.*

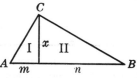

SUGGESTIONS. △ I ∼ △ II by § 405. Then *m* of △ I corresponds to *x* of △ II and *x* of △ I corresponds to *n* of △ II. ∴ $\frac{m}{x} = \frac{x}{n}$, or $x^2 = mn$.

NOTE. This corollary was known by Archytas (400 B.C.).

407. Projection of a Line Segment. The *projection of a line segment* on a line is the segment that is cut off on the line by perpendiculars to the line from the extremities of the line segment.

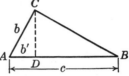

Thus, in the figures, $A'B'$ is the projection of AB on the line l.

408. Corollary II. *Either leg of a right triangle is the mean proportional between the hypotenuse and its projection on the hypotenuse.*

SUGGESTIONS. b' is the projection of b on c.
$\triangle ADC \sim \triangle ACB$. Why? b' of $\triangle ADC$ corresponds to b of $\triangle ACB$ and b of $\triangle ADC$ corresponds to c of $\triangle ACB$.

$\therefore \dfrac{b'}{b} = \dfrac{b}{c}$, or $b^2 = b'c$. Why?

409. Corollary III. *The perpendicular from any point on a circle to a diameter of the circle is the mean proportional between the segments of the diameter.*

Example 1. Given rt. $\triangle ACB$ with $CD \perp$ hypotenuse AB, $AD = 11$, and $BD = 15$. Find CD.

Solution. From § 406, $\dfrac{AD}{CD} = \dfrac{CD}{BD}$.

Substituting, $\dfrac{11}{CD} = \dfrac{CD}{15}$.

$\therefore \overline{CD}^2 = 165.$

$CD = 12.845 +.$

Example 2. If, in the figure of Ex. 1, $AC = 6$ and $BD = 10$, what is the length of AD?

Solution. From § 408, $\dfrac{AB}{AC} = \dfrac{AC}{AD}$.

Let $x = AD$. Substituting, $\dfrac{x+10}{6} = \dfrac{6}{x}$.

$x^2 + 10\,x = 36.$

Adding ($\frac{1}{2}$ of 10)^2, $\quad x^2 + 10\,x + 25 = 61.$

Extracting the square roots, $\quad x + 5 = 7.81 +.$

$x = 2.81$, to the nearest hundredth.

EXERCISES

A

1. Name two methods of proving that a line segment is the mean proportional between two other line segments.

2. In △ *ABC*, ∠ *ACB* = 90°, and *CD* ⊥ *AB*.
a. Find *DB* if *AD* = 5 and *CD* = 10.
b. Find *AD* if *DB* = 24 and *CD* = 72.
c. Find *AB* if *CD* = 8 and *DB* = 4.
d. Find *CD* if *AB* = 35 and *DB* = 7.
e. Find *BD* if *AD* = 20 and *BC* = 24.
f. Find *AC* if *AD* = 15 and *DB* = 25.

3. In △ *MNP*, ∠ *P* is a right angle and *PS* is perpendicular to *MN*.
a. If *MS* = 9 and *SN* = 4, find *PS*.
b. If *MS* = 21 and *PS* = 56, find *SN* to the nearest tenth.
c. If *PS* = 24 and *SN* = 18, find *MS*.
d. If *MS* = 18 and *SN* = 20, find *PS* to the nearest tenth.
e. If *MN* = 20 and *SN* = 5, find *PS* to the nearest tenth.
f. If *PS* = 12.3 and *SN* = 5.4, find *MS* to the nearest tenth.

4. *AB* is a diameter of circle *O*, *C* is a point on the circle, and *CD* is perpendicular to *AB*.
a. If *AD* = 3 and *DB* = 27, find *CD*.
b. If *AD* = 4 and *AB* = 20, find *CD*.
c. If *CD* = 9 and *DB* = 16.2, find *AD*.
d. If *AD* = 8.2 and *DB* = 24.6, find *CD* to the nearest tenth.

B

5. In △ *ABC*, *CD* is perpendicular to the hypotenuse *AB*.
a. If *BD* = 4 and *BA* = 9, find *BC*.
b. If *BC* = 8 and *BD* = 4, find *DA*.
c. If *AD* = 24 and *DB* = 18, find *CA* to the nearest tenth.
d. If *CA* = 12 and *DB* = 10, find *AB*.

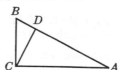

6. From any point *C* on a circle whose center is *O*, *CE* is drawn perpendicular to a diameter *AB*. Then line segment *BC* is drawn. Prove that $\overline{BC}^2 = 2\ AO \times BE$.

7. Prove that the line which joins the midpoints of two sides of a triangle cuts off a triangle similar to the given triangle.

★★Proposition V. Problem

410. *To construct the mean proportional between two given line segments.*

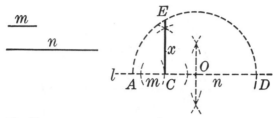

Given the line segments m and n.

To construct the segment x so that $\dfrac{m}{x} = \dfrac{x}{n}$.

Construction:

STATEMENTS	*REASONS*
1. On a line l construct $AC = m$ and $CD = n$.	1. Why possible?
2. Construct a semicircle having AD as a diameter.	2. Why possible?
3. At C construct $CE \perp AD$, meeting the semicircle at E.	3. Why possible?

Then CE is the required mean proportional.

Proof: (The proof is left to the student.)

EXERCISES

A

1. Construct the mean proportional between a line segment of 2 inches and one of $4\frac{1}{2}$ inches.

2. Construct a line segment equal to $\sqrt{5}$ inches.

SUGGESTION. Construct $m = 1$ inch and $n = 5$ inches.

B

3. Find the square root of 6 geometrically; arithmetically. Which method did the early Greeks use?

4. Given line segments a and b. Find the segment x so that $x = \dfrac{b^2}{a}$.

HINT. Which segment is the mean proportional?

★★ Proposition VI. Pythagorean Theorem

411. *The square of the hypotenuse of a right triangle is equal to the sum of the squares of the legs.*

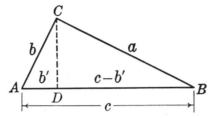

Given $\triangle ABC$ having the hypotenuse AB denoted by c, side AC denoted by b, and side BC denoted by a.

To prove that $c^2 = a^2 + b^2$.

Selection of Method: 1. Known methods of proving relations of sides of ⚌: §§ 401, 406, 408.
2. Method to be used: § 408; Ax. 1.

Proof:

STATEMENTS	REASONS
1. $\angle ACB$ is a rt. $\angle$.	1. Why?
2. Draw $CD \perp AB$.	2. Why possible?
3. Let $AD = b'$. Then $DB = c - b'$.	3. Why?
4. $\dfrac{c}{b} = \dfrac{b}{b'}$ and $\dfrac{c}{a} = \dfrac{a}{c-b'}$.	4. § 408.
5. $b^2 = b'c$ and $a^2 = c^2 - b'c$.	5. Why?
6. $\therefore a^2 + b^2 = c^2$.	6. Why?

NOTE. This theorem derives its name from Pythagoras, the Greek mathematician who formulated it. The above proof is attributed to Hindu mathematicians. Another proof of this proposition was given on page 222.

EXERCISE

See if you can prove Prop. VI, using the figure at the right. The proof is similar to that of Garfield (§ 235).

★★ Proposition VII. Theorem

412. *If two chords intersect within a circle, the product of the segments of one chord is equal to the product of the segments of the other.*

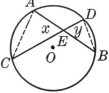

Given AB and *CD* two chords of ⊙ *O* intersecting at *E*.

To prove that $AE \cdot EB = CE \cdot ED$.

Selection of Method: 1. Known methods of proving products of line segments =: § 402.
2. Method to be used: § 402 *a*.

Proof: *STATEMENTS*   *REASONS*

1. Draw *AC* and *DB*.	1. Why possible?
In ⊿ *AEC* and *DEB*,	
2. $\angle x = \angle y$ and $\angle A = \angle D$.	2. §§ 50 *d*, 314.
3. ∴ △ *AEC* ∼ △ *DEB*.	3. Why?
4. ∴ $\dfrac{AE}{ED} = \dfrac{CE}{EB}$.	4. Why?
5. ∴ $AE \cdot EB = CE \cdot ED$.	5. Why?

413. Segment of a Secant. In § 258 a secant of a circle was defined as a line which meets the circle in two points and passes through it in at least one of them. If a secant drawn from a point *P* intersects a circle in point *B* and meets it in point *A*, as in the figure, it is customary to speak of segment *PA* as the secant from *P* to the circle. *PB* is the *external* segment of the secant and *BA* is the *internal* segment, or chord, of the secant. Name the external and internal segments of the secant *RT*.

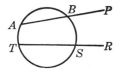

EXERCISES

A

1. The segments of one of two intersecting chords of a circle are 4 inches and 8 inches respectively. One segment of the other chord is 6 inches. Compute the length of the other segment.

2. The segments of one of two intersecting chords of a circle are 15 inches and 6 inches respectively. The length of the second chord is 23 inches. Find the lengths of the segments of the second chord.

3. A chord 16 inches long is 6 inches from the center of the circle. Find the length of the diameter of the circle.

4. Two chords intersect within a circle. The segments of one chord are 6 inches and 14 inches respectively. The length of the second chord is 25 inches. Find the lengths of its segments.

5. The distance from the center of a chord 36 inches long to the midpoint of its arc is 9 inches. Find the radius of the circle.

6. Chords RS and EM intersect in point H. If $RH \times HS = 56$ and $EH = 6$, find HM.

B

7. The radius of the larger of two concentric circles is 30 inches, and a chord of the larger circle is tangent to the smaller circle. Find the radius of the smaller circle if the length of this chord is 36 inches.

8. A contractor wishes to construct a circular arch having a span of 24 feet and a height of 9 feet. Find the radius of the circle of which the arch is an arc.

9. A chord is drawn through a point 5 inches from the center of a circle having a radius of 15 inches. What is the product of the segments into which the chord is divided?

C

10. Find the height of a circular arch having a radius of 5 feet if the height of the arch is one fourth of its span.

11. A chord 24 inches long is 9 inches from the center of the circle. Find the length of another chord of the circle which is 3 inches from the center.

12. Using Prop. VII, construct the fourth proportional to three given line segments.

★Proposition VIII. Theorem

414. *If a tangent and a secant are drawn to a circle from the same point, the tangent is the mean proportional between the secant and its external segment.*

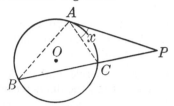

Given the tangent PA touching $\odot O$ at A and the secant PB intersecting the $\odot$ at C.

To prove that $\dfrac{PC}{PA} = \dfrac{PA}{PB}$, or $\overline{PA}^2 = PB \cdot PC$.

Selection of Method: 1. Known methods of proving a line segment the mean proportional: §§ 401 *c*, 406, 408, 409.
2. Method to be used: § 401 *c*.

Proof: *STATEMENTS* | *REASONS*

STATEMENTS	REASONS
1. Draw AB and AC.	1. Why possible?
In ⊿ PAC and PBA,	
2. $\angle P = \angle P$,	2. Why?
3. $\angle x \overset{\circ}{=} \tfrac{1}{2} \widehat{AC}$, and	3. Why?
4. $\angle B \overset{\circ}{=} \tfrac{1}{2} \widehat{AC}$.	4. Why?
5. $\therefore \angle x = \angle B$.	5. Why?
6. $\therefore \triangle PAC \sim \triangle PBA$.	6. Why?
7. $\dfrac{PC}{PA} = \dfrac{PA}{PB}$, or $\overline{PA}^2 = PB \cdot PC$.	7. Why?

EXERCISES

A

1. From a point outside a circle a tangent 7 inches long and a secant are drawn to the circle. If the secant is 10 inches long, what is the length of its external segment? of its chord?

2. Find the length of a tangent drawn to a circle from an external point if a secant from this point is 18 inches long and its external segment is 8 inches long.

3. Find the length of a tangent drawn to a circle from an external point if a secant from this point is 36 inches long and the chord of the secant is 10 inches.

4. A tangent and a secant are drawn to a circle from the same point. If the tangent is 24 inches in length and the secant is 20 inches longer than its external segment, find the length of the secant.

5. A point is 9 inches from a circle, and the length of the tangent from this point is 24 inches. Find the diameter of the circle.

B

6. Prove that tangents to two intersecting circles from any point in their common chord produced are equal.

7. The product of any secant from a fixed point without a circle and its external segment is constant.

SUGGESTION. The length of a tangent from the fixed point is constant.

8. Two circles are tangent internally. From any point in their common tangent secants are drawn to the two circles respectively. Prove that the product of one secant and its external segment is equal to the product of the other secant and its external segment.

C

9. Construct the mean proportional between two line segments, a and b, making use of Prop. VIII.

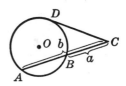

SUGGESTION. Does center O lie on the perpendicular bisector of AB?

10. Construct a circle passing through two given points and tangent to a given line.

11. If the radius of a circle intersects a chord of the circle, the product of the segments of the chord is equal to the square of the radius minus the square of the segment of the radius adjacent to the center.

12. If a secant CBA and a tangent CE are drawn to a circle from point C and AE is a diameter of the circle, prove that $\overline{AE}^2 = AC \cdot AB$.

Proposition IX.   Theorem

415. *The perimeters of two similar polygons have the same ratio as any two corresponding sides.*

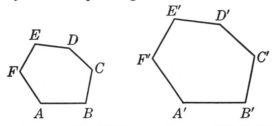

Given polygon $ABCDEF \sim$ polygon $A'B'C'D'E'F'$ with vertex A corresponding to A', B to B', etc., and with the perimeters denoted by P and P' respectively.

To prove that $\dfrac{P}{P'} = \dfrac{AB}{A'B'}$.

Selection of Method: 1. Known methods of proving proportions: §§ 366, 369, 370, 371, 372, 389, 394, 398.
2. Method to be used: §§ 394 and 369.

Proof: *STATEMENTS*	*REASONS*
1. $ABCDEF \sim A'B'C'D'E'F'$.	1. Why?
2. $\therefore \dfrac{AB}{A'B'} = \dfrac{BC}{B'C'} = \dfrac{CD}{C'D'} = \cdots$.	2. Why?
3. $\therefore \dfrac{AB + BC + CD + \cdots}{A'B' + B'C' + C'D' + \cdots} = \dfrac{AB}{A'B'}$.	3. Why?
4. $\therefore \dfrac{P}{P'} = \dfrac{AB}{A'B'}$.	4. Why?

EXERCISES [A]

1. Does Prop. IX apply to triangles?

2. The sides of one polygon are 3, 7, 6, 8, and 15. The longest side of a similar polygon is 20. Find its perimeter.

3. The sides of a pentagon are 3, 4, 5, 6, and 7 inches respectively Find the sides of a similar pentagon if its perimeter is 45 inches.

★Proposition X. Theorem

416. *If two polygons are similar, they can be separated into the same number of triangles which are similar each to each.*

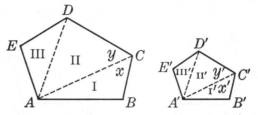

Given polygon $ABCDE \sim$ polygon $A'B'C'D'E'$ with AB corresponding to $A'B'$, BC to $B'C'$, etc.

To prove that each polygon can be separated into the same number of △ which are similar each to each.

Selection of Method: 1. Known methods of proving △ $\sim$: §§ 394, 396, 397, 399, 403, 404, 405.
2. Method to be used: § 403.

Proof: STATEMENTS	REASONS
1. Draw AC, AD, $A'C'$, and $A'D'$.	1. Why possible?
2. In △ I and I', $\angle B = \angle B'$, and	2. Why?
3. $\dfrac{AB}{A'B'} = \dfrac{BC}{B'C'}$.	3. Why?
4. $\therefore \triangle$ I $\sim \triangle$ I'.	4. Why?
5. $\angle BCD = \angle B'C'D'$.	5. Why?
6. $\angle x = \angle x'$.	6. Why?
7. $\therefore \angle y = \angle y'$.	7. Ax. 2.
8. Since $\triangle$ I $\sim \triangle$ I', $\dfrac{BC}{B'C'} = \dfrac{AC}{A'C'}$.	8. Why?
9. But $\dfrac{BC}{B'C'} = \dfrac{CD}{C'D'}$.	9. Why?
10. $\therefore \dfrac{AC}{A'C'} = \dfrac{CD}{C'D'}$.	10. Why?
11. From (7) and (10), $\triangle$ II $\sim \triangle$ II'.	11. Why?
12. In like manner, $\triangle$ III $\sim \triangle$ III'.	12. Why?

Proposition XI. Theorem

417. *If two polygons are composed of the same number of triangles, similar each to each and similarly placed, the polygons are similar.*

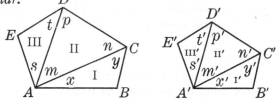

Given polygons $ABCDE$ and $A'B'C'D'E'$ with $\triangle$ I $\sim \triangle$ I', $\triangle$ II $\sim \triangle$ II', and $\triangle$ III $\sim \triangle$ III'.

To prove that $ABCDE \sim A'B'C'D'E'$.

Selection of Method: 1. Known methods of proving polygons $\sim$: § 394.
 2. Method to be used: § 394.

Proof:

STATEMENTS	REASONS
1. Since $\triangle$ I $\sim \triangle$ I', $\angle B = \angle B'$, $\angle x = \angle x'$, and $\angle y = \angle y'$.	1. Why?
2. Since $\triangle$ II $\sim \triangle$ II', $\angle m = \angle m'$, $\angle n = \angle n'$, and $\angle p = \angle p'$.	2. Why?
3. Since $\triangle$ III $\sim \triangle$ III', $\angle s = \angle s'$, $\angle t = \angle t'$, and $\angle E = \angle E'$.	3. Why?
4. $\therefore \angle EAB = \angle E'A'B'$, $\angle BCD = \angle B'C'D'$, and $\angle CDE = \angle C'D'E'$.	4. Ax. 1.
5. $\therefore$ the $\angle$ of $ABCDE$ = corr. $\angle$ of $A'B'C'D'E'$.	5. Sts. 1–4.
6. Since $\triangle$ I $\sim \triangle$ I', $\dfrac{AB}{A'B'} = \dfrac{BC}{B'C'} = \left(\dfrac{AC}{A'C'}\right)$.	6. Why?
7. Since $\triangle$ II $\sim \triangle$ II', $\left(\dfrac{AC}{A'C'}\right) = \dfrac{CD}{C'D'} = \left(\dfrac{AD}{A'D'}\right)$.	7. Why?
8. Since $\triangle$ III $\sim \triangle$ III', $\left(\dfrac{AD}{A'D'}\right) = \dfrac{DE}{D'E'} = \dfrac{EA}{E'A'}$.	8. Why?
9. $\therefore \dfrac{AB}{A'B'} = \dfrac{BC}{B'C'} = \dfrac{CD}{C'D'} = \dfrac{DE}{D'E'} = \dfrac{EA}{E'A'}$.	9. Why?
10. $\therefore ABCDE \sim A'B'C'D'E'$.	10. Why?

EXERCISES

A

1. The sides of a polygon are 6, 10, 12, and 14 inches respectively. Find the perimeter of a similar polygon whose shortest side is 9 inches.

2. The sides of a quadrilateral are 9, 10, 12, and 15 inches respectively. The perimeter of a similar quadrilateral is 61⅓ inches. Find its sides.

3. What theorems have you studied that bear on map-making?

4. A certain township is a square 6 miles on a side. Make a map of this township, using the scale of 1 to 100,000. In this township two post offices are 4 miles apart. What is the distance between the locations of the post offices on the map? How long on your map is the diagonal of the township?

5. The diagonals of a rhombus are 15 and 20 inches respectively. Find the perimeter of the rhombus.

6. The dimensions of one rectangle are $a + 3$ and $2a - 1$, and the dimensions of another rectangle are $3a + 2$ and $2a - 1$. What is the ratio of the area of the first rectangle to the area of the second?

B

7. Find the altitude of an equilateral triangle whose sides are 8 inches in length.

8. Find the length of each side of an equilateral triangle whose altitude is 20 inches.

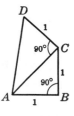

9. How long is AC in the figure? How long is AD? How would you construct a line segment $\sqrt{3}$ inches in length if you had given a line segment 1 inch long?

10. Find the side of a regular hexagon having an area of $150\sqrt{3}$.

C

11. Given a line segment m, construct a line segment $m\sqrt{2}$ by using the method of Ex. 9.

12. Given a line segment m, construct a line segment $m\sqrt{2}$ by using § 410.

13. Find the distance between two parallel sides of the rhombus in Ex. 5.

Proposition XII. Problem

418. *Upon a given line segment corresponding to one side of a given polygon to construct a polygon similar to the given polygon.*

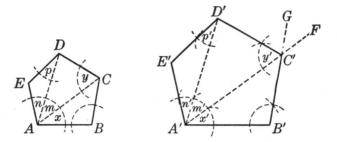

Given polygon *ABCDE* and *A'B'* corresponding to *AB*.

To construct on *A'B'* a polygon ∼ *ABCDE*.

Construction: *STATEMENTS*   *REASONS*

1. From *A* draw all the diagonals, as *AC* and *AD*.	1. Why possible?
2. At *A'* construct *A'F*, making ∠ *x'* = ∠ *x*, and then at *B'* construct *B'G*, making ∠ *B'* = ∠ *B*.	2. Why possible?
3. *A'F* and *B'G* will intersect at some point *C'*.	3. Prove it.
4. In the same manner, using *A'C'* as a side, construct ∠ *m'* = ∠ *m* and ∠ *y'* = ∠ *y*, forming △ *A'C'D'*.	4. Why possible?
5. Likewise, construct ∠ *n'* = ∠ *n* and ∠ *p'* = ∠ *p*, forming △ *A'D'E'*.	5. Why possible?

Then A'B'C'D'E' ∼ *ABCDE*.

Proof: (The proof is left to the student.)

Suggestions.   Prove △ *A'B'C'* ∼ △ *ABC*, △ *A'C'D'* ∼ △ *ACD*, etc . and then use § 417.

★★Proposition XIII. Theorem

419. *The areas of two similar triangles have the same ratio as the squares of any two corresponding sides.*

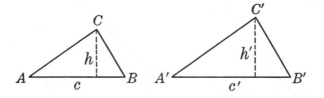

Given $\triangle ABC \sim \triangle A'B'C'$ having c and c' any pair of corresponding sides.

To prove that $\dfrac{\triangle ABC}{\triangle A'B'C'} = \dfrac{c^2}{c'^2}$.

Selection of Method: 1. Known methods of comparing areas of polygons: §§ 253, 255.
2. Method to be used: § 253 c.

Proof: STATEMENTS   REASONS

1. Draw the altitudes h and h' to the sides c and c' respectively.	1. Why possible?
2. $\dfrac{\triangle ABC}{\triangle A'B'C'} = \dfrac{ch}{c'h'}$.	2. § 253 c.
3. $\dfrac{\triangle ABC}{\triangle A'B'C'} = \dfrac{c}{c'} \times \dfrac{h}{h'}$.	3. Why?
4. But $\dfrac{h}{h'} = \dfrac{c}{c'}$.	4. Why?
5. $\therefore \dfrac{\triangle ABC}{\triangle A'B'C'} = \dfrac{c}{c'} \times \dfrac{c}{c'} = \dfrac{c^2}{c'^2}$.	5. Why?

420. Corollary. *The areas of two similar triangles have the same ratio as the squares of any two corresponding altitudes.*

★★Proposition XIV. Theorem

421. *The areas of two similar polygons have the same ratio as the squares of any two corresponding sides.*

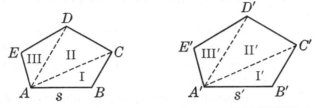

Given polygon $ABCDE \sim$ polygon $A'B'C'D'E'$ having any pair of corresponding sides s and s'.

To prove that $\dfrac{ABCDE}{A'B'C'D'E'} = \dfrac{s^2}{s'^2}$.

Selection of Method: 1. Known methods of comparing areas of polygons: §§ 253, 255, 419, 420.
2. Method to be used: § 419.

Proof:

STATEMENTS	REASONS
1. From any two corresponding vertices, A and A', draw the diagonals of each polygon.	1. Why possible?
2. $\triangle\,\mathrm{I} \sim \triangle\,\mathrm{I'}, \triangle\,\mathrm{II} \sim \triangle\,\mathrm{II'}$, and $\triangle\,\mathrm{III} \sim \triangle\,\mathrm{III'}$.	2. Why?
3. $\dfrac{\triangle\,\mathrm{I}}{\triangle\,\mathrm{I'}} = \dfrac{\overline{AC}^2}{\overline{A'C'}^2} = \dfrac{\triangle\,\mathrm{II}}{\triangle\,\mathrm{II'}} = \dfrac{\overline{AD}^2}{\overline{A'D'}^2} = \dfrac{\triangle\,\mathrm{III}}{\triangle\,\mathrm{III'}}$.	3. Why?
4. $\therefore\ \dfrac{\triangle\,\mathrm{I}}{\triangle\,\mathrm{I'}} = \dfrac{\triangle\,\mathrm{II}}{\triangle\,\mathrm{II'}} = \dfrac{\triangle\,\mathrm{III}}{\triangle\,\mathrm{III'}}$.	4. Ax. 6.
5. $\therefore\ \dfrac{\triangle\,\mathrm{I} + \triangle\,\mathrm{II} + \triangle\,\mathrm{III}}{\triangle\,\mathrm{I'} + \triangle\,\mathrm{II'} + \triangle\,\mathrm{III'}} = \dfrac{\triangle\,\mathrm{I}}{\triangle\,\mathrm{I'}}$.	5. Why?
6. But $\triangle\,\mathrm{I} + \triangle\,\mathrm{II} + \triangle\,\mathrm{III} = $ polygon $ABCDE$ and $\triangle\,\mathrm{I'} + \triangle\,\mathrm{II'} + \triangle\,\mathrm{III'} = $ polygon $A'B'C'D'E'$.	6. Ax. 8.
7. $\dfrac{\triangle\,\mathrm{I}}{\triangle\,\mathrm{I'}} = \dfrac{s^2}{s'^2}$.	7. § 419.
8. $\therefore\ \dfrac{ABCDE}{A'B'C'D'E'} = \dfrac{s^2}{s'^2}$.	8. Ax. 5.

EXERCISES. SIMILAR POLYGONS

A

1. The corresponding sides of two similar triangles have the ratio 1 : 2. What is the ratio of their altitudes? of their perimeters? of their areas?

2. Two corresponding sides of two similar polygons are 6 and 18 respectively. What is the ratio of their areas? of their perimeters?

3. The area of a triangle is 16 times that of a similar one. Find the ratio of two corresponding sides.

4. Construct a triangle that is similar to a given triangle and equal to one ninth of it.

5. The areas of two similar polygons are 64 square inches and 100 square inches. If a side of the first is 6 inches, find the corresponding side of the second.

6. Two similar polygons have areas of 200 square inches and 1152 square inches respectively. If a side of the first is 20 inches, find the corresponding side of the second.

B

7. The ratio of the sides of two squares is 2 : 3, and the difference of the areas of the squares is 405. What is the area of each of the squares?

8. The altitude of one equilateral triangle is equal to the side of another equilateral triangle. What is the ratio of their areas?

9. In $\triangle DEF$, $DE = 6$ inches and $EF = 4$ inches. G and H are points on DE and EF respectively such that $DG = 4$ inches and $EH = 3$ inches. Is $\triangle DEF \sim \triangle EHG$? Give reason for your answer.

C

10. Divide a triangle into three equal parts by drawing lines parallel to the base.

11. Two triangles which have an angle of one equal to an angle of the other have the same ratio as the products of the sides including the equal angles.

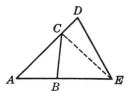

Suggestions. $\dfrac{\triangle ABC}{\triangle AEC} = ?$ $\qquad$ $\dfrac{\triangle AEC}{\triangle AED} = ?$ $\qquad$ $\dfrac{\triangle ABC}{\triangle AEC} \times \dfrac{\triangle AEC}{\triangle AED} = ?$

Proposition XV. Problem

422. *To construct a square equal to a given parallelogram.*

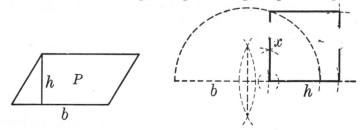

Given the $\square P$ having base b and altitude h.

To construct a square $S = P$.

Construction: STATEMENTS	REASONS
1. Construct x, the mean proportional between h and b.	1. § 410.
2. Construct a square S having x as a side.	2. § 157
Then $S = P$	

Proof:

1. $x^2 = hb$.	1. Const.
2. But $x^2 = S$.	2. Why?
3. $P = hb$.	3. Why?
4. $\therefore S = P$.	4. Why?

423. Solving Problems. At this time you should review the directions in § 159 for the solution of construction problems. In addition to these directions, if the construction exercise involves area or other numerical relations, you will often be able to discover the method of construction by the use of algebra. For example, in Prop. XV, $S = x^2$ and $P = hb$. Since S must equal P, then $x^2 = hb$. Then x is the mean proportional between h and b. Also the area of a rectangle with base b and altitude h, and equal in area to a square with side s, is given by

$$bh = s^2, \text{ or } \frac{b}{s} = \frac{s}{h}.$$

CONSTRUCTION EXERCISES

A

1. Construct a square equal to the sum of two given squares whose sides are 3 inches and 4 inches respectively.

2. Construct a square equal to a given rectangle.

3. Construct a square equal to a given triangle.

SUGGESTIONS. Let x be a side of the required square, b the base of the given triangle, and a its altitude. Then $x^2 = \frac{1}{2} a \cdot b$, or $\dfrac{\frac{1}{2}a}{x} = \dfrac{x}{b}$.

4. Construct a right triangle equal to a given triangle and having the same base.

B

5. Construct a square equal to a given quadrilateral.

SUGGESTION. Construct a triangle equal to the quadrilateral and then construct a square equal to the triangle.

6. Construct a square equal to a given polygon.

7. Construct a rectangle which has a given base and is equal in area to another rectangle. (Use proportion.)

8. Construct an isosceles triangle on a given line segment as a base and equal to a given triangle.

9. Construct a square having $\frac{9}{16}$ of the area of a given square.

10. Construct a triangle equal to the sum of two given triangles.

11. Construct a right triangle equal to a given triangle and having its hypotenuse equal to a given line segment.

12. Construct a square equal to a given trapezoid.

13. Divide a parallelogram into three equal parts by lines from one vertex.

14. Construct a line parallel to the base of a given triangle dividing the triangle into two parts which have the ratio 4 : 5.

C

15. Construct $\triangle ABC$ similar to a given $\triangle DEF$ and having a perimeter equal to a given line segment m.

16. Construct an equilateral triangle equal to a given triangle.

SUGGESTION. $\frac{1}{4} s^2 \sqrt{3} = \frac{1}{2} bh$. Then $s^2 = \frac{2}{3}\sqrt{3}\, bh$.

MISCELLANEOUS EXERCISES

A

1. A chord 6 inches long is 4 inches from the center of the circle. What is the length of the radius of the circle?

2. A chord 30 inches long is in a circle with a radius of 34 inches. How far is the chord from the center of the circle?

3. Construct a polygon similar to a given hexagon and having its sides one half as long.

4. The diagonal of a square is $7\sqrt{2}$. Find the length of a side.

5. Find the altitude of an isosceles triangle whose base is 14 inches and whose perimeter is 50 inches.

6. Construct a rectangle similar to a given rectangle and having its base three times as long as the given rectangle. What is the ratio of the two rectangles?

7. The radii of two concentric circles are 9 inches and 15 inches respectively. Find the length of a chord of the larger circle that is tangent to the smaller circle.

8. The corresponding sides of two similar polygons are 6 inches and 9 inches. If the area of the first polygon is 48 square inches, what is the area of the second?

9. The base of one rectangle is 56 feet and its altitude is 27 feet. The base of another rectangle is 18 feet and its altitude is 24 feet. Are the rectangles similar? Give reason for your answer.

10. In the figure, AB, a diameter of circle O, is 26 inches long and DB is 8 inches long. Find the length of the perpendicular CD; of AC; of BC.

11. If the ratio of the areas of two similar triangles is 16 : 25, what is the ratio of their perimeters?

12. Two corresponding sides of two similar polygons are 15 feet and 18 feet. What is the ratio of their perimeters? of their areas?

13. $\triangle ABC$ has a right angle at C. CA is extended through A to D. $DE \perp BA$ extended at E. Prove that $DA : AB = DE : CB$.

14. Find the side of a square equal to the sum of three squares whose sides are 3, 4, and 12 respectively.

15. The diagonals AC and BD of trapezoid $ABCD$ intersect in O; $AB \parallel DC$; $AB = 3 DC$. Compare $\triangle AOB$ and COD; $\triangle AOD$ and BOC.

B, C

16. *Prove:* If two triangles have their sides respectively parallel, they are similar.

17. *Prove:* If two triangles have their sides respectively perpendicular, they are similar.

18. *Prove:* A line parallel to the base of a triangle and intersecting the other two sides forms a triangle similar to the given triangle.

19. If one leg of a right triangle is $2\,ab$ and the other leg is $a^2 - b^2$, show that the hypotenuse is $a^2 + b^2$.

20. The product of the two legs of a right triangle is equal to the product of the hypotenuse and the altitude on the hypotenuse.

21. The legs of a right triangle are 16 feet and 20 feet respectively. Find the length of the radius of the circumcircle.

22. The diagonal of a rectangle is 143 inches and one side is 55 inches. Find the area of the rectangle.

23. *Given* ⊙ O, diameter AB, tangent BC, and secant CA.

Prove that $AB = \sqrt{AD \times AC}$.

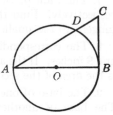

24. Construct the locus of a point if the sum of the squares of its distances from two given perpendicular lines is 25.

SUGGESTION. How far is the point from the intersection of the two lines?

25. Two circles having radii of 10 inches and 20 inches are tangent externally. Find the length of their common external tangents.

26. Find the area of a triangle whose medians are 30 inches, 30 inches, and 48 inches.

27. The area of a rectangle is 320 square inches and the perimeter is 72 inches. Find the dimensions of the rectangle.

28. *Given* rectangle $ABCD$ with $DE \perp AC$ and $FE \perp BC$.

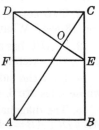

    a. *Prove:* $\triangle AOD \sim \triangle COE$.

    b. *Prove:* $\triangle AOD \sim \triangle ADC$.

    c. *Prove:* $\triangle ADC \sim \triangle DCE$.

    d. *Prove:* $\dfrac{AD}{DC} = \dfrac{DC}{CE}$.

    e. *Prove:* rectangle $ABCD \sim$ rectangle $FECD$.

29. The altitude of an equilateral triangle is $2\sqrt{3}$. Find the altitude of an equilateral triangle 25 times as large.

30. Find the area of a rectangle having diagonal d and length l.

31. Find the area of a triangle whose sides are b, b, and c.

32. Through P, a point within $\angle ABC$, construct a line segment whose end points are in AB and CB and which is divided by P into segments having the ratio 1 : 2.

33. In trapezoid $ABCD$, $AB \parallel DC$, $AB = 14$ inches, $BC = 13$ inches, $CD = 9$ inches, and $AD = 12$ inches. Find the area of $ABCD$. If AD and BC are produced to meet in E, what is the perimeter of $\triangle ABE$?

34. The sum of the three perpendiculars from any point within an equilateral triangle to the sides is constant.

SUGGESTION. Prove the sum equal to the altitude of the triangle.

35. Through a given point P within a given circle construct a chord so that its segments have a given ratio, $m : n$.

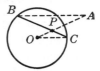

SUGGESTIONS. Draw OPA so that $\dfrac{OP}{PA} = \dfrac{m}{n}$. Construct AB, the fourth proportional to m, n, and the radius of the circle. Construct $OC \parallel BA$. Draw BP and PC. Prove that BPC is a straight line.

36. Find the locus of the midpoints of the chords of a given circle if the chords pass through a given point within the circle.

37. If PA is a secant which intersects a circle at A and B, determine the locus of point P so that $PA \cdot PB$ is constant.

38. Prove that in a 30°-60° right triangle the altitude on the hypotenuse divides the hypotenuse in the ratio 1 : 3.

39. Prove that if one leg of a right triangle is twice the other, the altitude on the hypotenuse divides the hypotenuse in the ratio 1 : 4.

40. If AB is the hypotenuse of a right triangle and the leg BC is bisected in D, $\overline{AB}^2 - \overline{AD}^2 = 3\,\overline{CD}^2$.

41. In the right triangle ABC, BE and AF bisect the legs AC and BC in the points E and F. Prove that $4\,\overline{BE}^2 + 4\,\overline{AF}^2 = 5\,\overline{AB}^2$.

42. Two chords intersect within a circle whose center is O. The shorter chord is divided into segments $2x$ and $3x$ and the longer chord into segments y and $6y$. Find the lengths of the chords if one exceeds the other by 8 inch s

43. *Given* □ *ABCD with DE intersecting diagonal AC at F, BC at G, and AB produced at E.*

Prove that $\dfrac{FG}{DF} = \dfrac{DF}{FE}$.

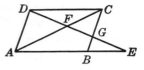

44. Construct $\sqrt{7}$ geometrically.

45. If a third tangent is included between two parallel tangents to a circle, the radius of the circle is the mean proportional between the segments of the third tangent.

46. If two circles are tangent internally, any chord of the larger circle drawn from the point of tangency is divided by the smaller circle in a constant ratio.

SUGGESTION. Prove that $\dfrac{AB}{AC} = \dfrac{AD}{AE}$.

47. *Given* ⊙ *O* and ⊙ *O'* tangent externally at *C*, with *DE* a straight line segment through *C* terminated by the circles and *AB* a straight line segment passing through the centers *O* and *O'*.

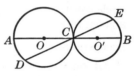

Prove that $CE : CD = CB : CA$.

48. In a triangle the product of two sides is equal to the product of the altitude on the third side and the diameter of the circumcircle.

SUGGESTION. Prove that $\triangle ACD \sim \triangle ECB$.

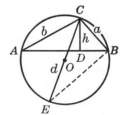

49. Prove that the area of $\triangle ABC$ in the figure is given by the formula $A = \dfrac{abc}{4R}$. $(R = \tfrac{1}{2}d.)$

50. Construct *x*, if $ax = b^2$.

51. *Given* ⊙ *O* and ⊙ *O'* with the common chord *AB*, chord *AC* of ⊙ *O* tangent to ⊙ *O'* at *A*, chord *AD* of ⊙ *O'* tangent to ⊙ *O* at *A*, and chords *BC* and *BD*.

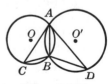

Prove that *AB* is the mean proportional between *BC* and *BD*.

52. About a given circle circumscribe a triangle similar to a given triangle.

53. In a given circle inscribe a triangle similar to a given triangle.

54. *Given* □ *ABCD*, with *CE* bisecting *AB*, *CF* bisecting *A BD* intersecting *CE* in *H* and *CF* in *G*.
To prove that *BH = HG = GD*.

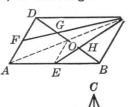

SUGGESTIONS. Draw *AC* intersecting *BD* in *O*; draw *EO*; prove △ *OEH* ~ △ *BCH*.

55. Inscribe a square in a semicircle.

56. Solve $x^2 = 6$ geometrically by § 410.

57. *Given* the isosceles △ *ABC* with *AC = BC* and the altitudes *CD* and *AE* intersecting at *F*.
Prove that *AC : AF = CD : DB*.

58. Inscribe a square in a given triangle so that one side of the square lies on the base of the triangle.

59. If three circles intersect one another, their common chords are concurrent.

SUGGESTIONS. *AB* and *CD* will intersect at some point *P*. Join *E* to *P*. Produce *EP* and let it meet ⑨ *O'* and *O''* at *F* and *G*. Prove that *PF = PG* by § 412, and hence *F* and *G* coincide.

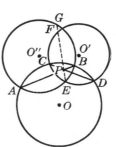

60. Given the altitude, construct a triangle similar to a given triangle.

61. Through a given point in the arc of a given chord, construct another chord which shall be bisected by the given chord.

SUGGESTIONS. On radius *OP* produced take *CD=CP* and construct *DE* ∥ *AB*. Then *EP* is the required chord.

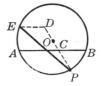

62. If the centers of arcs *AC* and *BC* are at *B* and *A* respectively, the arch *ACB* is equilateral. Construct an equilateral arch on a given line segment and inscribe a circle in it.

SUGGESTIONS. $AD = \frac{1}{2} AB$ and $EF = 2r$. $AE \cdot AF = \overline{AD}^2$. Why? $(AB - 2r)AB = \frac{1}{4}\overline{AB}^2$ (Ax. 6). Then $AB - 2r = \frac{1}{4} AB$. Why? Then $r = \frac{3}{8} AB$.

63. Construct a triangle, given two angles and the sum of the included side and the altitude on the included side.

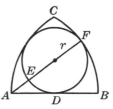

SUGGESTIONS. Construct any triangle with the two given angles and from it determine the ratio of the base and the altitude for the required triangle.

64. Prove that if two squares are constructed equal respectively to two given similar polygons, the sides of the squares have the same ratio as a pair of corresponding sides of the two polygons.

65. Construct a polygon similar to a given polygon and equal to a given square.

66. *Given* *PB'* tangent to ⑤ *O* and *O'* at *B* and *B'* respectively, *POO'* through the line of centers, *PAA'* a common secant, and radii *OA* and *O'A'*. *Prove* that *OA* ∥ *O'A'*.

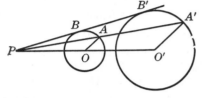

67. Find a point such that tangents from it to two given circles are equal.

68. The lines from the vertex of a triangle that trisect the opposite side do not trisect the angle.

69. *PQ* intersects *AB* in *F*, *AP* ⊥ *PF*, and *BQ* ⊥ *FQ*. *PQ* rotates about the point *F*. Prove that the ratio *PF* : *FQ* is constant.

70. Prove that the line segment joining the midpoints of two adjacent sides of a parallelogram forms with the parallel diagonal a trapezoid whose area is three eighths the area of the parallelogram.

71. *Ptolemy's Theorem.*
Given quadrilateral *ABCD* inscribed in ⊙ *O* and having diagonals *AC* and *BD*.

Prove: $AC \times BD = AD \times BC + AB \times DC$.

SUGGESTIONS. Draw *DF*, making ∠*FDC* = ∠*ADB*. Prove △ *ABD* ∼ △ *FDC* and △ *ADF* ∼ △ *BDC*.

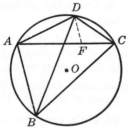

424. Scale Drawings. A *map* or *plan* is a scale drawing.* Its lines are proportional to the lines they represent. By Props. III and XI a map or plan of any plane figure is similar to the figure.

The *scale of a drawing* is the ratio of any line of the drawing to the corresponding line of the object. Thus when 1 inch of the drawing represents 40 feet (480 inches) of the object, the scale is 1 : 480 (usually written in the form *Scale 1″* = 40′).

---

* Pages 521–535 on maps may be studied at this time.

EXERCISES [A]

1. This is the first-floor plan of a dwelling, with the dimensions erased, drawn to the scale $\frac{1}{16}'' = 1'$. The living room is 16 feet wide. How long is it? What are the dimensions of each of the other rooms?

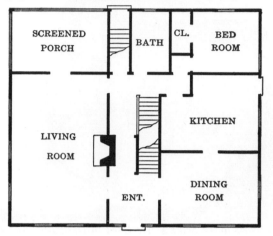

2. Using a map of Texas, find the distance from Galveston to Austin.

3. Excluding the end zones, a football field is 300 feet long and 160 feet wide. It is marked off with lines 5 yards apart and parallel to the end lines. Make a plan of the field using the scale $1'' = 50'$.

4. It is shown in physics that when two concurring forces act at an angle upon an object, their *resultant* (the single force which will produce the same effect on the motion of the object) is represented by the diagonal of a parallelogram constructed on the two segments representing the two given forces. In the figure, AB and AC represent two forces acting at A, and AD represents the resultant of these forces. Two forces, of 30 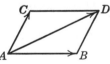 and 40 pounds respectively, act upon a body at an angle of 90°. Find their resultant by constructing the parallelogram of forces to scale.

5. Construct the resultant of two forces, of 100 and 120 pounds respectively, which act at an angle of 60°; at an angle of 90°; at an angle of 120°. Which resultant is the greatest?

6. Two forces act on a body at an angle of 90° and produce a resulting force of 50 pounds. If one force is 40 pounds, what is the other?

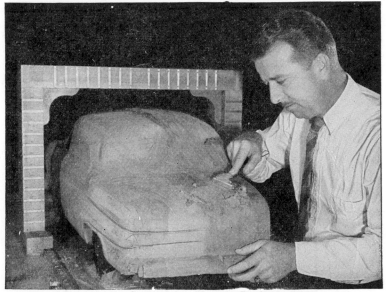

Clay Models to the Scale ⅛ Are Used in Designing Automobiles

7. Two equal forces of 100 pounds each act on a body at an angle of 60°. Find their resultant.

*8. When a plane is flying with the wind blowing against it from a side, the plane is not going in the direction in which its nose is pointed. Thus, if a plane is flying from A toward B at 100 miles an hour and the wind is blowing in the direction AC at 30 miles an hour, in one hour's time the plane will be at D.

Due to its own velocity it has gone from A to B and due to the wind it is carried from B to D. The diagonal AD of the $\Box$ $ABDC$ represents the ground velocity and direction of the plane's path.

A plane is headed east at 240 m.p.h. in a wind that is blowing from the southwest at 30 m.p.h. What is the ground speed of the plane?

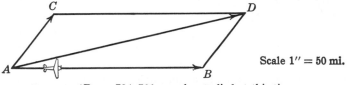

Scale $1'' = 50$ mi.

*Pages 504–511 may be studied at this time.

425. Theorem (*Optional*). *In any triangle, the square of a side opposite an acute angle is equal to the sum of the squares of the other two sides, diminished by twice the product of one of those sides and the projection of the other side on it.*

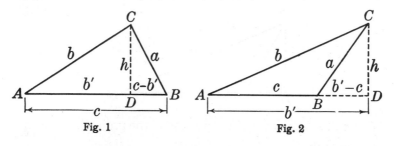

Fig. 1   Fig. 2

Given $\triangle ABC$ with $\angle A$ acute and $AD = b'$ the projection of b on c.

To prove that $a^2 = b^2 + c^2 - 2\,cb'$.

Proof: *STATEMENTS*   *REASONS*

STATEMENTS	REASONS
1. In Fig. 1, $a^2 = h^2 + (c - b')^2$ $\qquad = h^2 + c^2 - 2\,cb' + b'^2.$	1. Why?
2. In Fig. 2, $a^2 = h^2 + (b' - c)^2$ $\qquad = h^2 + c^2 - 2\,cb' + b'^2.$	2. Why?
3. But $h^2 + b'^2 = b^2.$	3. Why?
4. Then, for either triangle, $\qquad a^2 = b^2 + c^2 - 2\,cb'.$	4. Why?

EXERCISES

1. In the theorem above, if $b = 13$, $c = 14$, and $b' = 5$, find a.

2. In the theorem above, if $a = 96$, $b = 58$, and the projection of c on $b = 22$, find c.

3. In $\triangle ABC$, $AB = 10$, $AC = 8$, and $b' = 6.95$. Find BC.

4. In $\triangle ABC$, $AC = 12$, $AB = 17$, and $BC = 19$. Find the projection of AC on AB.

5. In $\triangle DEF$, $DE = 15$, $DF = 12$, and $EF = 10$. Find the projection of EF on DE.

426. Theorem (*Optional**). *In any obtuse triangle, the square of the side opposite the obtuse angle is equal to the sum of the squares of the other two sides, increased by twice the product of one of those sides and the projection of the other side on it.*

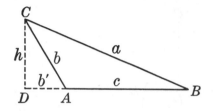

Given $\triangle ABC$ with $\angle A$ obtuse and b' the projection of b on c.

To prove that $a^2 = b^2 + c^2 + 2\,cb'$.

Proof:

STATEMENTS	REASONS
1. $a^2 = h^2 + (b' + c)^2$ $ = h^2 + b'^2 + 2\,b'c + c^2.$	1. Why?
2. But $h^2 + b'^2 = b^2$.	2. Why?
3. $a^2 = b^2 + c^2 + 2\,b'c.$	3. Why?

427. Theorem. *In $\triangle ABC$, if $a^2 < b^2 + c^2$, $\angle A$ is acute; and if $a^2 > b^2 + c^2$, $\angle A$ is obtuse.*

EXERCISES

1. The sides of a triangle are 6 inches, 7 inches, and 9 inches. Is the largest angle of the triangle acute, right, or obtuse?

2. The sides of a triangle are 7, 24, and 25. Is the largest angle acute, obtuse, or right?

3. In $\triangle ABC$, $AC = 10$, $AB = 12$, and the projection of AC on $AB = 3\frac{1}{3}$; $\angle A$ is obtuse. Find BC.

4. The sides of a triangle are 9, 15, and 17. Is the triangle acute, obtuse, or right?

5. *Prove:* The sum of the squares of the diagonals of a parallelogram is equal to the sum of the squares of the four sides

*The law of cosines states that $a^2 = b^2 + c^2 - 2\,bc \cos A$. This law holds for $\angle A$ being an acute angle, an obtuse angle, or a right angle.

428.* **Formulas for the Median and Angle Bisector of a Triangle** (*Optional*). The median of a triangle is given by the formula $m_c = \frac{1}{2}\sqrt{2(a^2 + b^2) - c^2}$. (Fig. 1.) The bisector of an angle of a triangle can be expressed by $t_c = \sqrt{ab - mn}$ where m and n are the segments of c made by the bisector t_c. (Fig. 2.)

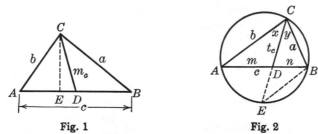

Fig. 1   Fig. 2

The bisector of an angle of a triangle in terms of its sides is given by $t_c = \dfrac{2}{a+b} \sqrt{abs(s-c)}$ where $s = \frac{1}{2}(a+b+c)$. (Fig. 2.)

EXERCISES

1. The sides of a triangle are 18, 24, and 30. Find the median to the side 24.

2. The sides of a triangle are 8, 15, and 17. Find the altitude to the side 15.

3. In triangle ABC, $AB = 30$, $AC = 15$, and $BC = 18$. Find the segments of AB made by the bisector of angle C. Find the length of the bisector of angle C.

4. In $\triangle ABC$, $AB = 17$, $AC = 8$, and $BC = 15$. Find the lengths of the three medians.

5. In $\triangle ABC$, $AB = 18$, $BC = 20$, and $AC = 16$. Find the lengths of the bisectors of the three angles.

6. In $\triangle RST$, $RS = 8$, $ST = 10$, and $RT = 12$. Find the three altitudes.

7. In $\triangle ABC$, $AB = 10$, $AC = 13$, and $BC = 13$. Find the lengths of the three medians; of the three altitudes; of the bisectors of the three angles.

*The formulas in § 428 are given without proof because of the time element.

APPLIED PROBLEMS

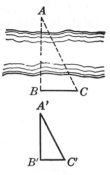

1. Some boys at the point B wished to find the distance across a stream to A. They proceeded as follows: First they set a stake at the point C so that $BC = 100$ feet. From C they sighted the point A. Then on paper they constructed $\triangle A'B'C'$, making $B'C' = 8$ inches, $\angle B' = \angle B$, and $\angle C' = \angle C$. Then they measured $A'B'$ and found it to be 15.5 inches. See if you can find the length of AB by using their measurements.

2. This figure represents a pair of *proportional dividers*. They are adjusted by a thumbscrew at O so that $\dfrac{AO}{OB} = \dfrac{CO}{OD}$. Prove that $\triangle AOC \sim \triangle DOB$. If the dividers are adjusted so that $\dfrac{AO}{OB} = \dfrac{3}{2}$, how will any measurement made with the points A and C compare with a measurement made by D and B? How could you use the dividers to make a line segment two thirds as large as another line segment?

3. The *pantograph* is an instrument used to draw a plane figure similar to a given plane figure. With it, drawings and maps may be enlarged or reduced in size. There are many different forms of pantographs, but they are all based on the same principle. The instrument consists of two pairs of parallel bars joined to form a parallelogram. The point A is fixed and the points B and C are movable. All three points, A, B, and C, lie in a straight line and no two of them are on the same bar.

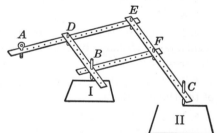

a. Prove that $\triangle ABD \sim \triangle ACE$.

b. Prove that $\dfrac{AD}{AE} = \dfrac{EF}{EC}$.

c. Prove that quadrilateral I $\sim$ quadrilateral II. (Draw diagonals.)

4. See if you can discover a practical method of finding the height of a flagpole by using similar triangles.

5. An engineer wishes to construct a circular arch having a span of 12 feet and a height of 4 feet. Find the radius of the arc.

6. To lay out the strongest rectangular beam (one that will carry the heaviest load without breaking) that can be cut from a circular log, the sawyer trisects the diameter of a cross section. At *C* and *D*, the points of trisection, he then draws *CE* and *DF*, each perpendicular to *AB*. Next he draws *BF*, *FA*, *AE*, and *EB*.

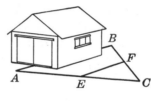

  a. *Prove* that *AEBF* is a rectangle.
  b. *Prove* that $\triangle ACE \sim \triangle AEB$.
  c. *Prove* that $\overline{AE}^2 = \frac{1}{3}\overline{AB}^2$.
  d. *Prove* that $\overline{BE}^2 = \frac{2}{3}\overline{AB}^2$.
  e. *Prove* that $\dfrac{AE}{BE} = \dfrac{1}{\sqrt{2}}$.

7. A geometry class was asked to find the distance between two points *A* and *B*, which were on opposite sides of a building. Show how the figure *AECFB* can be used to find *AB*.

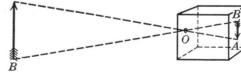

8. A girl scout found the height of a tree by placing a mirror horizontally on the ground and walking backwards until she could see the reflection of the top of the tree in it. Her eye was 4 feet 3 inches from the ground when her feet were 6 feet from the mirror. What was the height of the tree if it was 42 feet from the mirror?

9. *A'B'* is the image of *AB* in a pinhole box camera. Notice that the image is inverted. The object *AB* is 10 inches long and the camera is 8 inches long. How far should the camera be from *AB* to make the image one inch long?

[Space geometry. Optional]

429. Theorem. *If two lines are cut by three parallel planes, their corresponding segments are proportional.*

Given AB and *CD* cut by the ∥ planes *m, n,* and *s* at *A, E, B,* and *C, F, D* respectively.

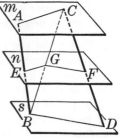

To prove that $\dfrac{AE}{EB} = \dfrac{CF}{FD}$.

Proof:

STATEMENTS	REASONS
1. Draw *BC*, intersecting *n* in *G*.	1. Why possible?
2. The plane of *BA* and *BC* intersects *n* in *EG* and *m* in *AC*. Also the plane of *BC* and *DC* intersects *s* in *BD* and *n* in *GF*.	2. Why?
3. *EG* ∥ *AC* and *GF* ∥ *BD*.	3. Why?
4. ∴ $\dfrac{AE}{EB} = \dfrac{CG}{GB}$ and $\dfrac{CG}{GB} = \dfrac{CF}{FD}$.	4. Why?
5. ∴ $\dfrac{AE}{EB} = \dfrac{CF}{FD}$.	5. Why?

EXERCISES

1. In the figure above, if *AE* = 24, *EB* = 15, and *CF* = 36, find *FD*.

2. In the figure above, if *AE* = 12, *EB* = 18, and *CD* = 40, find *CF*.

3. In the figure above, find *EG* if *AE* = 10, *EB* = 6, and *AC* = 8.

4. In the figure above, find *BD* if *CD* = 20, *CF* = 8, and *GF* = 6.

5. Find *AB* and *CD* in the figure above if *BG* = *GC*, *AE* = 4, and *CF* = 6.

6. What is the locus of a point whose distances from two parallel planes are in the ratio 1 : 2?

7. What is the locus of a line which intersects a given line at a given point and makes an angle of 45 degrees with the given line?

430. Theorem. *If a pyramid is cut by a plane parallel to the base, the lateral edges and the altitude are divided proportionally.*

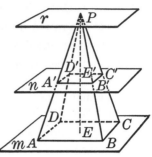

Given the pyramid *P-ABCD*, and plane *n* parallel to plane *m* of the base and cutting the lateral edges in *A'*, *B'*, *C'*, *D'*, and the altitude *PE* in *E'*.

To prove that
$$\frac{PA'}{PA} = \frac{PB'}{PB} = \frac{PC'}{PC} = \frac{PD'}{PD} = \frac{PE'}{PE}.$$

Proof:

STATEMENTS	REASONS
1. Pass plane *r* through *P* ∥ *m*.	1. Why possible?
2. Then *r* ∥ *n* ∥ *m*.	2. Why?
3. Then $\dfrac{PA'}{PA} = \dfrac{PB'}{PB} = \dfrac{PC'}{PC} = \dfrac{PD'}{PD} = \dfrac{PE'}{PE}.$	3. Why?

EXERCISES

1. It is proved in solid geometry that, in the figure above, polygon *ABCD* ∼ polygon *A'B'C'D'*; also that the area of the section is to the area of the base as the square of the distance of the section from the vertex is to the square of the altitude of the pyramid. In the figure, find the area of the base if $PE' = 2$, $PE = 4$, and the area of the section is 12 square inches.

2. It is shown by experiments in physics that the intensity of light on a screen varies inversely as the square of the distance from the source of light *S*. If the distance from *S* to *A'B'C'D'* is 2 inches and from *S* to *ABCD* is 6 inches, how many times as great is the

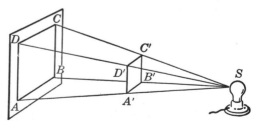

intensity on the screen when placed at *A'B'C'D'* as when placed at *ABCD*?

REVIEW QUESTIONS

1. When is the projection of one line upon another a point?

2. What is a ratio? a proportion?

3. State five methods of proving triangles similar.

4. What are the two conditions necessary for the similarity of two polygons?

5. How many pairs of similar triangles are formed when an altitude is drawn to the hypotenuse of a right triangle?

6. State two propositions in which a mean proportional is mentioned.

7. If the altitude is drawn to the hypotenuse of a right triangle, state three geometric truths which follow.

8. For what purposes are triangles proved congruent?

9. For what purposes are triangles proved similar?

10. What fact do you know about the altitudes of similar triangles?

11. Is the side of a square the mean proportional between the whole diagonal and half the diagonal?

12. What is the most common method of proving triangles similar?

13. What special kind of triangles are similar?

14. What special kind of quadrilaterals are similar?

15. If the altitude of a triangle is 4, what is the altitude of a similar triangle whose perimeter is five times as great?

16. Are two polygons always similar if their corresponding sides are proportional? Are two triangles always similar if their corresponding sides are proportional?

17. State the Pythagorean Theorem.

18. State the theorem concerning a tangent and a secant from a point outside a circle.

19. What is the ratio of a diagonal of a square to one of its sides?

20. State a proposition in which the product of two line segments equals the product of two other line segments.

21. How can you find a leg of a right triangle when the hypotenuse and the other leg are known?

22. Must similar polygons have the same number of sides?

SUMMARY OF PRINCIPAL METHODS OF PROOF

431. *Two triangles are similar*

a. If two angles of one triangle are equal respectively to two angles of another.

b. If they have their sides respectively proportional.

c. If an angle of one triangle equals an angle of the other and the including sides are proportional.

d. If they are each similar to a third triangle.

e. If they are corresponding triangles of similar polygons.

f. If they are right triangles and have an acute angle of one equal to an acute angle of the other.

g. If they are right triangles and one of them is formed by the altitude on the hypotenuse of the other.

h. If they are formed by the altitude on the hypotenuse of a right triangle.

432. *Line segments in proportion*

a. Two corresponding sides of similar polygons have the same ratio as any two other corresponding sides.

b. Two corresponding altitudes of two similar triangles have the same ratio as any two corresponding sides.

c. The perimeters of two similar polygons have the same ratio as any two corresponding sides.

433. *Products of line segments*

If two chords intersect within a circle, the product of the segments of one is equal to the product of the segments of the other.

434. *A line segment the mean proportional*

a. The altitude on the hypotenuse of a right triangle is the mean proportional between the segments of the hypotenuse.

b. Either leg of a right triangle is the mean proportional between the hypotenuse and its projection on the hypotenuse.

c. The perpendicular from any point on a circle to a diameter of the circle is the mean proportional between the segments of the diameter.

d. If a tangent and a secant are drawn to a circle from the same point, the tangent is the mean proportional between the secant and its external segment.

435. *Two polygons are similar*

a. If their corresponding angles are equal and their corresponding sides are proportional.

b. If they are composed of the same number of triangles, similar each to each and similarly placed.

436. *Ratios of areas*

a. The areas of two similar triangles have the same ratio as the squares of any two corresponding sides, or as the squares of any two corresponding altitudes.

b. The areas of any two similar polygons have the same ratio as the squares of any two corresponding sides.

437. *Constructions*

a. To construct the mean proportional between two given line segments.

b. Upon a given line segment corresponding to one side of a given polygon construct a polygon similar to the given polygon.

c. To construct a square equal to a given parallelogram.

TEST 31

True-False Statements (*Eight Minutes*)

Copy the numbers of these statements on your paper. Then if a statement is *always* true, write T after its number. If a statement is *not always* true, write F after its number. Do not guess.

1. Two congruent polygons are similar.

2. All squares are similar.

3. All rectangles are similar.

4. If the sides of one quadrilateral are respectively proportional to the sides of another quadrilateral, the corresponding angles are equal.

5. If the angles of one triangle are respectively equal to the angles of another triangle, the corresponding sides are proportional.

6. The altitude upon the hypotenuse of a right triangle forms two similar right triangles.

7. Two isosceles triangles are similar if an angle of one is equal to a corresponding angle of the other.

8. In the figure, $\triangle ABC \sim \triangle BCD$.

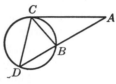

9. Either leg of a right triangle is a mean proportional between the hypotenuse and the other leg.

10. Two similar polygons are congruent.

11. The hypotenuse of a right triangle is equal to the sum of the other two sides.

12. The side of a square is the mean proportional between a diagonal and one half a diagonal.

13. If two chords intersect in a circle, the sum of the segments of one is equal to the sum of the segments of the other.

14. If a tangent and a secant are drawn to a circle from the same point, the tangent is the mean proportional between the secant and its internal segment.

15. If the nonparallel sides of a trapezoid are produced until they meet, two similar triangles are formed.

16. A median of a triangle separates the triangle into two similar triangles.

TEST 32

Completing Statements (Ten Minutes)

On your paper write one word, and only one, for each blank to make the following statements true:

1. Two polygons are similar if their corresponding sides are __?__ and their corresponding angles are __?__.

2. If two triangles have two angles of one equal respectively to two angles of the other, the __?__ are __?__.

3. The corresponding altitudes of two similar triangles have the same ratio as any two __?__ __?__.

4. If two triangles have an angle of one equal to an angle of the other and the including __?__ __?__, the triangles are similar.

5. The perpendicular from any point on a circle to a diameter of the circle is the mean proportional between the __?__ of the __?__.

6. Not all rectangles are similar, because their __?__ __?__ are not necessarily __?__.

7. Not all rhombuses are similar, because their __?__ __?__ are not necessarily __?__.

8. The __?__ of a line segment upon a line is the segment that is cut off on the line by the perpendiculars drawn from the end points of the given line segment.

9. If two polygons can be separated into the same number of triangles, similar each to each and similarly placed, the polygons __?__ __?__.

10. If a tangent and a secant are drawn to a circle from the same point, the tangent is the mean proportional between the _ ?__ and its __?__ __?__.

TEST 33

Constructions (Twelve Minutes)

Make the following geometric constructions accurately.

1. Construct a triangle similar to a given triangle and having its sides twice as long.

2. Given two line segments, m and n, construct a line segment p so that $p = \sqrt{mn}$.

TEST 34

Applications (Thirty Minutes)

1. The sides of one triangle are 8, 10, and 12. The smallest side of a similar triangle is 20. Find the length of the greatest side.

2. In a circle, chords AB and CD intersect in E. If $CE = 8$, $ED = 6$, and $EB = 3$, find AE.

3. The perimeter of a rectangle is 50 inches and the width is 8 inches. Find the perimeter of a similar rectangle whose width is 12 inches.

4. In the figures below, ▲ ABC and $A'B'C'$ are similar. Find $B'C'$,

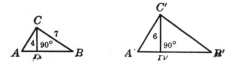

5. The diagonal of a square is $\sqrt{8}$. Find the length of a side.

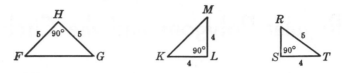

6. Which two triangles are similar in the figures above? Find FG Find RS.

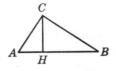

7. In the figure above, CH is the altitude upon hypotenuse AB of rt. $\triangle ABC$. If $AH = 4$ and $CH = 6$, find HB.

8. Using the figure in Ex. 7, if $AH = 5$ and $HB = 45$, find CH.

9. Using the figure in Ex. 7, if $AH = 4$ and $HB = 12$, find AC.

10. AB is a diameter of $\odot$ O, C is a point on the circle, and $CD \perp AB$ at D. Find CD if AD is 9 inches and AB is 25 inches.

11. In the figure above, AB is a tangent to $\odot$ O and secant ACD passes through O. If $AC = 4$ and $AB = 6$, find AD. If $AC = 3$ and $CD = 24$, find AB.

12. The sides of a polygon are 7, 10, 12, and 14 respectively. Find the perimeter of a similar polygon whose longest side is 3.

13. A line segment 10 inches long makes an angle of 60° with another line. Find the length of the projection of the first line on the second.

14. What is the ratio of similitude of the similar triangles in Ex. 6 above?

CHAPTER XIII

Regular Polygons and the Circle

438. In this chapter we shall study the relations of a circle to the regular polygons inscribed in and circumscribed about the circle. From these relations we shall be able to determine the approximate value of π and to express the area of a circle in terms of its radius.

It is essential at this time to review some of the important facts about polygons and circles.

REVIEW EXERCISES [A]

1. What two conditions are necessary for a polygon to be regular? to be similar to another polygon?

2. What is the name of a regular polygon of three sides? of four sides? of five sides? of six sides?

3. When is a polygon said to be inscribed in a circle? circumscribed about a circle? In each case what can you say about the circle?

4. State a theorem concerning the perimeters of two similar polygons.

5. State a theorem concerning the areas of two similar polygons.

6. What have you proved concerning two equal chords of a circle? about equal arcs of a circle?

7. What arc has the same number of degrees as a central angle? as an inscribed angle? as an angle formed by a tangent and a chord intersecting on a circle?

8. Name a quadrilateral which is equilateral but not regular.

9. State the theorem concerning the sum of the exterior angles of a polygon.

10. State the theorem concerning the sum of the interior angles of a polygon.

★Proposition I. Theorem

439. *A circle can be circumscribed about any regular polygon.*

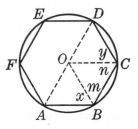

Given the regular polygon *ABCDEF*.

To prove that a ⊙ can be circumscribed about *ABCDEF*.

Selection of Method: 1. Known methods of proving a ⊙ is circumscribed: §§ 343, 269.
2. Method to be used: §§ 343, 269.

Proof: *STATEMENTS* *REASONS*

STATEMENTS	REASONS
1. Construct ⊙ *O* through *A*, *B*, and *C*.	1. § 343.
2. Draw *OA*, *OB*, *OC*, and *OD*.	2. Why possible?
3. *OB* = *OC*.	3. Why?
4. ∴ ∠ *m* = ∠ *n*.	4. Why?
5. But ∠ *ABC* = ∠ *BCD*.	5. Why?
6. ∴ ∠ *x* = ∠ *y*.	6. Ax. 2.
7. *AB* = *CD*.	7. Why?
8. From (3), (6), (7), △ *AOB* ≅ △ *COD*.	8. Why?
9. ∴ *OA* = *OD*, or *OD* = a radius.	9. Why?
10. ∴ ⊙ *O* passes through *D*.	10. § 262 *b*.
11. In like manner, we can prove that the ⊙ passes through the remaining vertices.	11. Reasons 3–10.
12. ∴ the ⊙ *O* is circumscribed about *ABCDEF*.	12. § 269.

Proposition II. Theorem

440. *A circle can be inscribed in any regular polygon.*

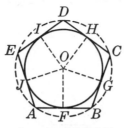

Given the regular polygon *ABCDE*.

To prove that a ⊙ can be inscribed in *ABCDE*.

Selection of Method: 1. Known methods of proving a ⊙ is inscribed: §§ 305, 348.
2. Method to be used: § 305.

Proof:

STATEMENTS	REASONS
1. Circumscribe ⊙ *O* about *ABCDE*.	1. § 439.
2. *AB = BC = CD = DE = EA*.	2. Why?
3. Construct ⊥s from *O* to each side of *ABCDE*.	3. Why possible?
4. *OF = OG = OH = OI = OJ*.	4. § 274.
5. With *O* as a center and *OF* as a radius construct a ⊙.	5. Why possible?
6. The sides of *ABCDE* are tangent to this ⊙.	6. §§ 262 *b*, 279.
7. ∴ this ⊙ is inscribed in *ABCDE*.	7. § 305.

441. Corollary I. *The circumscribed circle and the inscribed circle of a regular polygon are concentric.*

442. Names Associated with a Regular Polygon. The *center* of a regular polygon is the common center of the circumcircle and the incircle.

The *radius* of a regular polygon is the radius of the circumcircle. It connects the center to a vertex of the polygon.

The *apothem* (ăp′ŏ thĕm) of a regular polygon is the radius of the incircle, or the perpendicular from the center to a side.

A *central angle* of a regular polygon is an angle formed by two radii drawn to the extremities of a side.

443. Corollary II. *The central angle of a regular polygon of n sides is* $\dfrac{360°}{n}$.

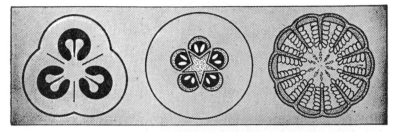

Cross Sections of Seed Pods

EXERCISES

A

1. Find the number of degrees in the central angle and in each interior angle of each of the following regular polygons:

   a. Triangle.   *c.* Quadrilateral.   *e.* Octagon.
   b. Pentagon.   *d.* Hexagon.   *f.* Heptagon.

2. A central angle of a regular polygon is the supplement of an interior angle of the polygon.

3. The apothem of a regular polygon bisects the side to which it is drawn. (Draw the circumcircle.)

4. Each angle of a regular polygon is bisected by the radius of the polygon drawn to its vertex.

5. A central angle of a regular polygon is equal to an exterior angle of the polygon.

B

6. Show that the apothem of a regular inscribed hexagon is $\frac{1}{2} R\sqrt{3}$ and that the area of the polygon is $\frac{3}{2} R^2\sqrt{3}$, where R is the radius of the polygon.

7. Find the area of a regular hexagon with a side of 4 inches.

Proposition III. Theorem

444. *If a circle is divided into any number of equal arcs, the chords of these arcs form a regular inscribed polygon.*

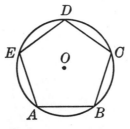

Given ⊙ *O*, with $\widehat{AB} = \widehat{BC} = \widehat{CD} = \widehat{DE} = \widehat{EA}$ and chords *AB*, *BC*, *CD*, *DE*, and *EA*.

To prove that *ABCDE* is a regular inscribed polygon.

Selection of Method: 1. Known methods of proving polygons regular: § 168.
2. Method to be used: § 168.

Proof:

STATEMENTS	REASONS
1. $\widehat{AB} = \widehat{BC} = \widehat{CD} = \widehat{DE} = \widehat{EA}$.	1. Why?
2. ∴ $AB = BC = CD = DE = EA$.	2. Why?
3. $\widehat{BCDE} = \widehat{CDEA} = \widehat{DEAB}$ = etc.	3. Ax. 1.
4. $\angle A \stackrel{\circ}{=} \frac{1}{2} \widehat{BCDE}$, $\angle B \stackrel{\circ}{=} \frac{1}{2} \widehat{CDEA}$, $\angle C \stackrel{\circ}{=} \frac{1}{2} \widehat{DEAB}$, etc.	4. Why?
5. ∴ $\angle A = \angle B = \angle C = \angle D = \angle E$.	5. Why?
6. ∴ *ABCDE* is a regular inscribed polygon.	6. §§ 168, 269.

445. Corollary I. *An equilateral polygon inscribed in a circle is a regular polygon.*

446. Corollary II. *If the midpoints of the arcs of a regular inscribed polygon are joined to the extremities of the respective sides, a regular inscribed polygon of double the number of sides is formed.*

Proposition IV. Theorem

447. *If a circle is divided into any number of equal arcs, the tangents drawn to the circle at the successive points of division form a regular circumscribed polygon.*

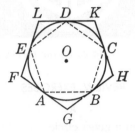

Given $\odot$ *O* with $\overarc{AB} = \overarc{BC} = \overarc{CD} = \overarc{DE} = \overarc{EA}$ and *FG, GH, HK, KL,* and *LF* tangent to the $\odot$ at *A, B, C, D,* and *E* respectively.

To prove that *FGHKL* is a regular circumscribed polygon.

Selection of Method: 1. Known methods of proving polygons regular: §§ 168, 444, 445, 446.
2. Method to be used: § 168.

Proof: STATEMENTS   REASONS

STATEMENTS	REASONS
1. Draw the chords *AB, BC, CD, DE,* and *EA*.	1. Why possible?
2. $AB = BC = CD = DE = EA$.	2. Why?
3. $\angle BAG = \angle ABG = \angle CBH = \angle BCH = \angle DCK = \angle CDK = $ etc.	3. § 302; Ax. 6.
4. $\therefore \triangle AGB \cong \triangle BHC \cong \triangle CKD \cong$ etc.	4. Why?
5. $\therefore \angle G = \angle H = \angle K = $ etc.	5. Why?
6. $\triangle AGB, BHC, CKD,$ etc. are isosceles.	6. Why?
7. $AG = GB = BH = HC = $ etc.	7. Why?
8. $\therefore FG = GH = HK = KL = $ etc.	8. Ax. 1.
9. $\therefore$ *FGHKL* is a regular circumscribed polygon.	9. §§ 168, 305.

Designs Based on the Hexagon

REVIEW EXERCISES

A

1. Inscribe a square in a given circle.

2. Inscribe a regular hexagon in a given circle.

3. How would you inscribe a regular octagon in a circle?

4. How would you inscribe a regular polygon of 12 sides in a circle?

5. Circumscribe a square about a circle.

6. Circumscribe a circle about a given square.

7. Draw a hexagon which is equiangular but not regular.

8. Draw a hexagon which is equilateral but not regular.

B

9. Draw a regular polygon. Prove that the lines which join the midpoints of its sides in order form another regular polygon.

10. The apothem of an equilateral triangle is one half the radius.

11. An equiangular polygon circumscribed about a circle is regular.

12. Prove that the diagonals of a regular pentagon are equal.

C

13. If s is a side of an equilateral triangle inscribed in a circle whose radius is R, show that $s = R\sqrt{3}$.

14. If s is a side of an equilateral octagon inscribed in a circle whose radius is R, show that $s = R\sqrt{2 - \sqrt{2}}$.

15. If two diagonals of a regular pentagon intersect, prove that the greater segment of each is equal to a side of the pentagon.

★★ Proposition V. Theorem

448. *The area of a regular polygon is equal to one half the product of its apothem and its perimeter.*

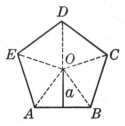

Given the regular polygon *ABCDE*, with apothem *a*, perimeter *p*, and area *S*.

To prove that $S = \frac{1}{2} ap$.

Selection of Method: 1. Known methods of finding areas of polygons: § 254.
2. Method to be used: § 254 *c*.

Proof: STATEMENTS	REASONS
1. Draw the radii *OA, OB, OC* · · ·.	1. Why possible?
2. The altitude of each triangle = *a*.	2. Why?
3. $\triangle OAB = \frac{1}{2} a \cdot AB$, $\triangle OBC = \frac{1}{2} a \cdot BC$, $\triangle OCD = \frac{1}{2} a \cdot CD$, etc.	3. § 254 *c*.
4. $\triangle OAB + \triangle OBC + \triangle OCD + \cdots$ $= \frac{1}{2} a(AB + BC + CD + \cdots)$.	4. Why?
5. $\therefore S = \frac{1}{2} ap$.	5. Why?

EXERCISE

Prove that the area of a polygon circumscribed about a circle is equal to one half the product of the perimeter of the polygon and the radius of the circle.

Proposition VI. Theorem

449. *Two regular polygons of the same number of sides are similar.*

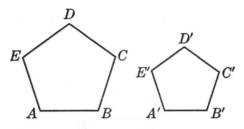

Given the regular polygons $ABCDE$ and $A'B'C'D'E'$, each having n sides.

To prove that $ABCDE \sim A'B'C'D'E'$.

Selection of Method: 1. Known methods of proving polygons $\sim$: § 435.
2. Method to be used: § 435 *a*.

Proof: STATEMENTS	REASONS
1. $\angle A = \angle B = \angle C = \cdots = \dfrac{180(n-2)^\circ}{n}$.	1. § 194.
2. $\angle A' = \angle B' = \angle C' = \cdots = \dfrac{180(n-2)^\circ}{n}$.	2. Why?
3. $\therefore \angle A = \angle A', \angle B = \angle B', \angle C = \angle C', \cdots$.	3. Why?
4. $AB = BC = CD = \cdots$.	4. Why?
5. $A'B' = B'C' = C'D' = \cdots$.	5. Why?
6. $\therefore \dfrac{AB}{A'B'} = \dfrac{BC}{B'C'} = \dfrac{CD}{C'D'} = \cdots$.	6. Ax. 4.
7. $\therefore ABCDE \sim A'B'C'D'E'$.	7. § 435 *a*.

450. Corollary. *The areas of two regular polygons of the same number of sides have the same ratio as the squares of any two corresponding sides.* (See § 421.)

Proposition VII. Theorem

451. *The perimeters of two regular polygons of the same number of sides have the same ratio as their radii or as their apothems.*

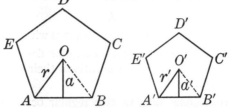

Given the regular polygons $ABCDE$ and $A'B'C'D'E'$ each having n sides, with centers O and O', radii r and r', apothems a and a', and perimeters p and p'.

To prove that $\dfrac{p}{p'} = \dfrac{r}{r'} = \dfrac{a}{a'}$.

Selection of Method: 1. Known methods of proving line segments proportional: §§ 389, 432.
2. Method to be used: § 432 *c*, *b*.

Proof: *STATEMENTS* *REASONS*

1. Draw OB and $O'B'$.	1. Why possible?
2. $ABCDE \sim A'B'C'D'E'$.	2. Why?
3. $\therefore \dfrac{p}{p'} = \dfrac{AB}{A'B'}$.	3. Why?
4. In ⧍ AOB and $A'O'B'$, $\angle AOB = \dfrac{360°}{n} = \angle A'O'B'$.	4. Give proof.
5. $AO = OB$ and $A'O' = O'B'$.	5. Why?
6. $\therefore \dfrac{AO}{A'O'} = \dfrac{OB}{O'B'}$.	6. Ax. 4.
7. $\therefore \triangle AOB \sim \triangle A'O'B'$.	7. § 403.
8. $\therefore \dfrac{a}{a'} = \dfrac{r}{r'} = \dfrac{AB}{A'B'}$.	8. § 432 *b*.
9. From (3) and (8), $\dfrac{p}{p'} = \dfrac{a}{a'} = \dfrac{r}{r'}$.	9. Ax. 6.

452. Corollary. *The areas of two regular polygons of the same number of sides have the same ratio as the squares of their radii or as the squares of their apothems.*

EXERCISES. REGULAR POLYGONS

A

1. Find the apothem of an inscribed square whose side is 10 inches.

2. The corresponding sides of two regular decagons are 2 inches and 6 inches respectively. Find the ratio of their perimeters and the ratio of their areas.

3. The corresponding sides of two regular octagons are 3 inches and 5 inches respectively. What is the ratio of their radii? of their apothems? of their perimeters? of their areas?

4. Find the side of a square inscribed in a circle whose radius is 10 inches.

5. Find the area of a regular hexagon if each side is 5 inches.

6. The perimeters of two regular polygons having the same number of sides are 36 inches and 63 inches respectively. If the radius of the first polygon is 6 inches, what is the radius of the other?

7. The area of one regular nonagon is 212 square inches, and the area of another regular nonagon is 53 square inches. Find the ratio of their radii; of their apothems.

B

8. Find the ratio of the perimeters of two regular octagons whose areas are 25 square feet and 50 square feet respectively.

9. The altitudes of two equilateral triangles are 3 inches and 8 inches respectively. Find the ratio of their perimeters; the ratio of their areas.

10. The area of the cross section of a steel beam 3 inches thick is 28 square inches. What is the area of a cross section of a beam of similar proportions and $4\frac{1}{2}$ inches thick?

11. What is the area of the cross section of the largest possible square piece of timber that can be sawed from a round log 18 inches in diameter?

12. Find the apothem of an equilateral triangle whose side is 12 feet.

13. Find the radius of an equilateral triangle whose side is 16 feet.

14. The area of one regular pentagon is $2\frac{1}{4}$ times that of another. What is the ratio of their perimeters?

15. The area of one equilateral triangle is 9 times that of another. Find the ratio of their altitudes.

16. Compare the radii of the circumcircle and incircle of an equilateral triangle.

17. Compare the radii of the circumcircle and incircle of a square.

18. The side of a square inscribed in a circle is 6 inches. Find the diameter of the circle.

19. Find the area of a square whose radius is 8.

20. The radius of a circle is 8 inches. Find the areas and the perimeters of the inscribed and circumscribed squares.

C

21. Every equiangular polygon inscribed in a circle is regular if it has an odd number of sides. Is this true if the polygon has an even number of sides?

22. The side of an inscribed regular hexagon is twice the apothem of an inscribed equilateral triangle.

23. If the side of a square is 4 inches, find the area of the square formed by joining the midpoints of the apothems.

24. Find the area of a rhombus whose shorter diagonal and whose sides are each 18 inches.

25. Each side of the regular hexagon $ABCDEF$ is $8\sqrt{3}$ inches. AE and AD are diagonals. Find the area of $\triangle AED$.

453. Method of Measuring the Circle. A line segment is measured by finding how many times a unit line segment is contained in it. An arc of a circle is measured in terms of a unit of arc of that circle by finding how many times it contains the unit of arc. It is often desirable to measure a circle, or an arc of it, in terms of a straight line segment. Since we cannot directly apply a straight line segment as a unit of measure to a curve line, we shall resort to a process known as the *method of limits* in the measurement of the circle.

To find the approximate value of π (the ratio of the circumference of a circle to the length of the diameter), first we shall inscribe a regular hexagon in a circle. Next, we shall inscribe in the circle regular polygons having 12, 24, 48, 96, 192, 384, and 768 sides respectively. Then compute the perimeter of the regular polygon having 768 sides. Divide the

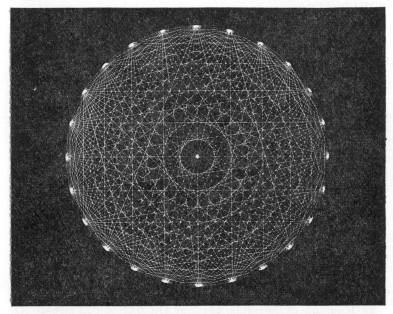

This Figure, Which Represents a Regular Polygon with Its Diagonals, Consists of Two Hundred Seventy-six Straight Line Segments

perimeter of this polygon, which is a close approximation of the circumference of the circle, by the diameter of the circle. This gives an approximate value of π.

By doubling the number of sides of a regular circumscribed polygon, a polygon may be obtained whose area will be almost the same as the area of the circle. In this manner it will be shown that the approximate area of the circle can be expressed in terms of the radius.

Before studying the theorems on the circumferences and areas of circles, students should have a thorough understanding of the terms "variable," "constant," and "limit of a variable."

454. Constants and Variables. A *constant* is a quantity which has a fixed value throughout a given discussion; and a *variable* is a quantity which may have different successive values during a discussion.

If we inscribe a regular polygon in a circle and then continue to double the number of its sides, the successive perimeters become greater and greater, and the successive apothems become greater and greater. In this case, the polygon is a variable, for it changes; the perimeter is a variable, for it has different values; but the circle is a constant, for it does not change. Is the apothem a constant or a variable? Is the radius a constant or a variable?

455.* Limits. When a variable so approaches a constant that the difference between the two *becomes* and *remains* less than any assigned positive value, however small, the constant is called the *limit of the variable.*

Consider the decimal which has the successive values .3, .33, .333, · · ·. As the digit 3 is continually annexed, the value of the decimal becomes greater and greater but always remains less than $\frac{1}{3}$. This decimal is a variable quantity and approaches the fraction $\frac{1}{3}$ as a limit.

The symbol for "approaches as a limit" is →. Thus $x \rightarrow c$ is read "x approaches c as a limit."

ORAL EXERCISES. LIMITS

1. Two regular polygons, of 16 and 32 sides respectively, are inscribed in a circle. Which polygon has the greater apothem? Why? Which polygon has the greater perimeter? Why?

2. As the number of sides of a regular inscribed polygon is indefinitely increased, what do you think will be the limit of its apothem? of its perimeter?

*If desired, §§ 455–458 and 460 may be omitted and the theorems in §§ 461 and 468 may be postulated.

3. As the number of 6's in the decimal .666 is increased indefinitely, what common fraction will the decimal approach as a limit?

4. As the number of 7's in the decimal .777 is increased indefinitely, what common fraction will the decimal approach as a limit?

5. As the number of 8's in the decimal .888 is increased indefinitely, what common fraction will the decimal approach as a limit?

6. If the number of sides of a regular circumscribed polygon is increased indefinitely,

    a. What is the limit of the perimeter of the polygon?

    b. What is the limit of the area of the polygon?

    c. Is the apothem of the polygon a variable?

7. Zeno, one of the most prominent investigators of problems of infinite series in the fifth century B.C., argued that Achilles could not pass a tortoise even though he went faster than the tortoise. He argued that if Achilles could run ten times as fast as a tortoise and if the tortoise had a start of 1000 yards, when Achilles had gone the 1000 yards, the tortoise would be 100 yards ahead of him. When Achilles had covered these 100 yards, the tortoise would be 10 yards ahead of him. This would continue forever. Thus Achilles would come nearer and nearer the tortoise but would never reach it. Was Zeno right in his reasoning?

456. Theorems on Limits. The two theorems which follow are used in proving equalities involving the circumferences of circles. Their proofs are too difficult for high-school students, and they will be accepted as true without proof.

457. Theorem. *If a variable x approaches a limit k and if c is a constant, then cx approaches ck as a limit, and $\frac{x}{c}$ approaches $\frac{k}{c}$ as a limit.*

Thus, if x is the variable decimal .333 $\cdots$ and if c is 2, and it is known that .333 $\cdots \rightarrow \frac{1}{3}$, the theorem states that .666 $\cdots \rightarrow \frac{2}{3}$.

458. Theorem. *If two variables are always equal while approaching their respective limits, their limits are equal.*

If the limits were not equal, could the variables be equal when they are very near their limits?

ORAL EXERCISES. LIMITS

1. If the repeating decimal .333 $\cdots \rightarrow \frac{1}{3}$, why will the repeating decimal .04166 $\cdots \rightarrow \frac{1}{24}$?

2. If the repeating decimal .142857142857 $\cdots \rightarrow \frac{1}{7}$, why will .047619047619 $\cdots \rightarrow \frac{1}{21}$?

3. If $x = y$, $x \rightarrow m$, and $y \rightarrow n$, what do you know of m and n? Why?

4. If $p \rightarrow c$ and if r is a constant, what do you know of pr?

5. If the number of sides of a regular inscribed polygon is indefinitely increased, what is the limit of each of its angles? of each of its central angles?

459. Area of a Circle. The area of a circle is the area of the plane surface enclosed by the circle.

460. Postulates on Limits Related to the Circle. Below are three postulates on limits expressing relations of the circle to the inscribed and circumscribed regular polygons.

a. **Post. 32.** *If the number of sides of a regular inscribed (or circumscribed) polygon is indefinitely increased, the perimeter of the polygon approaches the circumference of the circle as a limit.*

b. **Post. 33.** *If the number of sides of a regular inscribed (or circumscribed) polygon is indefinitely increased, the area of the polygon approaches the area of the circle as a limit.*

c. **Post. 34.** *If the number of sides of a regular inscribed polygon is indefinitely increased, the apothem of the polygon approaches the radius of the circle as a limit.*

ORAL EXERCISES. LIMITS

1. A circle is inscribed in one square and circumscribed about another. Which square has the greater area? the greater apothem?

2. A square, a regular octagon, and a regular polygon of 16 sides are circumscribed about a circle. Of the three polygons, which has an area nearest that of the circle?

3. Two regular polygons, of 96 and 384 sides respectively, are circumscribed about a circle. Which polygon has the greater area? the greater perimeter? the greater apothem?

★Proposition VIII. Theorem

461. *The circumferences of two circles have the same ratio as their radii.*

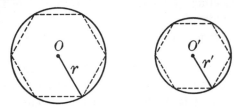

Given the ⊙ O and O' with circumferences c and c' and radii r and r' respectively.

To prove that $\dfrac{c}{c'} = \dfrac{r}{r'}$.

Selection of Method: 1. Known methods of proving line segments proportional: §§ 389, 432, 451.
2. Method to be used: § 451.

Proof: *STATEMENTS* *REASONS*

1. Inscribe regular hexagons in the ⊙ and denote their perimeters by p and p'.	1. § 312.
2. Then $\dfrac{p}{p'} = \dfrac{r}{r'}$.	2. § 451.
3. ∴ $pr' = p'r$.	3. Why?
4. Form regular inscribed polygons of double the number of sides and continue this process indefinitely, keeping the number of sides the same in each ⊙.	4. § 446.
5. Then $p \to c$ and $p' \to c'$.	5. § 460 *a.*
6. ∴ $pr' \to cr'$ and $p'r \to c'r$.	6. § 457.
7. ∴ $cr' = c'r$.	7. § 458.
8. ∴ $\dfrac{c}{c'} = \dfrac{r}{r'}$.	8. § 366.

462. Corollary I. *The circumferences of two circles have the same ratio as their diameters.*

Since $\dfrac{c}{c'} = \dfrac{r}{r'}$, $\dfrac{c}{c'} = \dfrac{2\,r}{2\,r'}$. Why? Then $\dfrac{c}{c'} = \dfrac{d}{d'}$.

463. The Ratio of the Circumference of a Circle to Its Diameter. Since $\dfrac{c}{c'} = \dfrac{d}{d'}$, then $\dfrac{c}{d} = \dfrac{c'}{d'}$. Why? Since $\dfrac{c}{d}$ of one circle is equal to $\dfrac{c'}{d'}$ of any other circle, Corollary I may be stated thus: *The ratio of the circumference of a circle to its diameter is constant.* This constant is represented by the Greek letter π (pī).

★464. Corollary II. *The circumference of a circle is expressed by the formula $c = \pi d$, or $c = 2\,\pi r$.*

465. Historical Note on π. The early Babylonians and Hebrews used 3 as the value of π. Later Ahmes, an Egyptian, found the area of a circle by squaring eight ninths of the diameter, which is approximately the same as using 3.1605 as the value of π. Archimedes (287–212 B.C.) inscribed in and circumscribed about a circle regular polygons of ninety-six sides. He then calculated their perimeters and assumed the circumference of the circle to lie between them. From these results he found the value of π to lie between $3\frac{1}{7}$ and $3\frac{10}{71}$. To make these calculations, Archimedes must have had some method of finding square roots of numbers. The value of π has been worked out by Shanks correct to 707 decimal places. The value of π to ten decimal places is 3.1415926535. This value of π will give the circumference of the earth correct to within a fraction of an inch. In 1766 Lambert proved that π is not rational and in 1882 Lindermann proved that π is a transcendental number—that is, it cannot be the root of an algebraic equation. The fact that π is not the root of an algebraic equation makes it impossible, using only the straightedge and compasses, to construct a line segment equal to the circumference of a circle, or to square a circle (to construct a square whose area is equal to that of a given circle).

Proposition IX. Problem

466. *Given a side of a regular inscribed polygon of n sides, to find the side of a regular inscribed polygon of 2 n sides.*

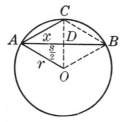

Given $\odot$ O with radius r, AB (s) a side of a regular inscribed polygon of n sides, and AC (x) a side of a regular inscribed polygon of $2\,n$ sides.

To find the value of x.

Solution:

STATEMENTS	REASONS
1. Draw CO, intersecting AB at D.	1. Why possible?
2. Draw BC and BO.	2. Why possible?
3. $AC = BC$.	3. Give proof.
4. $AO = BO$.	4. Why?
5. CO is the $\perp$ bisector of AB.	5. Why?
6. Then $AD = \dfrac{s}{2}$.	6. Why?
7. $OD = \sqrt{r^2 - \dfrac{s^2}{4}}$.	7. By § 411.
8. $CD = r - \sqrt{r^2 - \dfrac{s^2}{4}}$.	8. Why?
9. $x = \sqrt{\dfrac{s^2}{4} + \left(r - \sqrt{r^2 - \dfrac{s^2}{4}}\right)^2}$.	9. By § 41'
10. $x = \sqrt{\dfrac{s^2}{4} + r^2 - 2\,r\sqrt{r^2 - \dfrac{s^2}{4}} + r^2 - \dfrac{s^2}{4}}$.	10. Why?
11. $x = \sqrt{2\,r^2 - 2\,r\sqrt{r^2 - \dfrac{s^2}{4}}}$, or	11. Why?
12. $x = \sqrt{2\,r^2 - r\sqrt{4\,r^2 - s^2}}$.	12. Why?

Proposition X. Problem

467. *To compute the approximate value of* π.

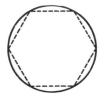

Solution. Inscribe a regular hexagon in a $\odot$ having a radius of 1 inch and denote a side by s_6. Then the perimeter of the hexagon is 6. Why? Doubling the number of sides to obtain a regular polygon of 12 sides and denoting each of its sides by s_{12}, we obtain

$$s_{12} = \sqrt{2\,r^2 - r\sqrt{4\,r^2 - s_6{}^2}} = \sqrt{2 - \sqrt{3}} = .51763809$$

by § 466. The perimeter of the polygon of 12 sides = $12 \times .51763809 = 6.21165708$. Continuing this process we obtain the following:

Number of Sides	One Side *	Perimeter	$P + D$
6	1	6	3
12	$\sqrt{2 - \sqrt{4 - (1)^2}} = .51763809$	6.21165708	3.10582854
24	$\sqrt{2 - \sqrt{4 - (.51763809)^2}} = .26105238$	6.26525722	3.13262861
48	$\sqrt{2 - \sqrt{4 - (.26105238)^2}} = .13080626$	6.27870041	3.13935020
96	$\sqrt{2 - \sqrt{4 - (.13080626)^2}} = .06543817$	6.28206396	3.14103198
192	$\sqrt{2 - \sqrt{4 - (.06543817)^2}} = .03272346$	6.28290510	3.14145255
384	$\sqrt{2 - \sqrt{4 - (.03272346)^2}} = .01636228$	6.28311544	3.14155772
768	$\sqrt{2 - \sqrt{4 - (.01636228)^2}} = .00818121$	6.28316941	3.14158470

Hence $\pi = 3.1416$, approximately.

*The length of each side has been computed to 17 decimal places but is given correct to only 8 decimal places.

★★Proposition XI. Theorem

468. *The area of a circle is equal to one half the product of its radius and its circumference.*

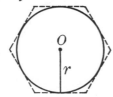

Given the ⊙ *O* with circumference *c*, radius *r*, and area *S*.

To prove that $S = \frac{1}{2} rc$.

Selection of Method: 1. Known methods of finding areas: §§ 254, 448, 460 *b*.
2. Method to be used: §§ 448, 460 *b*.

Proof: STATEMENTS   REASONS

STATEMENTS	REASONS
1. Circumscribe a regular polygon about the ⊙ and let S' denote its area and p its perimeter.	1. § 447.
2. Then $S' = \frac{1}{2} rp$.	2. § 448.
3. Form a regular circumscribed polygon of double the number of sides and continue this process indefinitely.	3. § 447.
4. Then $S' \rightarrow S$ and $p \rightarrow c$.	4. § 460 *b, a.*
5. ∴ $\frac{1}{2} rp \rightarrow \frac{1}{2} rc$.	5. § 457.
6. From (2), (4), and (5), $S = \frac{1}{2} rc$.	6. § 458.

★**469. Corollary I.** *The area of a circle is given by the formula* $S = \pi r^2$.

470. Corollary II. *The areas of two circles have the same ratio as the squares of their radii, or as the squares of their diameters.*

471. Corollary III. *The area of a sector of a circle is to the area of the circle as the angle of the sector is to 360°.* (In the figure of § 472, *OACB* is a sector.)

472. Area of a Segment. The area of segment ACB of circle O (§ 350) may be found by subtracting the area of $\triangle AOB$ from the area of the sector $OACB$.

Example. Find the area of a segment of a circle formed by one side of an inscribed equilateral triangle and its arc if the radius of the circle is 12.

Solution. $\angle AOB = 120°$. Why? Area of sector $OAEB = \frac{1}{3}\pi r^2 = \frac{1}{3}\pi\,12^2 = 150.8$. $\angle AOD = 60°$. Why? $\therefore \angle DAO = 30°$ and $DO = 6$. Why? $\overline{AD}^2 + \overline{DO}^2 = \overline{AO}^2$, or $\overline{AD}^2 + 36 = 144$. Solving, $AD = 6\sqrt{3} = 10.4$. Then $AB = 20.8$. Area of $\triangle ABO = \frac{1}{2} \times DO \times AB = \frac{1}{2} \times 6 \times 20.8 = 62.4$. $\therefore$ area of segment $AEB = 150.8 - 62.4 = 88.4$.

EXERCISES. CIRCLES

A

1. Find the circumference of a circle whose radius is
    a. 6.   *b.* 4.53.   *c.* 12.96.   *d.* 125.

2. Find the area of a circle whose radius is
    a. 3.   *b.* 15.   *c.* 42.   *d.* 13.4.

3. Find the diameter of a circle whose circumference is
    a. 12.5664.   *b.* 78.54.   *c.* 34.5576.   *d.* 100.

4. Find the radius of a circle whose area is
    a. 13.0946.   *b.* 18.8496.   *c.* 324 π.

5. Find the radius of a circle whose circumference is
    a. 27.2744.   *b.* 30.   *c.* 68.

6. Find the area of a semicircle whose diameter is 12.

7. The radii of two circles are 5 inches and 10 inches respectively. Find the ratio of their circumferences; of their areas.

8. Find the radius of a circle equal in area to a square whose area is 16.

9. Find the area of a circular ring formed by two concentric circles of radii 6 inches and 8 inches respectively.

10. A barn is 40 feet wide and 50 feet long. A horse is tied outside the barn at one corner by a rope 50 feet long. Over how many square feet of ground can the horse graze?

11. Find the length of a belt which connects two pulleys having radii of 4 inches, if their centers are 20 inches apart.

12. The radius of one circle is three times that of another. If the area of the smaller circle is 36 square inches, find the area of the larger circle.

B

13. A circular pond with an area of two acres is surrounded by a walk 2 yards wide. Find the cost of graveling the walk at 9 cents a square yard.

14. Find the length of a belt connecting two pulleys having radii of 3 inches and 26 inches respectively if their centers are 46 inches apart.

15. A square is inscribed in a circle whose diameter is 10 inches. Find the difference between the area of the circle and that of the square.

16. In the figure, $AO = OB$. Prove that the area of the shaded portion is equal to the sum of the areas of the smaller semicircles.

17. Find the diameter of a circle whose circumference and area are numerically equal.

18. Find the area of the equilateral arch ACB if the radius of each arc is 6 feet.

19. The area of the cross section of a $\frac{1}{2}$-inch wire is how many times the area of the cross section of a $\frac{1}{8}$-inch wire?

20. In the figure, $AO = OB$ and semicircles are constructed on AO and OB as diameters. Prove that the area of the shaded portion of the circle equals the area of the unshaded portion.

21. If the drive wheels of a locomotive are 60 inches in diameter, find the number of revolutions a minute they make when the engine is going 60 miles an hour.

22 Prove that the area of a circle constructed upon the hypotenuse of a right triangle as a diameter is equal to the sum of the areas of the circles constructed upon the legs as diameters.

C

23. If upon the three sides of a right triangle three semicircles (as shown in the figure) are drawn, the area of the right triangle is equal to the sum of the areas of the two crescents (shaded portions).

24. Prove that the incircle of a square divides the area of the circumcircle into two equal parts.

25. If one side of an equilateral triangle is 6 inches, compute the area of the three crescents bounded by the circumcircle of the triangle and the semicircles constructed on the sides of the triangle as diameters.

26. Prove that the area of the regular hexagon inscribed in a circle is a mean proportional between the area of the inscribed equilateral triangle and the area of the circumscribed equilateral triangle.

27. In the figure, if $CD \perp AB$, prove that the area bounded by the semicircles drawn on AB, AC, and CB as diameters is equal to the area of the circle whose diameter is CD.

473. Extreme and Mean Ratio. A line segment is divided in *extreme and mean ratio* if it is separated into two parts such

$$A \bullet\!\!-\!\!-\!\!-\!\!-\!\!-\!\!-\!\!\overset{C}{\underset{\bullet}{}}\!\!-\!\!-\!\!-\!\!-B$$

that the square of one part is equal to the product of the whole segment and the other part. Thus the line segment AB is divided in extreme and mean ratio by the point C if $\overline{AC}^2 = AB \times CB$, or $\dfrac{AB}{AC} = \dfrac{AC}{CB}$.

The point which divides a line segment in extreme and mean ratio is called the *golden section*. It is claimed that a line segment is most harmoniously divided when it is bisected or when it is divided in extreme and mean ratio by the golden section. Nature has made use of this fact in the construction of many plants. Artists often place the central figure of their paintings in accordance with the principle of the golden 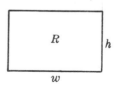 section. Picture frames and book covers are pleasing to the eye when the width and length have the ratio of the segments of a line divided in extreme and mean ratio. Thus the rectangle R has good proportions when $w^2 = h(w + h)$.

Proposition XII. Problem

474. *To divide a given line segment in extreme and mean ratio.*

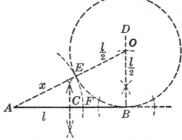

Given the line segment *AB*, or *l*.

To divide AB in extreme and mean ratio.

Construction: STATEMENTS	REASONS
1. Bisect *AB*, locating *C*, the midpoint of *AB*.	1. Why possible?
2. Construct *BD* ⊥ *AB*.	2. Why possible?
3. On *BD* construct $BO = BC = \dfrac{l}{2}$.	3. Why possible?
4. Construct the ⊙ having center *O* and radius $= BO$, or $\dfrac{l}{2}$.	4. Why possible?
5. Draw *AO*, meeting ⊙ *O* at *E*.	5. Why possible?
6. On *AB* construct $AF = AE = x$.	6. Why possible?

Then F divides AB in extreme and mean ratio, or $\overline{AF}^2 = AB \times FB$.

Proof:

1. $\left(x + \dfrac{l}{2}\right)^2 = \left(\dfrac{l}{2}\right)^2 + l^2.$	1. § 411.
2. $x^2 + lx + \dfrac{l^2}{4} = \dfrac{l^2}{4} + l^2.$	2. Why?
3. $x^2 = l^2 - lx.$	3. Why?
4. $x^2 = l(l - x)$, or	4. Why?
5. $\overline{AF}^2 = AB \times FB.$	5. Why?

EXERCISES [C]

1. A line segment 8 inches long is divided in extreme and mean ratio. Find the lengths of its segments.

Solution. Let $x =$ the number of inches in the longer segment.
Then $8 - x =$ the number of inches in the shorter segment.

$$x^2 = 8(8 - x). \text{ Why?}$$
$$x^2 = 64 - 8\,x.$$
$$x^2 + 8\,x = 64.$$
$$x = 4.94\ +, \text{ the number of inches in one segment.}$$
$$8 - x = 3.06\ -, \text{ the number of inches in the other segment.}$$

Check. Does $(4.94)^2 = 8 \times 3.06$? $24.4 = 24.5$, approximately.

2. Find the lengths of the parts of a line segment 5 inches long when the segment is divided in extreme and mean ratio.

3. Using straightedge and compasses, divide a line segment 5 inches long in extreme and mean ratio.

4. The longer dimension of a book cover is $5\frac{1}{2}$ inches. What should be the shorter dimension of the cover to conform to the principle of the golden section?

5. A line segment of length a is divided in extreme and mean ratio. Show that the lengths of the two parts are approximately .62 a and .38 a.

6. The veins of a certain fern leaf meet the main stem so as to divide the straight angle in extreme and mean ratio. Find the angles formed by a vein and the main stem. $[x^2 = 180(180 - x).]$

7. Divide a line segment 6 inches long in extreme and mean ratio. Measure the lengths of the two segments. Find the lengths by algebra.

8. Find the area of a circular segment formed by a chord 8 inches long and an arc of 106° 16′ if the radius of the circle is 5 inches.

9. Find the area of a circular segment formed by a chord 6 inches long and its arc if the radius of the circle is 6 inches.

10. If one side of the adjoining square is 8 inches, find the area of the shaded portion of the square formed by semicircles constructed on the sides as diameters.

Proposition XIII. Problem

475. *To inscribe a regular decagon in a given circle.*

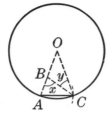

Given the ⊙ *O.*

To inscribe a regular decagon in ⊙ *O.*

Construction: STATEMENTS · REASONS

STATEMENTS	REASONS
1. Draw a radius *OA*.	1. Why possible?
2. Divide *OA* in extreme and mean ratio so that $\dfrac{AO}{BO} = \dfrac{BO}{AB}$.	2. § 474.
3. With *A* as a center and *BO* as a radius construct an arc intersecting the ⊙ at *C*.	3. Why possible?
4. Draw *AC*.	4. Why possible?

Then AC is a side of the required decagon.

Proof:

STATEMENTS	REASONS
1. Draw *CB* and *CO*.	1. Why possible?
2. $\dfrac{AO}{BO} = \dfrac{BO}{AB}$.	2. Const.
3. But *AC* = *BO*.	3. Const.
4. ∴ $\dfrac{AO}{AC} = \dfrac{AC}{AB}$.	4. Why?
5. In ▵ *AOC* and *ACB*, ∠ *A* = ∠ *A*.	5. Why?
6. ∴ △ *AOC* ∼ △ *ACB*.	6. Why?
7. Since △ *AOC* is isos., △ *ACB* is isos. and *AC* = *BC*.	7. Why?

(*Proof continued on opposite page.*)

8. But $BO = AC$.	8. Why?
9. ∴ $BC = BO$.	9. Why?
10. ∴ $\angle O = \angle y$.	10. Why?
11. $\angle x = \angle O + \angle y$, or $\angle x = 2 \angle O$.	11. § 110.
12. From (7), $\angle A = \angle x$.	12. Why?
13. ∴ $\angle A = 2 \angle O$.	13. Why?
14. $\angle ACO = \angle A$.	14. Why?
15. ∴ $\angle ACO = 2 \angle O$.	15. Why?
16. $\angle A + \angle ACO + \angle O = 180°$.	16. Why?
17. ∴ $2 \angle O + 2 \angle O + \angle O = 180°$.	17. Why?
18. ∴ $5 \angle O = 180°$.	18. Why?
19. ∴ $\angle O = 36°$.	19. Why?
20. ∴ $\overset{\frown}{AC} = 36°$, or $\frac{1}{10}$ of the ⊙.	20. Why?
21. ∴ chord AC is one side of the required decagon.	21. Why?

476. Corollary I. *A regular pentagon can be inscribed in a circle by joining the alternate vertices of a regular inscribed decagon.*

477. Corollary II. *A regular pentadecagon (a polygon of 15 sides) can be inscribed in a circle.*

SUGGESTIONS. Construct AB, the side of a regular inscribed hexagon, and AC, the side of a regular inscribed decagon (see § 475).

$$\overset{\frown}{AB} - \overset{\frown}{AC} = 60° - 36° = \overset{\frown}{BC} = 24°.$$

Chord BC is a side of the required pentadecagon.

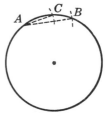

The division of the circle into any number of equal arcs by means of the straightedge and compasses can be done only in special cases. Gauss (1777–1855), when nineteen years of age, proved that a regular polygon of 17 sides could be inscribed in a circle. He also proved that a polygon of $(2^{2^n} + 1)$ sides can be inscribed in a circle if n is an integer and if $(2^{2^n} + 1)$ is a prime number.

What is the value of $(2^{2^n} + 1)$ if $n = 1$? if $n = 2$? if $n = 3$? if $n = 4$? Why can a regular polygon of $2^n(2^{2^n} + 1)$ sides, where n is a positive integer, be inscribed in a circle?

EXERCISES [C]

1. Construct a five-pointed star.

2. Construct a regular inscribed polygon of 20 sides.

3. Construct a regular inscribed polygon of 30 sides.

4. The draftsman has the following method of inscribing a regular pentagon and decagon in a circle. Draw a diameter AB. Construct radius $CO \perp AB$. Bisect OB at D. With D as a center and CD as a radius draw arc CE. Then CE is a side of the regular pentagon inscribed in the circle and EO is a side of the regular decagon inscribed in the circle.

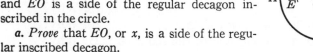

a. *Prove* that EO, or x, is a side of the regular inscribed decagon.

SUGGESTIONS. Let $OB = r$. Then $OD = \frac{1}{2} r$. $CD = \sqrt{r^2 + \frac{r^2}{4}} = \frac{r}{2}\sqrt{5}$. Why?
$ED = \frac{r}{2}\sqrt{5}$. $x = \frac{r}{2}\sqrt{5} - \frac{r}{2} = \frac{r}{2}(\sqrt{5} - 1)$.

In a circle of radius r, each side d of a regular inscribed decagon is given by $d^2 = r(r - d)$ (§§ 475, 473).

$$d^2 = r^2 - rd.$$
$$d^2 + rd = r^2.$$

Solving for d, $\qquad d = \frac{r}{2}(\sqrt{5} - 1)$.

$$\therefore x = d.$$

b. *Prove* that CE is a side of the regular inscribed pentagon.

SUGGESTIONS. Let p be a side of the regular inscribed pentagon.

Then $d = \sqrt{2 r^2 - r\sqrt{4 r^2 - p^2}}$, by § 466. But $d = \frac{r}{2}(\sqrt{5} - 1)$.

$$\therefore \frac{r}{2}(\sqrt{5} - 1) = \sqrt{2 r^2 - r\sqrt{4 r^2 - b^2}}.$$

Solving for p^2, $\qquad p^2 = r^2 + \frac{3 r^2}{2} - \frac{r^2}{2}\sqrt{5}.$

But $\qquad d^2 = \frac{3 r^2}{2} - \frac{r^2}{2}\sqrt{5}.$

Then $\qquad p^2 = r^2 + d^2.$

But $\qquad \overline{CE}^2 = r^2 + d^2.$

$\therefore \overline{CE}^2 = p^2$ and $CE = p$, a side of the regular inscribed pentagon.

5. Using the method given in Ex. 4, inscribe a regular pentagon and a regular decagon in a circle.

Cornelia Clarke; W. K. Fisher

478. How Nature Makes Use of the Golden Section.

Nature has used the golden section in both vegetable and animal life. When a flower has five or ten petals the principle of the golden section is applied. The starfish is a common example of the use of the golden section in animal life.

The stems of leaves are often arranged on the branch in the form of a spiral. In such an arrangement each stem appears at regular intervals on the spiral, each one being a little higher on the branch and farther around on it than the preceding one.

In the diagram of an oak twig at the right, notice that leaf bud 6 is directly above bud 1 on the stem. If 1 is the first bud of one cycle, then 6 is the first bud of the next cycle. A complete cycle consists of five leaves arranged equally distant apart in two revolutions of the spiral. We can represent this arrangement by the fraction $\frac{2}{5}$. The elm tree has the $\frac{1}{2}$ arrangement and the beech tree has the $\frac{1}{3}$ arrangement. Some trees have the $\frac{3}{8}$ arrangement, and some, including certain bushes, have the $\frac{5}{13}$ arrangement.

In most if not all the spiral arrangements of leaves on stems, both the numerator and the denominator of the fraction are members of the series 1, 2, 3, 5, 8, 13, 21, 34, ⋯ . In this series of numbers each number is equal to the sum of the two numbers immediately preceding it. As the numbers increase in size, the quotient obtained by dividing any number by the next consecutive one becomes nearer and nearer to $\dfrac{\sqrt{5}-1}{2}$, or .618 +. The fraction .618 + is the ratio of the larger segment to the whole when a segment of a line is divided into the golden section.

The sunflower illustrates the use of the golden section in two ways. The fruit sockets of a sunflower head form a series of intersecting curves which seem to be logarithmic spirals. A very small sunflower head has 21 curves crossing 34 curves, another has 34 curves crossing 55 curves, and a large head has 55 curves crossing 89 curves. The numbers of these curves are also of the series 1, 2, 3, 5, 8, 13, 21, 34, ⋯ .

The pine cone and the common teasel have a similar arrangement of the seed pods, except that their heads are not so flat as those of the sunflower.

479. The Most Beautiful Rectangle. We all know that some rectangles are more pleasing to the eye than others. The most beautiful rectangle is constructed as follows:

Divide the base AB into extreme and mean ratio so that $\dfrac{AB}{AE} = \dfrac{AE}{EB}$. Then construct the rectangle $ABCD$ having the

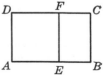

height $AD = AE$. This rectangle has many interesting properties. It consists of the similar rectangle $EBCF$ and the square $AEFD$. Its diagonal AC is perpendicular to BF, the diagonal oI *EBCF*. As explained below, it is sometimes called the *rectangle of whirling squares*. Since its numerical properties are related to plant and animal life, including the human skeleton, and since it has a property of dynamic symmetry, its use helps to give life to painting and sculpture. See how many of the following properties you can prove, and determine whether or not they apply to any rectangle.

EXERCISES [C]

1. The square *AF* is equal to a rectangle whose base is *AB* and whose altitude is equal to *EB*.

2. Rectangle *AC* ∼ rectangle *EC*.

SUGGESTIONS. $\dfrac{AB}{AE} = \dfrac{AE}{EB}$. Then $\dfrac{AB}{BC} = \dfrac{BC}{EB}$.

3. △ *ABC* ∼ △ *BCF*.

4. *BF* ⊥ *AC*.

5. *AB* is the mean proportional between *BC* and *AB* + *BC*.

6. $\dfrac{AO}{OB} = \dfrac{OB}{OC} = \dfrac{OC}{OF}$.

7. If *AD*=1, show that rectangle *EBCF* is the reciprocal of rectangle *ABCD*, or that $EBCF = \dfrac{1}{ABCD}$.

The Rectangle of the Whirling Squares. If the length of the most beautiful rectangle *ABCD* is represented by $\dfrac{\sqrt{5}+1}{2}$ units or 1.618, its width is represented by 1 unit. The rectangle *ABCD* is composed of the reciprocal rectangle *EBCF* and the square *AEFD*.

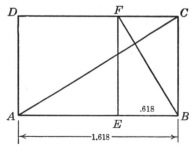

The reciprocal rectangle *EBCF* can be constructed by drawing *BF* ⊥ *AC* and then drawing *EF* ⊥ *DC*. The reciprocal rectangle *EBCF* cuts off the square *AEFD*. Likewise the rectangle *GHCF* is the reciprocal of the rectangle *EBCF* and cuts the square *EBHG* from rectangle *EBCF*. Again, the rectangle *GKMF* cuts the square *KHCM* from rectangle

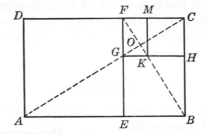

GHCF. If this process is continued indefinitely, a series is formed consisting of squares which continually get smaller and arrange themselves about *O* at intervals of 90°.

If the longer side of each rectangle is drawn as shown below, a broken line is formed which winds itself about the point *O*,

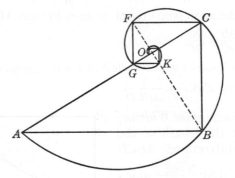

but never reaches *O*. The points *ABCFGK* · · · lie on a curve called the logarithmic spiral. This curve appears to be the growth curve of plants.

The line segments *OA, OB, OC,* · · · are called radius vectors. If one radius vector of a logarithmic spiral bisects the angle formed by two other radius vectors, it is the mean proportional between them. To find another point *P* of the curve, say between points *A* and *B*, bisect ∠ *AOB* and on this bisector construct *OP* so that *OA* : *OP* = *OP* : *OB*.

[Space geometry. Optional]

480. Area and Volume of a Circular Cylinder. In § 468 we saw that the theorem on the area of a circle was based on the area of a regular polygon. In solid geometry the theorems on the area and volume of a circular cylinder are based on the theorems on the area and volume of a prism having regular polygons as bases. These theorems are:

a. The lateral area of a right circular cylinder is equal to the product of the altitude and the circumference of the base, or $S = 2\,\pi rh$.

b. The volume of a right circular cylinder is equal to the product of the base and altitude, or $V = \pi r^2 h$.

EXERCISES

1. Show that the total area, T, of a right circular cylinder is given by the formula $T = 2\,\pi r(r + h)$.

SUGGESTIONS. Let A = area of one base. $A = \pi r^2$, $2\,A = 2\,\pi r^2$, and $S = 2\,\pi rh$. $S + 2\,A = T$.

2. Find the lateral areas of the following right circular cylinders, given

a. Altitude 6 inches, radius of base 4 inches.

b. Altitude 10 feet, radius of base 2 feet.

c. Altitude 4 feet, diameter of base 7 feet.

d. Altitude 14 inches, circumference of base 32 inches.

3. Find the volume of the following right circular cylinders, given

a. Radius of base 5 inches, altitude 12 inches.

b. Radius of base 11 feet, altitude 20 feet.

c. Diameter of base 10 inches, altitude 16 inches.

d. Circumference of base 80 inches, altitude 6 feet.

4. Find the total area and volume of a right circular cylinder if the radius of the base is 5 feet and the altitude is 20 feet.

5. The circumference of the base of a right circular cylinder is 28 inches, and its height is 15 inches. What is the lateral area of the cylinder?

6. What is the height of a cylindrical pail 8 inches in diameter if it holds a gallon?

481. Area and Volume of a Right Circular Cone. The theorems on the area and volume of a right circular cone from solid geometry are:

a. The lateral area of a right circular cone is equal to half the product of its slant height and the circumference of its base, or $S = \pi r l$.

b. The volume of a right circular cone is equal to one third of the product of its base and altitude, or $V = \frac{1}{3} \pi r^2 h$.

EXERCISES

1. Show that the total area of a right circular cone is given by the formula $T = \pi r(l + r)$.

2. Find the slant height and lateral area of a right circular cone if the radius of the base is 5 inches and the altitude is 12 inches.

3. Find the volume and lateral area of a right circular cone if the altitude is 8 inches and the radius of the base is 6 inches.

4. Find the lateral area and the volume of a right circular cone if the slant height is 17 feet and the radius of the base is 8 inches.

5. Find the total area of a right circular cone if the altitude is 24 inches and the diameter of the base is 14 inches.

482. Area and Volume of a Sphere. The theorems on the area and volume of a sphere are:

a. The area of a sphere is equal to the area of four great circles of the sphere, or $S = 4 \pi r^2$.

b. The volume of a sphere with radius r is given by the formula $V = \frac{4}{3} \pi r^3$.

EXERCISES

1. Find the area and volume of the following spheres:

    a. Radius 6 inches.   *c.* Radius 3 feet.
    b. Radius 4 inches.   *d.* Radius 5 feet.

2. A sphere 12 inches in diameter is inscribed in a right circular cylinder. What is the area of the sphere? the lateral area of the cylinder? What is the volume of the sphere? of the cylinder?

3. Solve the formula $S = 4 \pi r^2$ for r.

4. A right circular cylinder and a right circular cone have equal bases and equal altitudes. What is the ratio of their areas? the ratio of their volumes?

5. Find the cost at $3 a square foot of gilding a dome in the shape of a hemisphere whose diameter is 25 feet.

6. A sphere 14 inches in diameter is inscribed in a cylinder. What is the area of the sphere? the lateral area of the cylinder? What is the volume of the sphere? of the cylinder?

483. Mathematics and Science. Mathematics and science are closely interrelated. Sometimes the advance of science must wait until the necessary mathematics is developed, but more often the necessary mathematics has been developed years before and only waits on a keen scientific mind to make the application.

Prediction is probably one of the most important services that mathematics renders the sciences. Astronomers tell us that there will be an eclipse of the sun visible from this continent on October 26, 2144. This is not a guess, but a guarantee, for astronomers by use of mathematics can accurately predict the courses of the sun, moon, and earth for centuries to come.

The English physicist and mathematician James Clerk-Maxwell developed his electrical theory in the middle of the nineteenth century almost exclusively by mathematical methods without realizing the great importance it was to have fifty years later in the development of wireless telegraphy and radio.

The application of geometry to a new field, biology, is illustrated by the prediction made by Dr. Dorothy Wrinch. Dr. Wrinch, when a young mathematics instructor at Oxford University, England, decided to apply her knowledge of geometry to biology. After two years of study she was able to tie up the facts of biological and chemical research to foretell the structure of one of the chief types of protein molecules, cyclized polypeptides. She predicted that this molecule is shaped like a cage with eight sides. Later, Dr. Langmuir, an American, verified her prediction by means of X rays.

REVIEW QUESTIONS

1. What are the names of the four centers of a triangle?

2. Can a circle be circumscribed about

a. A triangle?   *d.* A square?

b. A quadrilateral?   *e.* A rectangle?

c. A rhombus?   *f.* A regular pentagon?

3. What two conditions are necessary for a polygon to be regular?

4. In what polygon that is not regular can a circle be inscribed?

5. When are two regular polygons similar?

6. If the number of sides of a regular inscribed polygon is increased indefinitely, what is the limit

a. Of the apothem?   *d.* Of the area of the polygon?

b. Of each side?   *e.* Of an angle of the polygon?

c. Of the perimeter?   *f.* Of a central angle?

7. How many of the regular polygons having less than twenty-five sides can be constructed with compasses and straightedge?

8. Why is the radius of a regular polygon so named?

9. What inscribed polygon has a side equal to the radius?

10. If the radius of a circle is doubled,

a. Is the area doubled?   *b.* Is the circumference doubled?

11. If the number of sides of a regular inscribed polygon is doubled, is its perimeter doubled?

12. What is a constant? a variable? Does a constant have a limit?

13. The ratio of the radii of two circles is 2 : 5. What is the ratio of their circumferences? of their areas?

14. Is the ratio of the area of a circle to its radius constant?

SUMMARY OF METHODS OF PROOF

484. *Regular polygons*

a. If a circle is divided into any number of equal arcs, the chords of these arcs form a regular inscribed polygon and the tangents at the points of division form a regular circumscribed polygon.

b. An equilateral polygon inscribed in a circle is regular.

c. If the midpoints of the arcs of a regular inscribed polygon are joined to the extremities of the respective sides, a regular inscribed polygon of double the number of sides is formed.

485. *Areas*

a. The area of a regular polygon is equal to one half the product of its apothem and its perimeter.

b. The area of a circle is equal to one half the product of its radius and its circumference.

c. The area of a circle is given by the formula $S = \pi r^2$.

486. *Proportions involving polygons and circles*

a. The areas of two regular polygons of the same number of sides have the same ratio as the squares of any two corresponding sides, as the squares of their radii, or as the squares of their apothems.

b. The perimeters of two regular polygons of the same number of sides have the same ratio as their radii or as their apothems.

c. The circumferences of two circles have the same ratio as their radii or as their diameters.

d. The areas of two circles have the same ratio as the squares of their radii or as the squares of their diameters.

e. The area of a sector of a circle is to the area of the circle as the angle of the sector is to 360°.

487. *Similar polygons*

Two regular polygons of the same number of sides are similar.

488. *Circumference of a circle*

The circumference of a circle is expressed by the formula $c = \pi d$ or $c = 2\pi r$.

489. *Constructions*

a. A circle can be circumscribed about any regular polygon.

b. A circle can be inscribed in any regular polygon.

c. To divide a given line segment in extreme and mean ratio.

d. To inscribe a regular decagon in a given circle.

e. A regular pentagon can be inscribed in a circle by joining the alternate vertices of a regular inscribed decagon.

f. A regular pentadecagon can be inscribed in a circle.

WORD LIST

Here are twenty words. Do you know the meaning of each one? Can you spell each one?

apothem	circumscribed	inscribed	polygon
arc	complementary	limit	radii
arch	diameter	measure	sector
central	divided	pentagon	similar
circumference	exercises	pi	variable

TEST 35

True-False Test (*Twelve Minutes*)

Copy the numbers of these statements on your paper. Then if a statement is *always* true, write T after its number. If a statement is *not always* true, write F after its number. Do not guess.

1. All regular polygons are similar.

2. The apothem of a regular polygon is the radius of the incircle.

3. The radius of a regular polygon is the radius of the circumcircle.

4. An equilateral polygon inscribed in a circle is a regular polygon.

5. A circle can be circumscribed about any polygon.

6. If a regular pentagon and a square have the same area, the pentagon has the greater perimeter.

7. The circumcircle and the incircle of a regular polygon are concentric.

8. The area of a regular polygon is equal to one half the product of its radius and its perimeter.

9. The perimeters of two regular polygons have the same ratio as their radii.

10. The areas of two circles have the same ratio as their radii.

11. The ratio of the circumference of a circle to its diameter is 3.1416.

12. The area of a circle is equal to one half the product of its radius and its circumference.

13. If the diameter of one circle is twice the diameter of a second circle, the area of the first circle is twice the area of the second circle.

14. The area of a sector of a circle is to the area of the circle as the angle of the sector is to 180°.

15. The apothem of an equilateral triangle is equal to one half the radius of the circumcircle.

16. If the perimeter of a regular polygon is doubled, its area is doubled.

17. Two polygons are similar if their sides are parallel each to each.

18. Two polygons are similar if their corresponding sides are proportional.

TEST 36

Applications (*Twenty-five Minutes*)

1. What is the ratio of the areas of two circles whose diameters are 4 and 5 inches respectively?

2. Find the area of the shaded portion in the figure if the diameter of the smaller circle is 2 inches and the diameter of the larger circle is 3 inches.

3. If the radius of a circle is 4, what is the area of an inscribed equilateral triangle?

4. If the radius of a circle is $\sqrt{2}$, what is the area of an inscribed square?

5. The area of a circle is 180 square feet. Find the area of a sector of 80°.

6. One side of a regular hexagon is 6 inches. Find the length of the apothem.

7. How large is the central angle of a regular quadrilateral?

8. Find the circumference of a circle whose radius is 8 inches.

9. A pentagon is circumscribed about a circle of radius 5. Find the area of the pentagon if its sides are 4, 6, 8, 9, and 10.5 respectively.

10. The area of one regular heptagon is $6\frac{1}{4}$ times that of another. What is the ratio of their perimeters?

11. Find the area of a segment of a circle formed by one side of an inscribed square and its arc if the radius of the circle is 10 inches.

12. Two tangents to a circle form an angle of 105°. Find the length of the minor arc if the radius of the circle is 10 inches.

Surveyors at Work

The leveling instrument pictured above, unlike the transit, can be
used to measure angles in the horizontal plane only

CHAPTER XIV

Elements of Trigonometry

The word "trigonometry" is derived from two Greek words which mean "triangle measurement." It is that branch of mathematics which deals with the relations between the sides and the angles of triangles.

One of the main purposes of trigonometry is to obtain formulas by means of which distances may be measured indirectly. You have seen how to construct a triangle when three parts are given, one of which · must be a side. When the numerical values of these parts are given, trigonometry will enable you to compute the values of the unknown parts. With the steel tape the engineer measures distances, and with the transit he measures angles. Then, using trigonometry, he

A Transit Is an Instrument for Measuring Angles

computes other distances and angles and is able to make plans and specifications for constructions of various kinds. Trigonometry is constantly used in surveying, engineering, physics, astronomy, and navigation. Without trigonometry, surveying and navigation would be very difficult and the distances from the earth to the sun, the moon, and the planets would be unknown.

490. Trigonometric Functions. We proved in § 397 that if right triangles have an acute angle of one equal to an acute angle of the other, the triangles are similar. In the figure, ∡ *ABC*, *AB′C′*, and *AB″C″* are right triangles having the same acute ∠ *A*. Hence

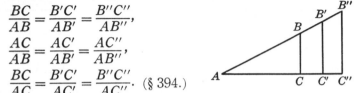

$$\frac{BC}{AB} = \frac{B'C'}{AB'} = \frac{B''C''}{AB''},$$

$$\frac{AC}{AB} = \frac{AC'}{AB'} = \frac{AC''}{AB''},$$

and $\dfrac{BC}{AC} = \dfrac{B'C'}{AC'} = \dfrac{B''C''}{AC''}.$ (§ 394.)

That is, the value of the ratios of the sides of the right triangles depends upon the size of angle *A* and not upon the size of the right triangles. The values of these ratios change as ∠ *A* changes and for this reason are called *functions* of ∠ *A*.

491. Trigonometric Functions of an Acute Angle.

1. *The sine of an acute angle of a right triangle is the ratio of the opposite side to the hypotenuse.*

2. *The cosine of an acute angle of a right triangle is the ratio of the adjacent side to the hypotenuse.*

3. *The tangent of an acute angle of a right triangle is the ratio of the opposite side to the adjacent side.*

It is customary, in the study of trigonometry, to let the capital letters *A*, *B*, and *C* denote the angles of a right triangle, *C* being the right angle, and the small letters *a*, *b*, and *c* denote the corresponding opposite sides. From the right △ *ABC*,

$\dfrac{a}{c}$ = sine of ∠ *A* (written **sin A**);

$\dfrac{b}{c}$ = cosine of ∠ *A* (written **cos A**);

$\dfrac{a}{b}$ = tangent of ∠ *A* (written **tan A**).

In like manner, $\dfrac{b}{c} = \sin B$; $\dfrac{a}{c} = \cos B$; $\dfrac{b}{a} = \tan B$.

The definitions in this section should be memorized so that the ratio for each function can be read from a figure instantly.

EXERCISES [B]

1. From the figures below, give the sine, cosine, and tangent of each acute angle in terms of the sides of the triangle. Thus, $\sin D = \dfrac{d}{e}$, $\cos D = \dfrac{f}{?}$, etc.

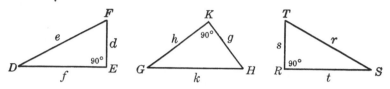

2. In the figures below, the lengths of the sides are indicated. Verify by § 411 that the triangles are right triangles and give the numerical value of the sine, cosine, and tangent of each acute angle to two decimal places.

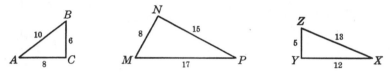

3. In rt. $\triangle RST$, $\angle S$ is the rt. $\angle$ and $SW \perp TR$. Give the three functions of $\angle T$ in terms of RS, ST, and TR. Also give these functions in terms of SW, ST, and TW.

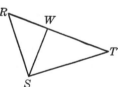

4. In the same figure, give the three functions of $\angle R$ in terms of RS, ST, and TR and also in terms of RS, SW, and RW.

5. In the figure of Ex. 3, give the three functions of $\angle TSW$ in terms of TW, SW, and ST.

6. With a protractor construct any right triangle having an acute angle of 20°, and by measurement find the numerical values of sin 20°, cos 20°, and tan 20° to two decimal places. From the same figure find the numerical values of sin 70°, cos 70°, and tan 70°. Do you notice any relation between sin 20° and cos 70°? between cos 20° and sin 70°?

7. Find the numerical values of the three functions of 30° and 60° in the same way as you did in Ex. 6 above.

492. Functions of 45°, 30°, and 60°. In the isosceles rt. △ ABC, $\angle A = 45°$ and $b = a$. $c^2 = a^2 + b^2$ (§ 411). $c^2 = 2\,a^2$ (Ax. 5). $\therefore c = a\sqrt{2}$ (Ax. 7).

$$\sin 45° = \frac{a}{c} = \frac{a}{a\sqrt{2}} = \frac{1}{\sqrt{2}} = \frac{1}{2}\sqrt{2}.$$

$$\cos 45° = \frac{b}{c} = \frac{a}{a\sqrt{2}} = \frac{1}{\sqrt{2}} = \frac{1}{2}\sqrt{2}.$$

$$\tan 45° = \frac{a}{b} = \frac{a}{a} = 1.$$

In a 30°-60° rt. △ ABC, $b = \frac{1}{2}c$ (§ 120) and $a^2 = c^2 - \frac{1}{4}c^2$ (§ 411). $a^2 = \frac{3}{4}c^2$. $\therefore a = \frac{1}{2}c\sqrt{3}$ (Ax. 7).

$$\sin 30° = \frac{b}{c} = \frac{\frac{1}{2}c}{c} = \frac{1}{2}.$$

$$\cos 30° = \frac{a}{c} = \frac{\frac{1}{2}c\sqrt{3}}{c} = \frac{1}{2}\sqrt{3}.$$

$$\tan 30° = \frac{b}{a} = \frac{\frac{1}{2}c}{\frac{1}{2}c\sqrt{3}} = \frac{1}{\sqrt{3}} = \frac{1}{3}\sqrt{3}.$$

$$\sin 60° = \frac{a}{c} = \frac{\frac{1}{2}c\sqrt{3}}{c} = \frac{1}{2}\sqrt{3}.$$

$$\cos 60° = \frac{b}{c} = \frac{\frac{1}{2}c}{c} = \frac{1}{2}.$$

$$\tan 60° = \frac{a}{b} = \frac{\frac{1}{2}c\sqrt{3}}{\frac{1}{2}c} = \sqrt{3}.$$

The sine and cosine of 30°, 45°, and 60° are easily remembered in the following way:

Function	30°	45°	60°
sin	$\frac{1}{2}\sqrt{1}$	$\frac{1}{2}\sqrt{2}$	$\frac{1}{2}\sqrt{3}$
cos	$\frac{1}{2}\sqrt{3}$	$\frac{1}{2}\sqrt{2}$	$\frac{1}{2}\sqrt{1}$

493. Trigonometric Tables. The functions of the angles given in § 492 are the only ones we can find by elementary algebra and geometry. We could find the approximate values of the functions of other angles by the method of Ex. 6, p. 459. For practical purposes, however, we refer to more accurate values computed by higher mathematics. In Table II, p. 564, the values of the functions from 0° to 90° are given to four decimal places.

EXERCISES [B]

Using Table II, find the value of each of the following functions:

1. sin 20°.	**4.** cos 70°.	**7.** sin 12°.
2. cos 14°.	**5.** tan 17°.	**8.** cos 54°.
3. sin 76°.	**6.** tan 63°.	**9.** tan 85°.

10. Which of the three functions increase as the angles increase and which decreases as the angles increase?

Find the number of degrees in the angle in each of the following exercises:

11. sin A = .2250.	**13.** tan A = .2679.	**15.** cos B = .1392.
12. cos A = .8988.	**14.** sin B = .7771.	**16.** tan B = 7.1154.

494. Interpolation. In order to find the value of the function of an angle expressed in degrees and a fractional part of a degree, it is necessary to resort to a process known as *interpolation*, which can be illustrated best by the solution of some examples.

Example 1. Find sin 16° 30′.

Solution. The sine of 16° 30′ is found by adding to the sine of 16° half the difference between sin 16° and sin 17°.

Thus
$$\begin{array}{r} \sin 17° = .2924 \\ \sin 16° = .2756 \\ \hline \text{Difference} = .0168 \end{array}$$

$\frac{30}{60}$, or $\frac{1}{2}$, of .0168 = .0084. Then .2756 + .0084 = .2840. Therefore sin 16° 30′ = .2840.

In the case of increasing functions, like the sine and tangent, the correction must be added to the value of the function of the smaller angle; but in a decreasing function, like the cosine, the correction must be subtracted.

Example 2. Find cos 32° 10′.

Solution.   cos 32° = .8480
                cos 33° = .8387

                Difference = .0093

$\frac{10}{60}$, or $\frac{1}{6}$, of .0093 = .0016.

Then .8480 − .0016 = .8464.

Therefore cos 32° 10′ = .8464.

Example 3. Find tan 45.3°.

Solution.   tan 46° = 1.0355
                tan 45° = 1.0000

                Difference = .0355

$\frac{3}{10}$ of .0355 = .0107.

Then 1.0000 + .0107 = 1.0107.

Therefore tan 45.3° = 1.0107.

EXERCISES [B]

Find the values of the following from Table II:

1. sin 36° 20′.	**5.** tan 62.3°.	**9.** cos 0°.	**13.** tan 60° 7′.
2. sin 47.4°.	**6.** cos 11.9°.	**10.** sin 41.6°.	**14.** sin 15° 15′.
3. tan 18° 50′.	**7.** cos 80° 40′.	**11.** cos 53° 5′.	**15.** sin 0°.
4. tan 72.7°.	**8.** cos 33.3°.	**12.** tan 90°.	**16.** cos 61.8°.

495. Inverse Use of Table. Finding the angle when the value of the function is given will now be illustrated.

Example 1. tan B = .2905. Find $\angle B$.

Solution. .2905 lies between .2867 and .3057.

                .3057 = tan 17°
                .2867 = tan 16°

                .0190 = difference

.2905 − .2867 = .0038. Then $\frac{.0038}{.0190}$ of 60′ = 12′, or .2°, the amount to be added to 16°. Therefore the required angle is 16° 12′, or 16.2°.

Notice that the result is taken to the nearest minute or tenth of a degree, depending upon which method you use in expressing the angle.

Example 2. cos B = .3140. Find $\angle B$.

Solution. .3140 lies between cos 72° and cos 71°.

                .3256 = cos 71°
                .3090 = cos 72°

                .0166 = difference

.3140 − .3090 = .0050. Then $\frac{.0050}{.0166}$ of 60′ = 18′, or .3°.

72° − 18′ = 71° 42′, or 71.7°. Therefore $\angle B$ = 71° 42′.

Since the cosine is a decreasing function, the correction is subtracted from 72°.

EXERCISES [B]

Find the number of degrees in each angle:

1. $\sin A = .1132$.
2. $\tan X = .3105$.
3. $\cos B = .4664$.
4. $\sin Y = .4664$.
5. $\cos A = .9788$.

6. $\tan B = 3.0841$.
7. $\sin A = .9930$.
8. $\cos A = .1422$.
9. $\tan A = .8233$.
10. $\sin B = .5618$.

11. $\cos B = .9630$.
12. $\tan B = .1500$.
13. $\cos C = .5180$.
14. $\tan C = 1.8045$.
15. $\sin C = .9460$.

496. Finding Parts of a Right Triangle. By the use of trigonometric functions, any part of a right triangle can be found if any two sides or a side and an acute angle are given.

Example 1. Given the rt. $\triangle ABC$ with $\angle A = 20° \ 10'$ and $b = 8.5$. Find a.

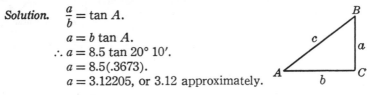

Solution. $\quad \dfrac{a}{b} = \tan A$.

$\qquad a = b \tan A$.

$\qquad \therefore a = 8.5 \tan 20° \ 10'$.

$\qquad a = 8.5(.3673)$.

$\qquad a = 3.12205$, or 3.12 approximately.

Example 2. Given $c = 12.66$, $a = 5.42$. Find B.

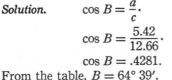

Solution. $\qquad \cos B = \dfrac{a}{c}$.

$\qquad \cos B = \dfrac{5.42}{12.66}$.

$\qquad \cos B = .4281$.

From the table, $B = 64° \ 39'$.

Example 3. In a circle of 6-inch radius find the length of a chord that has a central angle of 36°.

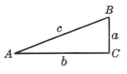

Solution. Draw $OC \perp AB$.

OC bisects $\angle O$. Why?

$\qquad \dfrac{AC}{OA} = \sin \tfrac{1}{2} O$.

$\qquad AC = OA \sin \tfrac{1}{2} O$.

$\qquad \therefore AC = 6 \sin 18° = 6(.3090)$.

$\qquad AC = 1.8540$, or 1.85 (inches) approximately.

EXERCISES

B

1. Given $A = 60°$, $b = 4$. Find c.

2. Given $A = 12°$, $b = 4$. Find a.

3. Given $B = 55°$, $b = 10$. Find a.

4. Given $A = 20.5°$, $c = 80$. Find a.

5. Given $B = 56° 10'$, $c = 16$. Find a.

6. Given $a = 4.84$, $b = 3.63$. Find A.

7. Given $a = 6.5$, $c = 9.8$. Find B.

8. A man standing 120 feet from the foot of a chimney finds that the angle of elevation of the top of the chimney is 51.3°. Find the height of the chimney.

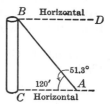

NOTE. In the figure, $\angle A$ is the *angle of elevation* of B from A. $\angle ABD$ is the *angle of depression* of A from B.

9. From the top of a building 80 feet high, the angle of depression of an automobile on a road is 26° 20'. How far is the automobile from the foot of the building?

10. At a horizontal distance of 112 feet from the base of a tower, the angle of elevation of the top is 72° 10'. Find the height of the tower.

11. Find the angle of elevation of the sun when a tree whose height is 96 feet casts a shadow 116 feet in length.

12. What is the angle of elevation of an inclined plane if it rises a foot in a horizontal distance of 12 feet?

13. The Washington Monument is 555 feet high. What is the angle of elevation of the top when viewed at a distance of half a mile?

14. Find the angles of an isosceles triangle if the equal sides are each 12 inches and the base 18 inches.

SUGGESTION. Draw the altitude on the base.

15. Find the angles of an isosceles triangle if the altitude is 8 inches and the equal sides are each 10 inches.

16. The average inclination of the bed of a stream is 3° 10'. Find its fall in a distance of 1 mile along the stream.

C

17. The sides of a right triangle are 3, 4, and 5. Find the number of degrees in each acute angle.

18. If a hillside has a slope of 5°, how far up the hillside will a dam 36 feet high force the water?

19. Find the area of an isosceles triangle if the base is 16 feet and each of the equal sides is 15 feet.

20. Find the area of an isosceles triangle if the vertex angle is 40° and the altitude is 6 feet.

21. In making a cylinder head for a steam engine five holes are to be placed equally about a circle 8 inches in diameter. How far apart will the holes be, center to center?

22. The hypotenuse of a right triangle is 24 feet and one acute angle is 36° 20′. Find the altitude on the hypotenuse.

23.* A captain of field artillery has his battery, consisting of four guns, 3 miles from a straight road. If the range of a gun is 4 miles, how far apart must the captain place his guns to command the maximum length of road? Through how large an angle must the captain be able to turn his guns?

24. Find the radius of a circle inscribed in an equilateral triangle whose perimeter is 36 inches.

25. Two sides and the included angle of a parallelogram are 40, 60, and 68° respectively. Find the altitude on side 60.

26. On a circular railway curve an arc of 30° has a chord 400 feet long. Find the radius of the curve.

27. Find the number of degrees in an arc whose chord is 18 feet if the radius of the circle is 12.5 feet.

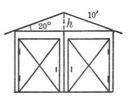

28. Gable rafters 10 feet long, with a pitch of 20°, project one foot beyond the walls of a garage. Find the height h of the ridgepole and the width of the garage.

29. One side of a regular decagon is 10 inches. Find the radii of the inscribed and circumscribed circles and the area of the polygon.

*Pages 512–520 on artillery fire may be studied at this time.

497. Relations of Trigonometric Functions. Two fundamental relations existing between the functions of an angle can be shown by simple formulas.

Theorem. *In any right triangle having an acute angle A,*

$$\sin^2 A + \cos^2 A = 1.*$$

Given the rt. $\triangle ABC$, A an acute $\angle$.

To prove that $\sin^2 A + \cos^2 A = 1$.

Proof:

STATEMENTS	REASONS
1. $a^2 + b^2 = c^2$.	1. § 411.
2. $a = c \sin A$ and $b = c \cos A$.	2. § 491.
3. $a^2 = c^2 \sin^2 A$ and $b^2 = c^2 \cos^2 A$.	3. Ax. 7.
4. $c^2 \sin^2 A + c^2 \cos^2 A = c^2$.	4. Ax. 1.
5. $\therefore \sin^2 A + \cos^2 A = 1$.	5. Ax. 4.

Theorem. *In any right triangle having an acute angle A,*

$$\tan A = \frac{\sin A}{\cos A}.$$

Proof:

STATEMENTS	REASONS
1. $\sin A = \dfrac{a}{c}$.	1. § 491.
2. $\cos A = \dfrac{b}{c}$.	2. § 491.
3. $\dfrac{\sin A}{\cos A} = \dfrac{\frac{a}{c}}{\frac{b}{c}} = \dfrac{a}{c} \times \dfrac{c}{b} = \dfrac{a}{b}$.	3. Ax. 4.
4. But $\tan A = \dfrac{a}{b}$.	4. § 491.
5. $\therefore \tan A = \dfrac{\sin A}{\cos A}$.	5. Ax. 5.

*(sin A)² is written sin² A to avoid the use of parentheses.

TEST 37

True-False Statements (*Ten Minutes*)

Copy the numbers of these statements on your paper. Then if a statement is *always* true, write T after its number. If a statement is *not always* true, write F after its number. Do not guess.

1. In a right triangle the sine of an acute angle is the ratio of the opposite side to the adjacent side.
2. $\cos 60° = .5$.
3. $\tan 30° = \sqrt{3}$.
4. As an angle increases from 0° to 90° the value of its sine increases from 0 to 1.
5. If A and B are the two acute angles of a right triangle, $\sin A = \cos B$.
6. In any right triangle having an acute angle A, $\sin^2 A - \cos^2 A = 1$.
7. The area of a parallelogram is equal to the product of two adjacent sides multiplied by the sine of the included angle.
8. $\sin A = \dfrac{1}{\cos A}$.

TEST 38

Applications (*Fifteen Minutes*)

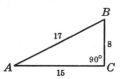

1. In $\triangle ABC$ above, give the value of $\sin A$ to four decimal places.
2. In $\triangle ABC$ above, give the value of $\cos A$ to four decimal places.
3. In $\triangle ABC$ above, give the value of $\tan B$ to three decimal places.

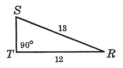

4. In $\triangle RST$, find $\angle R$ to the nearest minute.
5. In a circle of 4-inch radius, find the length of a side of a regular inscribed pentagon.

CHAPTER XV

Inequalities

In our study of geometry thus far we have learned several methods of proving line segments, angles, and arcs equal. In this chapter we shall study relations between line segments, angles, and arcs that are unequal.

The propositions and exercises listed in this chapter have not been considered as important as those dealing with equalities. However, the study of inequalities is very interesting and instructive.

498. Orders of Inequalities. The symbol for "is unequal to" is $\neq$; for "is greater than" is $>$; and for "is less than" is $<$. The inequalities $a > x$ and $b > y$ are said to be in the *same order*, since the same symbol is used in each inequality. The inequalities $a > x$ and $b < y$ are said to be in *reverse order*, since the symbol in one inequality is the reverse of the symbol in the other.

1. Read the following: $5 < x$; $x > 5$; $AB + BC > AC$.

2. State which of the following pairs of inequalities are in reverse order:

a. $\angle x > \angle y$ and $\angle m > \angle n$.
b. $7 < 9$ and $8 > 4$.
c. $6 < 8$ and $7 < 9$.
d. $c > d$ and $e < f$.

499. Axioms of Inequalities. In addition to the axioms listed in § 31 we shall need the following axioms of inequalities:

Ax. 10. *If the first of three quantities is greater than the second and the second is greater than the third, then the first is greater than the third.*

Thus if $a > b$ and $b > c$, then $a > c$.

Ax. 11. *If unequals are increased by, diminished by, multiplied by, or divided by positive equals, the results are unequal in the same order.*

Example 1. If $6 < 8$
and $\quad\quad\quad \dfrac{4 = 4}{10 < 12}$
then

Example 2. If $6 < 8$
and $\quad\quad\quad \dfrac{4 = 4}{2 < 4}$
then

Example 3. If $6 < 8$
and $\quad\quad\quad \dfrac{4 = 4}{24 < 32}$
then

Example 4. If $6 < 8$
and $\quad\quad\quad \dfrac{4 = 4}{1\frac{1}{2} < 2}$
then

Ax. 12. *If unequals are subtracted from equals, the remainders are unequal in the reverse order.*

Example 1. If $12 = 12$
and $\quad\quad\quad \dfrac{7 > 4}{5 < 8}$
then

Example 2. If $2x + 6 = 2x + 6$
and $\quad\quad\quad \dfrac{x + 2 < \quad x + 3}{x + 4 > \quad x + 3}$
then

Ax. 13. *If unequals are added to unequals in the same order, the sums are unequal in the same order.*

Example 1. If $5 < 8$
and $\quad\quad\quad \dfrac{3 < 4}{8 < 12}$
then

Example 2. If $3x + 5 > x + 6$
and $\quad\quad\quad \dfrac{x + 7 > \quad\quad 5}{4x + 12 > x + 11}$
then

Ax. 14. *Like powers and like positive roots of positive unequals are unequal in the same order.*

Example. If $x^2 > 9$, then $x > 3$.

ORAL EXERCISES [A]

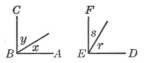   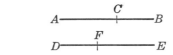

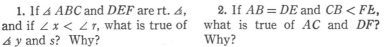

1. If $\measuredangle ABC$ and DEF are rt. $\measuredangle$, and if $\angle x < \angle r$, what is true of $\measuredangle y$ and s? Why?

2. If $AB = DE$ and $CB < FE$, what is true of AC and DF? Why?

3. If $AD + DC > AC$, why is $AD > AC - DC$?

4. If $\angle BAC > \angle y$ and $\angle y = \angle x$, why is $\angle BAC > \angle x$?

5. If $x^2 - r^2 = y^2 - s^2$ and $r^2 > s^2$, why is $x^2 > y^2$?

Proposition I. Theorem

500. *Each side of a triangle is less than the sum of the other two sides.*

(The demonstration is left to the student. Use Post. 4.)

Proposition II. Theorem

501. *If one side of a triangle is greater than a second side, the angle opposite the first side is greater than the angle opposite the second side.*

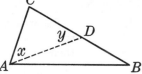

Given △ ABC with BC > AC.

To prove that ∠ A > ∠ B.

Selection of Method: 1. Known methods of proving ∡ unequal: Axs. 8, 9, 10, 11, 12, 13, 14, and § 82.
2. Method to be used: Axs. 8 and 10 and § 82.

Proof: STATEMENTS   REASONS

1. On *CB* construct *CD* = *AC*.	1. Why possible?
2. Draw *AD*.	2. Why possible?
3. ∠ x = ∠ y.	3. Why?
4. ∠ BAC > ∠ x.	4. Ax. 8.
5. ∴ ∠ BAC > ∠ y.	5. Ax. 5.
6. ∠ y > ∠ B.	6. § 82.
7. ∴ ∠ BAC > ∠ B.	7. Ax. 10.

EXERCISE [A]

In △ *ABC*, *AB* = 6, *BC* = 5, and *AC* = 7. Which angle of the triangle is the smallest? the largest?

Proposition III. Theorem

502. *If one angle of a triangle is greater than a second angle, the side opposite the first angle is greater than the side opposite the second angle.*

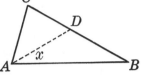

Given △ *ABC* with ∠ *A* > ∠ *B*

To prove that *BC* > *AC*.

Selection of Method: 1. Known methods of proving line segments unequal: Axs. 8–14; Posts. 4 and 11; and § 500.
2. Method to be used: § 500.

Proof:

STATEMENTS	REASONS
1. Draw *AD*, making ∠ *x* = ∠ *B*.	1. Why possible?
2. ∴ *AD* = *DB*.	2. Why?
3. *AD* + *DC* > *AC*.	3. § 500.
4. ∴ *BD* + *DC* > *AC*.	4. Why?
5. ∴ *BC* > *AC*.	5. Why?

503. Corollary I. *The perpendicular from a point to a line is the shortest line segment from the point to the line.*

NOTE. The proof of this corollary proves Post. 11. However, the proof of this corollary is not based on any theorems that depend on Post. 11.

504. Corollary II. *The hypotenuse of a right triangle is greater than either leg.*

EXERCISES

A

1. In △ *MNP*, ∠ *M* = 80° and ∠ *P* = 60°. Which side is the shortest? the longest?

2. In △ *ABC*. ∠ *A* = 59° and ∠ *C* = 60°. Which side is the longest? the shortest?

B

3. The difference between two sides of a triangle is less than the third side.

4. *Given* △ *ABC* with *CD* bisecting ∠ *ACB*. *Prove* that *AC* > *AD*.

SUGGESTION. ∠ *z* > ∠ *y*. Why?

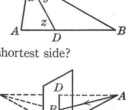

5. In a 30°-60° right triangle which is the shortest side?

6. *ABC* is the path of a ray of light reflected by a plane mirror *m* from *A* to *C*. Prove that the path *ABC* is shorter than the path *AFC*, *F* being any other point in the line *BD* of the mirror.

SUGGESTION. See Ex. 1, p. 139.

$$EBC < EF + FC.$$

7. *Given* △ *ABC* with *D* a point within the triangle.

a. Prove that *AC* + *CB* > *AD* + *DB*.
b. Prove that ∠ *ADB* > ∠ *C*.

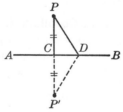

C

8. The perimeter of a quadrilateral is greater than the sum of its diagonals.

9. Prove Cor. I, § 503, using the figure shown at the right.

10. The sum of the line segments drawn from any point within a triangle to the vertices is greater than one half the perimeter of the triangle.

11. If two angles of a triangle are unequal, the bisector of the third angle is oblique to the opposite side.

12. The median of a triangle is less than half the sum of the two adjacent sides.

SUGGESTIONS. Let *CM* be the median of △ *ABC*. Extend *CM* to *C'* so that *MC'* = *MC*. Draw *AC'* and *BC'*. Compare *CC'* with *CB* + *BC'*. Prove that *AC* = *BC'*.

Proposition IV. Theorem

505. *If two triangles have two sides of one equal respectively to two sides of the other and the included angle of the first greater than the included angle of the second, the third side of the first is greater than the third side of the second.*

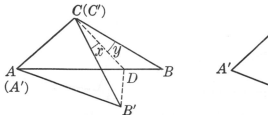

Given ⊿ ABC and $A'B'C'$ with $AC = A'C'$, $BC = B'C'$, and $\angle ACB > \angle A'C'B'$.

To prove that $AB > A'B'$.

Selection of Method: 1. Known methods of proving line segments unequal: §§ 500, 502, 503, 504; axioms and postulates.

                         2. Method to be used: Superposition; § 500; Ax. 5.

Proof: *STATEMENTS*   *REASONS*

1. Place △ $A'B'C'$ upon △ ABC so that $A'C'$ coincides with its equal, AC, and $C'B'$ falls within $\angle ACB$.	1. Why possible?
2. Draw CD bisecting $\angle B'CB$. Draw $B'D$.	2. Why possible?
3. In ⊿ $B'CD$ and BCD, $CB' = CB$,	3. Why?
4. $\angle x = \angle y$, and	4. Why?
5. $CD = CD$.	5. Why?
6. ∴ △ $B'CD \cong$ △ BCD.	6. Why?
7. ∴ $DB' = DB$.	7. Why?
8. $AD + DB' > AB'$.	8. Why?
9. ∴ $AD + DB > A'B'$.	9. Why?
10. ∴ $AB > A'B'$.	10. Why?

Proposition V. Theorem

506. *If two triangles have two sides of one equal respectively to two sides of the other and the third side of the first greater than the third side of the second, the angle opposite the third side of the first is greater than the angle opposite the third side of the second.*

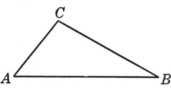
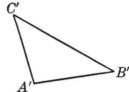

Given ⧌ *ABC* and *A'B'C'* with *AC = A'C'*, *BC = B'C'*, and *AB > A'B'*.

To prove that ∠ *C* > ∠ *C'*.

Selection of Method: 1. Known methods of proving ⧌ unequal: §§ 82, 501, axioms and postulates.
2. Method to be used: Ax. 9.

Proof: STATEMENTS   REASONS

1. ∠ *C* < ∠ *C'*, ∠ *C* = ∠ *C'*, or ∠ *C* > ∠ *C'*. | 1. Ax. 9.
2. If ∠ *C* < ∠ *C'*, then *AB* < *A'B'*. | 2. § 505.
3. But *AB* > *A'B'*. | 3. Given
4. ∴ ∠ *C* is not < ∠ *C'*. | 4. Why?
5. If ∠ *C* = ∠ *C'*, △ *ABC* ≅ △ *A'B'C'*. | 5. Why?
6. Then *AB* = *A'B'*. | 6. Why?
7. But *AB* > *A'B'*. | 7. Why?
8. ∴ ∠ *C* ≠ ∠ *C'*. | 8. Why?
9. ∴ ∠ *C* > ∠ *C'*. | 9. Ax. 9.

EXERCISES [A]

1. Compare the length of *AB* of △ *ABC* with that of *DF* of △ *DEF*, if *AC* = 10, *BC* = 12, *DE* = 10, *EF* = 12, ∠ *C* = 70°, and ∠ *E* = 65°.

2. The diagonals of a rhombus that is not a square are unequal.

Proposition VI. Theorem

507. *If two oblique line segments are drawn to a line from a point in a perpendicular to that line, the one having the greater projection upon the line is the greater.*

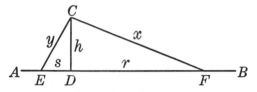

Given $CD \perp AB$, DE and DF the respective projections of CE and CF on AB, and $DF > DE$.

To prove that $CF > CE$.

Selection of Method: 1. Known methods of proving line segments unequal: §§ 500, 502, 503, 504, 505, axioms and postulates.

2. Method to be used: Axs. 11 and 14.

Proof: *STATEMENTS*	*REASONS*
1. $h^2 + r^2 = x^2$ and $h^2 + s^2 = y^2$.	1. Why?
2. Then $h^2 = x^2 - r^2$ and $h^2 = y^2 - s^2$.	2. Why?
3. $\therefore x^2 - r^2 = y^2 - s^2$.	3. Why?
4. But $r > s$, and	4. Why?
5. $r^2 > s^2$.	5. Ax. 14.
6. From (3) and (5), $x^2 > y^2$.	6. Ax. 11.
7. $\therefore x > y$.	7. Ax. 14.

EXERCISES [A]

1. In $\triangle DEF$, H is the foot of the perpendicular from F to DE. What is the projection of DF on DE? Compare DF and EF if $DH = 8$ and $HE = 10$.

2. Prove that the sum of the altitudes of a triangle is less than its perimeter.

3. Prove that either diagonal of a quadrilateral is less than half of its perimeter.

Proposition VII. Theorem

508. *If two unequal oblique line segments are drawn to a line from a point in a perpendicular to that line, the greater line segment has the greater projection upon the line.*

(The demonstration is left to the student.)

EXERCISES [C]

1. If the median of a triangle is oblique to the base, the adjacent sides are unequal.

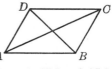

2. The diagonals of an oblique parallelogram are unequal.

SUGGESTION. In the oblique parallelogram *ABCD* compare ∆ *ABD* and *ABC*.

3. State and prove the converse of Ex. 1.

4. If a triangle is not isosceles, the median to any side is greater than the altitude to that side.

5. What theorems on the inequalities of triangles are illustrated by the operation of the shovel in the picture below?

Acme

Proposition VIII. Theorem

509. *In a circle or in equal circles the greater of two unequal central angles has the greater arc.*

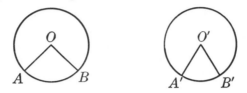

Given the $=$ ⑤ O and O' with $\angle O > \angle O'$.

To prove that $\widehat{AB} > \widehat{A'B'}$.*

Selection of Method: 1. Known methods of proving arcs unequal: axioms and postulates.
2. Method to be used: § 295 and Ax. 5.

Proof: *STATEMENTS*	*REASONS*
1. $\odot O = \odot O'$.	1. Why?
2. $\angle O \stackrel{\circ}{=} \widehat{AB}$, $\angle O' \stackrel{\circ}{=} \widehat{A'B'}$.	2. § 295.
3. $\angle O > \angle O'$.	3. Why?
4. $\therefore \widehat{AB} > \widehat{A'B'}$.	4. Ax. 5.

Proposition IX. Theorem

510. *In a circle or in equal circles the greater of two unequal arcs has the greater central angle.*

(The demonstration is left to the student.)

EXERCISES

1. In the same circle, do arcs have the same ratio as their central angles?

2. Prove that in a circle the chord of an arc of 180° is twice as long as the chord of an arc of 60°.

*The arcs referred to on this and on the following pages are minor arcs.

Proposition X. Theorem

511. *In a circle or in equal circles the greater of two unequal chords has the greater arc.*

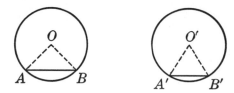

Given the = ⊚ O and O' with chord $AB >$ chord $A'B'$.

To prove that $\overarc{AB} > \overarc{A'B'}$.

Selection of Method: 1. Known methods of proving arcs unequal: § 509, axioms and postulates.
2. Method to be used: § 509.

Proof: *STATEMENTS*	*REASONS*
1. Draw radii OA, OB, $O'A'$, and $O'B'$. In △ AOB and $A'O'B'$,	1. Why possible?
2. $AO = A'O'$ and $BO = B'O'$.	2. Why?
3. $AB > A'B'$.	3. Why?
4. ∴ $\angle O > \angle O'$.	4. § 506.
5. ∴ $\overarc{AB} > \overarc{A'B'}$.	5. § 509

Proposition XI. Theorem

512. *In a circle or in equal circles the greater of two unequal arcs has the greater chord.*

(The demonstration is left to the student.)

EXERCISE

In a given circle, if $\overarc{AB} = 2\,\overarc{CD}$, is chord AB twice, more than twice, or less than twice chord CD? Prove that your answer is correct.

Proposition XII. Theorem

513. *In a circle or in equal circles the greater of two un-equal chords is nearer the center.*

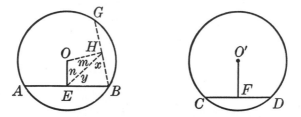

Given the = ⊚ *O* and *O'* with chord *AB* > chord *CD*, *OE* ⊥ *AB*, and *O'F* ⊥ *CD*.

To prove that *OE* < *O'F*.

Selection of Method: 1. Known methods of proving segments unequal: §§ 500, 502, 503, 504, 505, 507, 508, 512, axioms and postulates.
2. Method to be used: § 502.

Proof: STATEMENTS	REASONS
1. Draw *BG* = *CD*.	1. Why possible?
2. Draw *OH* ⊥ *BG*.	2. Why possible?
3. Draw *EH*.	3. Why possible?
4. *AB* > *CD*.	4. Why?
5. ∴ *AB* > *BG*.	5. Why?
6. *EB* = ½ *AB* and *BH* = ½ *BG*.	6. § 271.
7. ∴ *EB* > *BH*.	7. Why?
8. ∠ *OHB* = ∠ *OEB*.	8. Why?
9. From (7), ∠ *x* > ∠ *y*.	9. § 501.
10. ∴ ∠ *m* < ∠ *n*.	10. Ax. 12.
11. ∴ *OE* < *OH*.	11. § 502.
12. *GB* = *CD*.	12. Why?
13. Then *OH* = *O'F*.	13. § 274.
14. ∴ *OE* < *O'F*.	14. Why?

Proposition XIII. Theorem

514. *In a circle or in equal circles if two chords are un-equally distant from the center, the chord nearer the center is the greater.*

(The demonstration is left to the student. Prove by reversing the order of steps in Proposition XII.)

515. Corollary. *A diameter of a circle is greater than any other chord.*

EXERCISES

B

1. If $\triangle ABC$ is inscribed in a circle and if $\angle B > \angle A$, prove that $\overset{\frown}{AC} > \overset{\frown}{BC}$.

2. A $\triangle ABC$ is inscribed in a circle and $\overset{\frown}{AC} = 70°$ and $\overset{\frown}{BC} = 150°$. Name the angles of the triangle in order of size.

3. If a square and an equilateral triangle are inscribed in the same circle, prove that the apothem of the square is greater than the apothem of the triangle.

4. If two unequal chords intersect on a circle, the greater chord makes the smaller angle with the diameter through the point of intersection.

C

5. The shortest chord through a point inside a circle is perpendicular to the radius through this point.

6. If AB is a diameter of a circle and CD is an intersecting diameter of a smaller concentric circle, prove that $ACBD$ is an oblique parallelogram.

TEST 39

True-False Statements (*Six Minutes*)

Copy the numbers of these statements on your paper. If a statement is *always* true, write T after its number. If a statement is *not always* true, write F after its number. Do not guess.

1. If unequals are subtracted from equals, the remainders are unequal in the same order.

2. If one side of a triangle is greater than a second side, the angle opposite the first side is greater than the angle opposite the second side.

3. In a circle or in equal circles the greater of two unequal central angles has the greater arc.

4. If two oblique line segments are drawn to a line from a point in a perpendicular to that line, the one having the smaller projection upon the line is the greater.

5. In a circle or in equal circles the smaller of two unequal chords is nearer the center.

6. The bisector of an angle of a triangle is less than the median drawn from the vertex of the angle.

7. A median of a triangle is less than half the sum of the two adjacent sides.

8. Any side of a triangle is greater than half the perimeter.

TEST 40

Completing Statements (*Nine Minutes*)

On your paper write one word, and only one, for each blank to make the following statements true:

1. Like powers and like roots of unequals are _ _?_ _.

2. If one angle of a triangle is greater than a second angle, the side opposite the first angle is _ _?_ _ _ _?_ _ the side opposite the second angle.

3. A diameter of a circle is greater than _ _?_ _ _ _?_ _ _ _?_ _.

4. In a circle, the greater of two unequal _ _?_ _ has the greater arc.

5. If a central angle is increased, its arc is _ _?_ _.

6. The greater of two arcs of a circle has the _ _?_ _ chord.

7. The difference between two sides of a triangle is _ _?_ _ _ _?_ _ the third side.

8. The _ _?_ _ of a right triangle is greater than either leg.

9. The shortest chord through a point within a circle is _ _?_ _ to the radius through that point.

10. The area of the largest triangle inscribed in a semicircle with a radius of 20 inches is _ _?_ _ square inches.

CHAPTER XVI

Analytic Geometry

The geometry we have studied so far owes much of its development to the Greeks, when Greek culture was at its height, about 300 B.C. Algebra was developed much later, and it was not until the close of the Middle Ages that the symbols and notation which we use today were in common use.

In 1637 René Descartes, a French mathematician, showed in his *Géométrie* how the methods of algebra could be applied to geometry. This geometry, now known as *Analytic Geometry*, consists in associating numbers with points, and equations with geometrical figures.

The student is already familiar with the rectangular co-ordinate system and the graph of first-degree equations in two variables from his study of algebra and loci. (See § 331.)

EXERCISES

1. Plot each group of points, using a separate co-ordinate axis:

a. (2, 5), (3, 0), (− 2, 5), (5, − 8).
b. (5, − 12), (− 3, 0), (− 4, − 4), (− 1, 2).
c. (3, − 5), (− 2, − 6), (− 3, 1), (0, 2).

2. Draw the triangles whose vertices are as follows:

a. (3, − 1), (− 2, 6), (− 8, − 4).   *b.* (0, 0), (− 7, 7), (4, 6).
c. (4, − 5), (− 4, − 5), (0, 5).

3. Draw the quadrilaterals whose vertices are as follows:

a. (− 3, 0), (2, 4), (6, 0), (3, − 5).   *b.* (0, 0), (5, 3), (0, 8), (5, 11).
c. (1, − 6), (8, 2), (1, 6), (− 8, 2).

4. What is the locus of points:

a. Whose abscissas are − 3?   *c.* Satisfying the condition $x + y = 0$?
b. Whose ordinates are 5?   *d.* Satisfying the condition $x - y = 0$?

482

516. Distance between Two Points. It is readily apparent from the figure that the distance between the two points A and B, having the same ordinate, is the difference of their abscissas, or $6 - 1 = 5$. Also, the distance between the two points B and C, having the same abscissa, is the difference of their ordinates, or $4 - (- 2) = 6$. In like manner, we see that the distance $EF = - 2 - (- 5) = 3$.

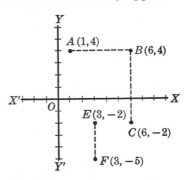

Theorem. *The distance between two points is given by the formula* $d = \sqrt{(x_2 - x_1)^2 + (y_2 - y_1)^2}$.

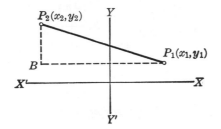

Given points P_1 and P_2 with the co-ordinates (x_1, y_1) and (x_2, y_2) respectively. $P_1P_2 = d$.

To prove that $d = \sqrt{(x_2 - x_1)^2 + (y_2 - y_1)^2}$.

Proof:

STATEMENTS	REASONS
1. Draw $P_1B \parallel$ to the x-axis and $P_2B \parallel$ to the y-axis.	1. Why possible?
2. $\angle P_2BP_1$ is a right angle.	2. Why?
3. $BP_1 = x_2 - x_1$ and $P_2B = y_2 - y_1$.	3. Why?
4. $\overline{P_2P_1}^2 = \overline{BP_1}^2 + \overline{P_2B}^2$.	4. Why?
5. $d^2 = (x_2 - x_1)^2 + (y_2 - y_1)^2$.	5. Why?
6. $d = \sqrt{(x_2 - x_1)^2 + (y_2 - y_1)^2}$.	6. Why?

Example 1. Show that $(3, 6)$, $(-6, 4)$, $(1, -2)$ are the vertices of an isosceles triangle.

Solution.

$d_1 = \sqrt{(3-1)^2 + (6+2)^2} = \sqrt{68}.$
$d_2 = \sqrt{(-6-1)^2 + (4+2)^2} = \sqrt{85}.$
$d_3 = \sqrt{(3+6)^2 + (6-4)^2} = \sqrt{85}.$

Since $d_2 = d_3$, the triangle is isosceles.

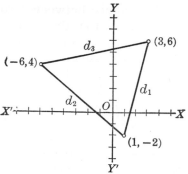

Example 2. Prove that $(-2, -3)$, $(4, 5)$, $(-4, 1)$ are the vertices of a right triangle.

Solution.

$d_1{}^2 = (4+4)^2 + (5-1)^2 = 80.$
$d_2{}^2 = (-4+2)^2 + (1+3)^2 = 20.$
$d_3{}^2 = (4+2)^2 + (5+3)^2 = 100.$

Since $d_1{}^2 + d_2{}^2 = d_3{}^2$, the triangle is a right triangle.

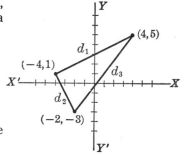

EXERCISES

1. Find the lengths of the sides of a triangle whose vertices are
a. $(1, -2)$, $(5, 6)$, $(-2, 3)$.　　*b.* $(3, 4)$, $(-2, 2)$, $(5, -3)$.

2. Show that the following triangles are isosceles:
a. $(9, 5)$, $(5, -1)$, $(-1, 3)$.　　*b.* $(4, 5)$, $(2, -1)$, $(-3, 4)$.

3. Show that the following are right triangles:
a. $(7, 4)$, $(4, 5)$, $(1, -4)$.　　*b.* $(1, 3)$, $(5, 6)$, $(4, -1)$.
c. $(-6, 2)$, $(5, -1)$, $(4, 4)$.　　*d.* $(13, -1)$, $(-9, 3)$, $(-3, -9)$.

4. Show *(a)* that $(-5, -3)$, $(1, -11)$, $(7, -6)$, and $(1, 2)$ are the vertices of a parallelogram; *(b)* that the quadrilateral $(3, 2)$, $(0, 5)$, $(-3, 2)$, $(0, -1)$ is a rhombus.

5. What kind of quadrilateral has vertices at $(6, 4)$, $(-1, 2)$, $(3, -2)$, $(2, 8)$?

6. Find the lengths of the diagonals of a quadrilateral whose vertices are $(1, 3)$, $(-2, -1)$, $(5, 0)$, and $(-4, 2)$.

517. Midpoint of a Line Segment.

Theorem. *The co-ordinates of the midpoint of a line segment are one half the sums of the co-ordinates of the end points, or*

$$x = \frac{x_1 + x_2}{2} \text{ and } y = \frac{y_1 + y_2}{2}.$$

Given P the midpoint of line segment P_1P_2.

To prove that $x = \frac{x_1 + x_2}{2}$ and $y = \frac{y_1 + y_2}{2}$.

Proof:

STATEMENTS	REASONS
1. Draw P_1A, PB, and $P_2C \perp$ the x-axis.	1. Why possible?
2. $P_1A \parallel PB \parallel P_2C$.	2. Why?
3. $P_1P = PP_2$.	3. Why?
4. $x - x_1 = x_2 - x$.	4. Why?
5. $2x = x_2 + x_1$.	5. Why?
6. $\therefore x = \frac{x_2 + x_1}{2}$.	6. Why?
7. Draw $P_1F \perp P_2C$.	7. Why possible?
8. $P_1F \perp PB$.	8. Why?
9. $P_1E = EF$.	9. Why?
10. $PE = \frac{1}{2} P_2F$.	10. Why?
11. $PE = y - y_1$ and $P_2F = y_2 - y_1$.	11. Why?
12. $\therefore y - y_1 = \frac{1}{2}(y_2 - y_1)$.	12. Why?
13. $2y - 2y_1 = y_2 - y_1$.	13. Why?
14. $2y = y_1 + y_2$ and $y = \frac{y_1 + y_2}{2}$.	14. Why?

EXERCISES

1. Find the co-ordinates of the midpoints of the sides, and the lengths of the medians, of these triangles:

   a. $(-1, 2)$, $(5, -2)$, $(5, 6)$.   *b.* $(-2, 3)$, $(-4, 3)$, $(6, 1)$.

2. The midpoint of a line segment is $(2, 1)$ and one end point is $(8, 10)$. Find the other end point.

518. Inclination and Slope of a Line. The inclination of
a line is the least angle it
makes with the positive end of
the x-axis measured counterclockwise from the x-axis to
the line. In the figure, w_1 is
the inclination of l_1, and w_2
is the inclination of l_2. The
tangent of the angle of inclination is called the *slope of
the line.* If we denote the

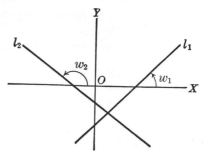

slope by m, then $m_1 = \tan w_1$ and $m_2 = \tan w_2$. If w is acute,
the slope is positive; and if w is obtuse, the slope is negative.
The slope of a line parallel to the x-axis is zero.

519. Parallel and Perpendicular Lines. If two lines, l_1
and l_2, are parallel, they have the same
slope, since their angles of inclination
w_1 and w_2 are equal. Conversely, if
two lines have the same slope, they
are parallel. Why?

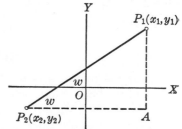

If two lines are perpendicular, their
slopes are negative reciprocals; that
is, $m_1 = -\dfrac{1}{m_2}$, or $m_1 m_2 = -1$. Conversely, if the slopes of two lines are
negative reciprocals, they are perpendicular.

520. Slope of a Line through Two Points. *The slope of a
line through two points is given
by the formula* $m = \dfrac{y_1 - y_2}{x_1 - x_2}$.

In the figure, $P_2A \perp P_1A$.

$\tan w = \dfrac{y_1 - y_2}{x_1 - x_2}$. Why?

$\tan w = m$. Why?

$\therefore m = \dfrac{y_1 - y_2}{x_1 - x_2}$. Why?

Example. Show that $(-5, -1)$, $(1, 1)$, $(7, 7)$, and $(1, 5)$ are the vertices of a parallelogram.

Solution.

$$m = \frac{y_1 - y_2}{x_1 - x_2}.$$

$$m_1 = \frac{-1 - 1}{-5 - 1} = \frac{-2}{-6} = \frac{1}{3}.$$

$$m_3 = \frac{5 - 7}{1 - 7} = \frac{-2}{-6} = \frac{1}{3}.$$

Since AB and DC have the same slope, they are parallel.

$$m_2 = \frac{7 - 1}{7 - 1} = \frac{6}{6} = 1, \quad \text{and} \quad m_4 = \frac{5 + 1}{1 + 5} = \frac{6}{6} = 1.$$

Since AD and BC have the same slope, they are parallel.
$\therefore ABCD$ is a $\square$. Why?

EXERCISES

1. Prove that $(2, 8)$, $(6, 4)$, $(3, -2)$, and $(-1, 2)$ are the vertices of a parallelogram.

2. Prove by means of slopes that the following points lie on a straight line in each case:

a. $(0, 0)$, $(2, 3)$, $(4, 6)$.   *c.* $(3, 1)$, $(3, 4)$, $(3, -2)$.
b. $(0, 0)$, $(2, 1)$, $(-4, -2)$.   *d.* $(1, 4)$, $(2, 3)$, $(4, 1)$.

3. Prove by means of slopes that $(5, 7)$, $(6, 2)$, and $(3, 5)$ are the vertices of a right triangle. (Use $m_1 m_2 = -1$.)

4. Prove that $(-1, 2)$, $(1, 3)$, $(-5, 10)$, and $(-3, 11)$ are the vertices of a rectangle.

5. Prove that $(0, -2)$, $(4, 2)$, $(0, 6)$, and $(-4, 2)$ are the vertices of a square.

521. Applications to Plane Geometry. Many of the theorems of plane geometry can be proved more easily by the methods of analytic geometry than by the methods the student has thus far employed.

The method of analytic proof will be illustrated by three examples.

Example 1. The diagonals of a rectangle are equal.

Solution. Place the given rectangle with one vertex at the origin and two adjacent sides along the x- and y-axes respectively. Label the vertices $(0, 0)$, $(a, 0)$, (a, b), and $(0, b)$.

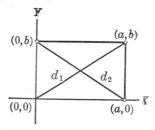

$d_1 = \sqrt{(a - 0)^2 + (b - 0)^2} = \sqrt{a^2 + b^2}$.

$d_2 = \sqrt{(a - 0)^2 + (0 - b)^2} = \sqrt{a^2 + b^2}$.

Therefore the diagonals of the rectangle are equal.

This example could have been proved by placing the rectangle in any position in reference to the axes, but the algebraic computation is simplified when a suitable position is chosen. The properties of a geometric figure depend upon the relation of its parts and not upon the position in which the figure is placed in reference to the axes.

Example 2. The diagonals of a parallelogram bisect each other.

Solution. Represent the $\square$ by $P_1P_2P_3P_4$ and place one vertex at the origin and one side along the x-axis. Represent P_2 by $(a, 0)$ and P_3 by (c, b). Then the fourth vertex will be $(c - a, b)$.

By means of the midpoint formula, we find that the midpoint of

P_1P_3 is $\left(\dfrac{c}{2}, \dfrac{b}{2}\right)$ and the midpoint of P_2P_4 is $\left(\dfrac{a + c - a}{2}, \dfrac{b}{2}\right)$, or $\left(\dfrac{c}{2}, \dfrac{b}{2}\right)$.

Since the diagonals have the same midpoint, they bisect each other.

Example 3. Prove that the diagonals of a square are perpendicular.

Solution. Place the square as shown.

Use $\qquad m = \dfrac{y_1 - y_2}{x_1 - x_2}$.

$m_1 = \dfrac{a - 0}{0 - a} = \dfrac{a}{-a} = -1$.

$m_2 = \dfrac{a - 0}{a - 0} = \dfrac{a}{a} = 1$.

$m_1 m_2 = (-1)(1) = -1$.

Therefore the diagonals are $\perp$ (§ 519).

EXERCISES

Prove the following theorems analytically:

1. The midpoint of the hypotenuse of a right triangle is equidistant from the vertices.

2. The line segment joining the midpoints of two sides of a triangle is parallel to the third side and equal in length to one half the third side. [Place the triangle with one vertex at the origin and the base along the x-axis. Label the vertices $(0, 0)$, $(a, 0)$, and (b, c).]

3. The line segments joining the midpoints of the sides of a square taken in order form a square.

4. The line segments joining the midpoints of the sides of a rectangle taken in order form a rhombus.

5. The diagonals of an isosceles trapezoid are equal. [Place the figure so that the vertices are $(0, 0)$, $(a, 0)$, (c, b), and $(a - c, b)$.]

6. The line segments joining the midpoints of the opposite sides of a quadrilateral bisect each other.

522. Equation of a Line. From algebra we know that the graph of a simple equation is a straight line. By means of analytic geometry, if given conditions that determine the line, such as two points or a point and the slope, we can write the equation of the line.

a. Point-Slope Form. $y - y_1 = m(x - x_1)$.

Given m the slope of the line and one point on the line, as $P_1(x_1, y_1)$. Represent any other point on the line as $P(x, y)$.

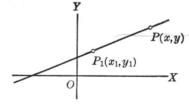

Then $\quad m = \dfrac{y - y_1}{x - x_1}$,

or $\quad y - y_1 = m(x - x_1)$.

Example. Find the equation of the line through $(3, 4)$ whose slope is $\frac{1}{2}$.

Solution.
$$y - y_1 = m(x - x_1).$$
$$y - 4 = \tfrac{1}{2}(x - 3).$$
$$2y - 8 = x - 3, \text{ or } x - 2y = -5.$$

b. *Slope-Intercept Form.* $y = mx + b.$

Given the slope m and the y-intercept equal to b. Represent any other point on the line by $P(x, y)$.

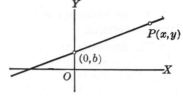

Then $m = \dfrac{y - b}{x - 0}.$

$mx = y - b.$

$y = mx + b.$

Example. Find the equation of a line whose slope is 2 and y-intercept 5.

Solution. $\quad\quad y = mx + b.$

$\quad\quad\quad\quad y = 2\,x + 5,$ or $2\,x - y = -5.$

c. *Two-Point Form.* $\dfrac{y - y_1}{x - x_1} = \dfrac{y_2 - y_1}{x_2 - x_1}.$

Given two points $P_1(x_1, y_1)$ and $P_2(x_2, y_2)$. Take any other point $P(x, y)$ on the line.

For PP_1,

$$m = \frac{y - y_1}{x - x_1}.$$

For P_2P_1,

$$m = \frac{y_2 - y_1}{x_2 - x_1}.$$

$$\therefore \frac{y - y_1}{x - x_1} = \frac{y_2 - y_1}{x_2 - x_1}.$$

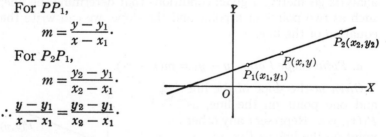

Example. Find the equation of the line determined by $(2, 3)$ and $(-3, 6)$.

Solution.

$$\frac{y - y_1}{x - x_1} = \frac{y_2 - y_1}{x_2 - x_1}.$$

$$\frac{y - 3}{x - 2} = \frac{6 - 3}{-3 - 2}.$$

$$\frac{y - 3}{x - 2} = \frac{3}{-5}.$$

$$-5\,y + 15 = 3\,x - 6, \text{ or } 3\,x + 5\,y = 21.$$

d. *Intercept Form.* $\dfrac{x}{a} + \dfrac{y}{b} = 1.$

Given x-intercept $= a$ and y-intercept $= b$. The line intersects the x-axis at $(a, 0)$ and the y-axis at $(0, b)$. Take any point on the line, as $P(x, y)$.

Use $\qquad m = \dfrac{y - y_1}{x - x_1}.$

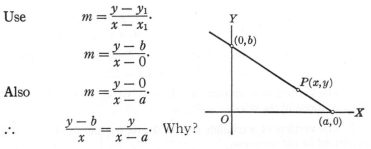

$$m = \dfrac{y - b}{x - 0}.$$

Also $\qquad m = \dfrac{y - 0}{x - a}.$

$\therefore \qquad \dfrac{y - b}{x} = \dfrac{y}{x - a}.$ Why?

$xy - bx - ay + ab = xy,$ or $bx + ay = ab.$

Dividing by ab, $\qquad \dfrac{x}{a} + \dfrac{y}{b} = 1.$

Example. Find the equation of a line whose x-intercept is 4 and y-intercept -5.

Solution.

$$\dfrac{x}{a} + \dfrac{y}{b} = 1.$$

$$\dfrac{x}{4} + \dfrac{y}{-5} = 1.$$

$$\dfrac{x}{4} - \dfrac{y}{5} = 1.$$

$$5x - 4y = 20.$$

EXERCISES

1. Find the equations of the lines through the following points and having the given slopes:

a. $(2, 3)$, $m = \frac{5}{2}$. *c.* $(2, -4)$, $m = -\frac{1}{2}$. *e.* $(-5, 2)$, $m = \frac{1}{2}$.
b. $(3, 0)$, $m = 1$. *d.* $(2, 7)$, $m = 0$. *f.* $(0, 6)$, $m = -2$.

2. Find the equations of the lines having the following slopes and y-intercepts:

a. $m = 2$, $b = 5$. *c.* $m = 5$, $b = -2$
b. $m = \frac{1}{3}$, $b = -3$. *d.* $m = \frac{1}{2}$, $b = 3$.

3. Find the equations of the lines through the points

    a. (4, 3), (− 2, 7).   *d.* (0, 3), (− 7, 5).

    b. (3, − 1), (5, 3).   *e.* (4, 2), (− 5, − 3).

    c. (6, − 4), (2, − 6).   *f.* (6, 0), (− 1, − 2).

4. Write the equations of the lines having the following *x*- and *y*-intercepts:

    a. $a = 3$, $b = 4$.   *c.* $a = -5$, $b = 2$.

    b. $a = 5$, $b = -1$.   *d.* $a = 3$, $b = -7$.

5. Write the equations of the following lines in intercept form:

    a. $3x + 5y = 15$.   *b.* $3x + 4y = 12$.   *c.* $x - 5y = 5$.

6. The vertices of a triangle are (1, − 4), (5, 4), and (− 5, 6). Find the equations of its sides.

7. The vertices of a triangle are (0, 0), (6, 0), and (8, 6). Find the equations of the medians.

8. The vertices of a triangle are (0, 8), (4, 0), and (− 4, 0). Find the equations of the medians.

523. Equation of a Circle. $(x - h)^2 + (y - k)^2 = r^2$.

Given a circle with radius r and center (h, k). Take (x, y) any point on the circle.

Then, by the distance formula,

$$\sqrt{(x - h)^2 + (y - k)^2} = r,$$

or $(x - h)^2 + (y - k)^2 = r^2.$

If h and k are both equal to 0, the center is at the origin and the equation becomes

$$x^2 + y^2 = r^2.$$

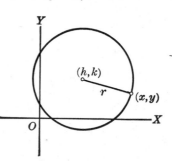

Example 1. Find the equation of a circle whose center is (3, − 4) and whose radius is equal to 6.

Solution.
$$(x - h)^2 + (y - k)^2 = r^2.$$
$$(x - 3)^2 + (y + 4)^2 = 6^2.$$
$$x^2 - 6x + 9 + y^2 + 8y + 16 = 36.$$
$$x^2 + y^2 - 6x + 8y = 11.$$

Example 2. Find the center and radius of the circle

$$x^2 + y^2 - 6x + 10y - 2 = 0.$$

Solution. To complete the squares in the left-hand member, we first write the equation in the form

$$(x^2 - 6x + \quad) + (y^2 + 10y + \quad) = \quad 2.$$

Since the coefficient of x^2 and of y^2 is unity, we can complete the squares by adding the squares of half the coefficient of x and of y respectively. Making these additions, we have

$$(x^2 - 6x + 9) + (y^2 + 10y + 25) = 9 + 25 + 2,$$

or $$(x - 3)^2 + (y + 5)^2 = 36.$$

Then the center is $(3, -5)$ and the radius is 6.

EXERCISES

1. Write the equations of the following circles and draw their graphs, using compasses:

a. Center $(0, 0)$, radius 5.

b. Center $(0, 2)$, radius 3.

c. Center $(-3, 0)$, radius 4.

d. Center $(-1, 3)$, radius 2.

e. Center $(1, -4)$, radius 8.

f. Center $(2, 5)$, radius 6.

2. Write the equation of the circle with center $(-4, 3)$ and passing through the origin.

3. Write the equation of a circle for which $(5, 2)$ and $(-1, 8)$ are the ends of a diameter.

4. Find the center and radius of each of the following circles and draw their graphs with compasses:

$$a.\ x^2 + y^2 + 10x + 8y + 25 = 0.$$
$$b.\ x^2 + y^2 + 10x - 24y = 0.$$
$$c.\ x^2 + y^2 - 6x - 7 = 0.$$

524. Summary of Formulas.

a. Distance Formula: $d = \sqrt{(x_2 - x_1)^2 + (y_2 - y_1)^2}$.

b. Midpoint Formulas: $x = \dfrac{x_1 + x_2}{2},\ y = \dfrac{y_1 + y_2}{2}$.

c. For ‖ Lines: $m_1 = m_2$.

d. For ⊥ Lines: $m_1 m_2 = -1$.

e. Slope Formula: $m = \dfrac{y_1 - y_2}{x_1 - x_2}$.

f. Line Formulas:

   (1) Point-Slope Form: $y - y_1 = m(x - x_1)$.

   (2) Slope-Intercept Form: $y = mx + b$.

   (3) Two-Point Form: $\dfrac{y - y_1}{x - x_1} = \dfrac{y_2 - y_1}{x_2 - x_1}$.

   (4) Intercept Form: $\dfrac{x}{a} + \dfrac{y}{b} = 1$.

g. Circle Formulas:

   (1) Any Center: $(x - h)^2 + (y - k)^2 = r^2$.

   (2) Center at Origin: $x^2 + y^2 = r^2$.

TEST 41

Applications (*Forty Minutes*)

1. Find the lengths of the sides of the triangle whose vertices **are** $(2, 3)$, $(- 5, 6)$, and $(- 4, - 3)$.

2. Find the midpoints of the sides of the triangle whose vertices **are** $(- 3, 6)$, $(5, 4)$, and $(7, - 6)$.

3. Find the slope of the line segment joining $(2, 1)$ and $(5, 4)$.

4. Prove that $(4, 0)$, $(7, 8)$, $(0, 10)$, and $(- 3, 2)$ are the vertices **of** a parallelogram.

5. Prove that $(- 1, - 3)$, $(- 3, 3)$, $(6, 6)$, and $(8, 0)$ are the vertices of a rectangle.

6. Find the equation of the line through $(2, 5)$ whose slope is $\frac{2}{3}$.

7. Find the equation of the line whose slope is 2 and y-intercept 5.

8. Write the equation of the line through $(3, 5)$ and $(7, - 1)$.

9. Write the equation of the line whose x-intercept is 3 and y-intercept $- 4$.

10. Find the equation of the circle whose center is at the origin and which has a radius equal to 6.

11. Write the equation of the circle which passes through the origin and has its center at $(4, - 3)$.

12. Find the equation of the circle whose center is $(6, 2)$ and radius 4.

CHAPTER XVII

Additional Topics

1. Aeronautics

Aeronautics, or air navigation, is the science or art of sailing in the air by means of a balloon, airship, glider, or airplane. Four of the most needed subjects in the study of aeronautics are mathematics, physics, physical geography, and meteorology.

It is the purpose in these few pages to present some simple applications of mathematics, and particularly geometry, to the flying of a plane. Let us first see why a plane flies.

525. Why a Kite Flies. When a boy flies his kite, he keeps it stationary as the wind flows past it. When a pilot flies a plane, the engine of the plane pulls it through the air. Since the kite and plane are kept aloft in equilibrium by the action of similar forces, we shall first make a short study of flying the simple kite.

When a boy flies his kite, he probably knows that three forces are acting upon it to keep it in the air. One force is the wind which blows against the surface of the kite. Another force is the pull of gravity. This force is called the weight of the kite. The third force is the one applied by the boy through the string. In Fig. 1 on page 496, AG shows the direction of the force of gravity, AP shows the direction of the pull of the boy through the string, and AB shows the direction of the effective force of the wind WA.

When two nonparallel forces act at a point on a body, their *resultant* (the single force which has the same effect on the mo-

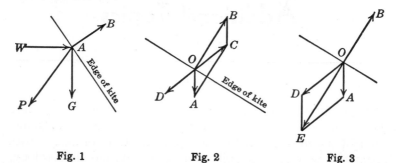

| Fig. 1 | Fig. 2 | Fig. 3 |

tion of the body as the two forces acting together) can be represented by the diagonal of a parallelogram which has two adjacent sides representing the two nonparallel forces. (See Ex. 4, p. 401.)

In Fig. 2, *OA* represents the magnitude and direction of the force of gravity, or the weight of the kite; *OB* represents the magnitude and direction of the effective force of the wind (part of the wind's force is directed along the face of the kite); and *OC* represents the resultant of these two forces both in magnitude and in direction. To keep the kite in equilibrium, the force *OD*, which is equal to the force *OC* but opposite in direction, must be applied at *O*. Then *OD* represents the pull of the string.

In the same manner one can find the resultant *OE* of the two forces *OA* and *OD*. Then *OB* (Fig. 3) represents the effective force of the wind.

EXERCISES

1. Two forces act at a point upon a body at an angle of 60°. One of the forces is 40 pounds and the other is 80 pounds. Construct their resultant, letting 1 cm. stand for 10 pounds. Measure their resultant and find what single force will have the same effect on the body as the two given forces.

2. Force AB is 30 pounds and force AC is 25 pounds. What is their resultant if they act in opposite directions?

3. Two forces, AB and AC, act on a body at A. If the force AB is 30 pounds, find the resultant of the two forces. What single force AD must be applied at A to maintain equilibrium? Find the number of degrees in $\angle BAD$.

526. Why a Plane Flies. All the forces which keep a kite in the air are present in the flight of a plane, but not all of them act on the plane in the same directions as they do on the kite. For example, in the level flight of a plane the propeller force is almost horizontal, while the string pull on the kite is toward a point on the ground.

One force which helps to keep the modern plane aloft is due to the streamlining of the plane. Let us see why the wings of a plane are streamlined. When an *airfoil* (any part of a plane which is used to keep the plane in the air), having a cross section like the one shown here, is pulled rapidly through the air toward 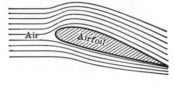 the left, there is a decrease in the atmospheric pressure on the upper side of the airfoil and an increase in the atmospheric pressure on the underside of the airfoil. The difference in pressure between these two pressures is called the *lift* of the airfoil.

When a plane is in a straight and level flight, the air forces acting against the plane may be resolved into one single force, OW, which tends to lift the plane. The weight of the plane, OG, is directed toward the center of the earth. The engine of the plane through the propeller acts on the 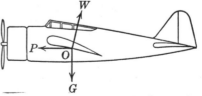 plane by the force OP. When the plane is in equilibrium, the forces OW, OP, and OG can be represented by the parallelogram of forces.

The Plan of Construction of a Modern Airplane Is Based on Experimentation and on the Application of Aerodynamics

EXERCISES

1. The lifting surface of the wings of a plane is 262 square feet. If the atmospheric pressure on the underside of the wings is 12.8 pounds per square inch and the atmospheric pressure above the wings is 12.1 pounds per square inch, what is the total lift?

2. The proportion $\dfrac{V_1}{V_2} = \sqrt{\dfrac{W_1}{W_2}}$ shows the relation of the velocities and loads of a plane. In this proportion V_1 and V_2 are the velocities when the respective loads are W_1 and W_2.

a. Show that the load of a plane varies directly as the square of its velocity.

b. If a plane weighing 2400 pounds can fly 100 m.p.h., what velocity must it have if its load is increased 600 pounds?

3. An airplane has an air speed of 100 m.p.h. If the wind is blowing east at 20 m.p.h., how far east can the plane go and return in $7\frac{1}{2}$ hours?

527. How Navigators Express Time. The navigator counts the time of day from midnight. Each day begins at midnight and ends at the following midnight. Instead of writing "4:37 A.M." the navigator writes "0437"; instead of writing "8:12 P.M." he writes "2012"; and instead of writing "11 A.M." he writes "1100."

Frequently it is necessary to add and subtract measures of time.

Example 1. Add: 2 hr. 32 min. 18 sec.
                         14 hr. 29 min. 45 sec.
The sum is   16 hr. 61 min. 63 sec. = 17 hr. 2 min. 3 sec.

Example 2. If the difference in sun time between two places is 2 hr. 48 min., find the slow time when the fast time is 1823.

Solution. 1823 = 18 hr. 23 min. = 17 hr. 83 min.
                                      2 hr. 48 min.
The difference is   15 hr. 35 min.

The slow time is 1535, or 3:35 P.M.

528. Meaning of Direction. The direction of any ray from a point A is the angle that the ray makes with the ray running north from A. The direction of any point on the ray is the same as that of the ray. The angle is measured clockwise. Thus the direction of C from A is 50° and the direction of D from A is 270°.

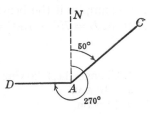

529. Direction of the Wind. When indicating the direction of the wind, it is customary to give the direction *from* which the wind is blowing. For example, a west wind means a wind blowing from the west. Remember that a west wind blows from the west toward the east and that a south wind blows from the south toward the north.

The direction of the wind at an airport is usually shown by an *air-sock,* which is attached to a pole and flies in the wind.

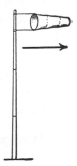

530. Bearing of a Point. The *bearing* of one point from another is the direction of the first point from the second. In Fig. 1 the bearing of C from P is 45°, the bearing of D from P is 120°, and the bearing of E from P is 200°.

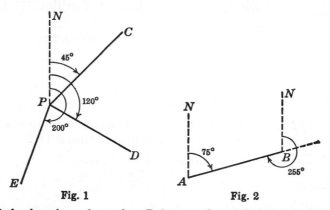

Fig. 1   Fig. 2

If the bearing of a point B from point A is known (Fig. 2), the bearing of point A from point B can be determined easily. For example, if the bearing of B from A is 75°, the bearing of A from $B = 75° + 180° = 255°$. Can you prove it?

EXERCISES

1. Change the following times to the form used by navigators:

a. 4:18 A.M.   **c.** 6:15 P.M.   **e.** 7 A.M.

b. 12 noon.   **d.** 11:32 P.M.   **f.** midnight.

2. When it is 0815 Wednesday, what is the time 17 hr. 4 min. later?

3. What was the time 16 hr. 50 min. before 1345 Tuesday?

4. $\angle x = 27° \, 18' \, 34''$ and $\angle y = 18° \, 37' \, 52''$.

a. Find $\angle m$ if $\angle m = \angle x + \angle y$.   **b.** Find $\angle n$ if $\angle n = \angle x - \angle y$.

Example 1. *Find the difference in latitude between that of a city 62° 18′ N. latitude and that of an airport 39° 42′ N. latitude.

Solution. $62° \, 18' = 61° \, 78'$

$39° \, 42' = 39° \, 42'$

The difference of latitude $= 22° \, 36'$

*Read §§ 544, 545.

Example 2. A is 18° 37′ E. longitude and B is 93° 41′ W. longitude. Find the difference of longitude of A and B.

Solution. 18° 37′
　　　　　　93° 41′
　　　　　　111° 78′ = 112° 18′, the difference of longitude.

5. Athens, Greece, is situated at 23° 44′ E. longitude and 38° 1′ N. latitude. Havana, Cuba, is situated at 82° 23′ W. longitude and 23° 7′ N. latitude. Find the difference of longitude and latitude of the two cities.

6. If the bearing of a ship from a lighthouse is 52° 18′, what is the bearing of the lighthouse from the ship?

7. A pilot finds that the bearing of an airport from his plane is 137°. What is the bearing of his plane from the airport?

8. What is the approximate bearing of the North Star?

9. Columbus, Ohio, is about 170 miles east of Indianapolis, Indiana. The pilot of a plane observed that the bearing of Columbus was 70° and the bearing of Indianapolis was 330°. Make a scale drawing to find his distance from Columbus.

531. Methods of Navigation. There are four general ways of navigating a plane—piloting, celestial navigating, radio navigating, and navigating by dead reckoning. *Avigation* is a word often used for air navigation because "navigation" has for many years been applied to steering ships at sea.

Piloting is finding one's way by the use of maps and charts and by the observation of certain landmarks such as railways, roads, rivers, and towns.

Celestial navigating is done by observing the position of the sun, moon, planets, and stars.

Radio navigating means finding one's way by radio communication with airports, planes, or ships.

Dead reckoning is flying by the use of a chart and compass. Before a pilot or navigator starts on a flight by dead reckoning, he must chart his course. To do this he uses his chart to find the bearing of his destination from the beginning of his flight. He determines the direction the plane must be *headed* (pointed) to make allowance for the *wind drift*. Since the compass needle at most places does not point true north, the pilot must add or subtract the magnetic variation to know what compass reading should be used in the flight. The pilot should be able to tell exactly where he is at any time in the flight.

532. How to Establish a Fix. *Establishing a fix* is finding one's position. A pilot may be sure that he is flying in the right direction toward his destination, but uncertain of the remaining distance to be covered. The following example illustrates a method of finding his position:

Example 1. While flying a straight course from airport A to airport B, the pilot wishes to find how far he is from the airport B. Hearing the radio signal from airport C, he finds the bearing of it from his position to be 125°. Find his distance to B.

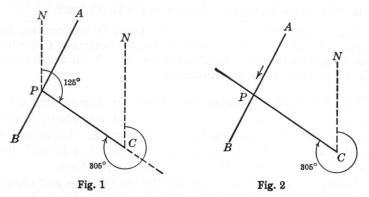

Fig. 1   Fig. 2

Analysis. (Fig. 1) 1. Suppose the problem solved and that P is his position in AB. Draw PC.

2. Draw the lines running north from P and C.

3. Since the bearing of C from P is 125°, the bearing of P from C is (125° + 180°), or 305°.

4. Then P is the intersection of AB and the line through C and with direction 305°.

Solution. (Fig. 2) 1. On the chart draw AB.

2. Draw the line through C in direction 305°.

3. This line intersects AB in point P, which is the fix.

4. By using the chart, the distance PB can be calculated.

Suppose a pilot is not flying a straight course and wishes to check his location by radio from two airports. The following example illustrates a method he may use:

Example 2. A pilot at a point P recognized the radio signals from two airports A and B. Using his direction-finder, he observed that the bearing of A was 78° and the bearing of B was 300°. Find his position.

Analysis. (Fig. 1) 1. Suppose the problem solved.

2. Since the bearing of A from P is 78°, the bearing of P from A is (180° + 78°), or 258°.

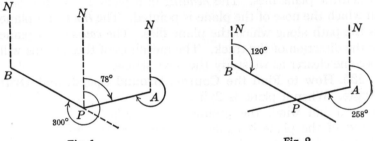

Fig. 1   Fig. 2

3. Since the bearing of B from P is 300°, the bearing of P from B is (300° − 180°), or 120°.

Solution. (Fig. 2) 1. On the map draw the line from A in direction 258°.

2. From B draw the line in direction 120°.

3. These two lines intersect in point P, which is the position or fix of the pilot.

EXERCISES

1. Airport S is 240 miles from airport R, and its bearing from R is 138°. Airport T has a bearing of 115° from R and a bearing of 10° from S. Find the distance of T from R and from S.

2. A pilot is flying course 225° from airport X. Determine his fix when the bearing of station Y is 76° from the plane, if station Y is in direction 115° from X and the distance of Y from X is 150 miles.

533. How the Wind Affects the Direction and Speed of a Plane. When an airplane is flying in still air toward a given destination, its nose is pointed in the direction it is going. A wind blowing in the same direction as the plane is flying is called a *tail wind*; and a wind blowing in the opposite direction is called a *head wind*. Neither a tail wind nor a head wind changes the direction of a plane's flight, but either one affects the speed of the plane relative to the ground.

534. Speed, Track, and Course. The *air speed* of a plane is the speed of the plane in still air. The *ground speed* of a plane is the speed of the plane relative to the ground over which the plane flies. The *heading* of a plane is the direction in which the nose of the plane is pointed. The *track* of a plane is the path along which the plane flies. The *course* of a plane is the direction of the track. The meanings of these terms will become clearer as we study the next article.

535. How to Find the Course, Ground Speed, and Drift Angle. When a plane is flying with a tail wind, the ground speed of the plane is equal to the sum of the air speed and the speed of the wind. Thus if AB represents the air speed of the plane and CD the speed of the wind, then AD represents the ground speed of the plane.

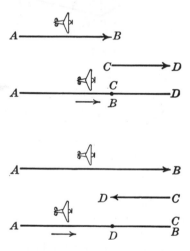

When a plane is flying against a head wind, the ground speed is equal to the air speed of the plane decreased by the speed of the wind.

When a plane is flying in a wind that is blowing obliquely to the heading of the plane, both the speed and the direction of the plane are affected.

Suppose that points A and B are 100 miles apart and that a plane at A is headed toward B at 100 m.p.h. Also suppose that the wind is blowing in the direction BC at 40 m.p.h. In 20 minutes the plane has traveled from A to B', but the wind has carried the plane from B' to C'; in 40 minutes the plane has traveled from A to B'', but the wind has carried the plane from B'' to C''; and

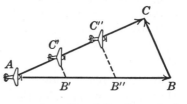

in 1 hour the plane has traveled from A to B, while the wind has caused it to arrive at C. If AB represents the air speed of the plane and BC represents the velocity of the air, then AC represents the course of the plane and its ground speed.

The parallelogram of velocities can be used to find the ground velocity of the plane.

AC is the diagonal of the parallelogram $ABCD$ drawn from A. In either figure, the plane is headed along AB, its track is along AC, and its course is in direction AC. Due to the wind the plane's direction of flight (course) is changed from AB to AC. The $\angle BAC$ is called the *drift angle*.

Example 1. A plane is headed east with an air speed of 100 m.p.h. The wind is blowing from direction 225° at 40 m.p.h. Find the course, ground speed, and drift angle.

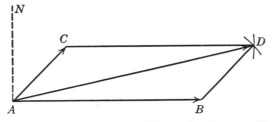

Solution. 1. If 1 cm. represents 20 m.p.h., 5 cm. will represent 100 m.p.h. Draw AB in direction 90° and 5 cm. long.

2. $40 \div 20 = 2$. Draw AC in direction $(225° - 180°)$, or 45°, and 2 cm. long.

(Solution continued on following page.)

3. Construct □ *ABDC* and draw diagonal *AD*.

4. Measure *AD*. It is 6.5 cm. long approximately.

5. 6.5 × 20 = 130. The ground speed is 130 m.p.h.

6. Measure ∠ *BAD*, the drift angle. It is 16° approximately.

7. 16° is the drift angle. The course is 130 m.p.h. in direction *AD*, 74°.

In Example 1 above, the line segments *AB, AC,* and *AD* that represent the velocities are called *vectors*.

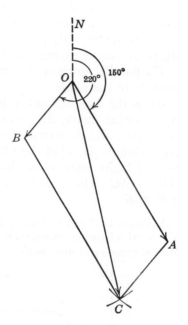

Example 2. Find the course, ground speed, and drift angle of an airplane with an air speed of 100 m.p.h. and headed at 150° if there is a 40 m.p.h. wind from direction 40°.

Solution. 1. Let 1 cm. represent 20 m.p.h. Then 5 cm. will represent 100 m.p.h. and 2 cm. will represent 40 m.p.h.

2. Draw *OA* = 5 cm. and in direction 150°.

3. Draw *OB* = 2 cm. and in direction 220°.

4. Construct □ *OACB* and draw diagonal *OC*.

5. *OC* = 6 cm.   6 × 20 = 120. The ground speed is 120 m.p.h.

6. Measure ∠ *NOC*.   ∠ *NOC* = 168°. The course is 168° from *O*.

7. The drift angle = ∠ *AOC* = 18°.

EXERCISES

1. An airplane is headed 30° with an air speed of 120 m.p.h. The wind is blowing 45 m.p.h. from due west. Find the course, ground speed, and drift angle.

2. Solve Ex. 1, assuming that the wind is blowing from 135° instead of from the west.

3. Solve Ex. 1, assuming that the wind is blowing from 340°.

536. How to Find the Ground Speed and the Wind-Correction Angle. On pages 504–505 it was shown how a pilot can determine the course and ground speed when the wind is blowing. More often a pilot must determine in what direction the plane must be headed so that he can fly the required course.

Study the following example and its solution:

Example. A pilot is to fly on course 70° when the wind is blowing 30 m.p.h. from direction 140°. If he plans on an air speed of 150 m.p.h., what wind-correction angle is needed and what will be his ground speed?

Solution. 1. Draw line *OK* in direction 70°.

2. Using the scale 1 cm. = 30 m.p.h., draw *OC* in direction (140° + 180°), or 320°, and 1 cm. long.

3. With *C* as the center and radius = 5 cm. draw an arc intersecting *OK* in *B*.

4. Complete the parallelogram *OABC*.

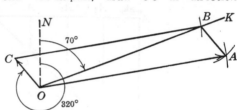

5. *OA* = *CB*. Why? The plane should be headed along *OA*. Measure ∠ *NOA*. The heading is about 81° and the wind-correction angle *AOB* is about 11°.

6. The ground speed represented by vector *OB* is about 137 m.p.h.

EXERCISES

1. A pilot must fly a course of 20° when the wind has a velocity of 20 m.p.h. from direction 135°. Find his heading and the ground speed if his air speed is 100 m.p.h.

2. The required course is 280°, the wind is blowing from 200° at 40 m.p.h., and the air speed is 240 m.p.h. Find the heading and ground speed.

3. A pilot wishes to take his plane on course 280° with a ground speed of 160 m.p.h. The wind is blowing due east at 40 m.p.h. Find the air speed and heading he must use. (Draw a sketch of the parallelogram and use analysis.)

537. Interception. Any boy or girl who has played basketball knows that in passing a ball to a running teammate the ball is aimed in the direction ahead of the intended receiver so that it will reach a certain place at the same time the receiver arrives. The antiaircraft gunner tries to aim his gun so that the shell and target will be in the same position at the same time. Likewise when a pilot wishes to intercept a moving plane or ship in the shortest time, he must fly a straight course to the spot where they will meet.

Suppose that a pilot at point C wishes to intercept a ship at A sailing east at constant speed. If he wishes to reach the ship in the shortest time possible, he must head his plane to-

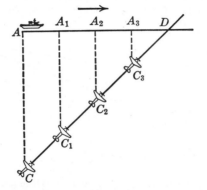

ward the point D where the plane and ship will meet. Suppose that they will meet in 60 minutes. If their velocities are uniform, at the end of 15 minutes the ship will be at A_1 and the plane at C_1; in 30 minutes their respective positions will be at A_2 and C_2; and at the end of 45 minutes their respective positions will be at A_3 and C_3. From the figure it can be seen that when the plane and the ship intercept each other under the above conditions, the bearing of one from the other is constant.

The converse of the last statement has long been known among seamen and is stated "constant bearing means collision." This means that if two objects are moving in straight courses and the bearing of one from the other remains constant, the two objects will meet.

Example. A plane at point C starts to meet a ship which starts to take course AB from port A at 20 m.p.h. If there is no wind, how long will it take the plane to intercept the ship at a speed of 100 m.p.h.?

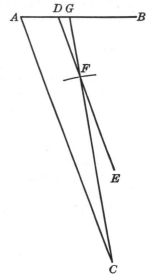

Scale: 1 cm. = 20 miles

Solution. 1. Draw AC.

2. On AB mark off $AD = 1$ cm. to represent the distance the ship will go in 1 hour.

3. Draw $DE \parallel AC$. When the ship is at D, the plane is somewhere in line DE. Why?

4. In 1 hour the plane is 100 miles from C. So with C as a center and a radius of 5 cm. draw an arc intersecting DE in F.

5. Draw CF intersecting AB in G, which is the place of interception.

6. If AD represents 1 hour of flying time, AG represents about 1 hr. 24 min., the time required for interception. AG is about 1.35 cm. and CG is about 6.65 cm. $1.35 \times 20 = 27$ and $6.65 \times 20 = 133$. Then the ship has gone about 27 miles, and the plane has gone about 133 miles.

EXERCISES

1. A pursuit plane starts to intercept a transport plane which is 60 miles due north and flying at 320 m.p.h. due east. Find the course of the pursuit plane if it flies 450 m.p.h. How soon after it starts will the pursuit plane intercept the transport plane?

2. At 6 A.M. a troopship sails on course 79° from a coastal town A at 25 m.p.h. At 8 A.M. an airplane leaves an airport 150 miles due south from A with a speed of 180 m.p.h. to intercept the ship. How far will the plane have to fly to intercept the ship? How far from A is the point of interception? How long does it take the plane to intercept the ship?

3. A bomber is flying due south at 220 m.p.h. A pursuit plane starts to intercept the bomber when the bearing of the bomber from the pursuit plane is 280° and the distance between the planes is 80 miles. Find the course of the pursuit plane and the time needed for the interception, if the pursuit plane flies 300 m.p.h.

4. At the hour 1600 a battleship starts on course 260° at 16 m.p.h. from island X. At the hour 2000 an airplane leaves an airport 340 miles south of X with a speed of 280 m.p.h. to intercept the battleship. Find the course of the airplane. How far from X will the point of interception be? How long will it take the airplane to make the interception?

5. A hunter fires a rifle at a hare when it is 120 feet due north of him and running due east at 40 feet a second. The rifle the hunter uses will give the bullet an average velocity of 2000 feet a second. In what direction must he sight the gun so that his shot will hit the hare? How far will the hare go from the time the hunter fires the gun until it is shot?

538. Radius of Action. One of a pilot's problems is finding how far he can safely fly a plane and return on a given amount of gasoline. After a plane is in the air and has attained its required speed, the consumption of gasoline is independent of the velocity of the air.

The distance from an airport that a plane can safely fly and return is called the *radius of action* for the plane at this port.

Example. The tank of a plane holds 56 gallons, and the plane consumes 10 gallons an hour. When no wind is blowing, what distance can the plane safely fly and return if 6 gallons are allowed for safety and getting into the air and the plane's speed is 100 m.p.h.?

Solution. 1. $56 - 6 = 50$.

2. $50 \div 10 = 5$, the number of hours of safe flying. The time going $= 2\frac{1}{2}$ hours.

3. $2\frac{1}{2} \times 100 = 250$, the distance in miles that the plane can go, or the radius of action.

When a pilot flies a straight course from one point as far as he can and returns on a straight course to a second point, the distance between the first point and the turning point is the radius of action for the plane at the first point.

Example. An airplane carrier is steaming on course 315° at 25 m.p.h. A scouting plane with a speed of 100 m.p.h. leaves the ship on course 270° with sufficient gasoline for 4 hours of flight. How far can the plane keep its course before starting its return to the carrier? What heading should it take in returning?

Solution. 1. Draw *AB* the distance the plane can go on course 270°
at 100 m.p.h. in 4 hours.

2. Draw *AC* the distance the carrier will go in 4 hours.

3. Draw *BC* and construct its ⊥ bisector, which intersects *AB*
in *D*.

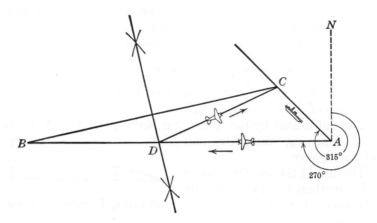

4. Draw *DC*. Prove *DC = DB*.

5. *D* is the point where the plane must start on its return trip
AD, the radius of action, is about 228 miles.

6. The course returning, *DC*, is about 65°.

EXERCISES

1. A pilot is flying a plane whose safe flying time is 6 hours. How
far southeast can he fly and return if no wind is blowing and his air
speed is 120 m.p.h.?

2. An airplane carrier is steaming on course 240° at 20 m.p.h. If
a plane with an air speed of 160 m.p.h. leaves the carrier to scout
on course 280° and no wind is blowing, how far can it go on its course
before starting its return to the carrier, allowing 1½ hours flying time?
What heading should it take on its returning course?

3. The wind is blowing 20 m.p.h. and the air speed of the plane is
110 m.p.h. How far can the pilot fly with the wind and return
against the wind in 4 hours?

2. Artillery Fire

539. Mil. The *mil* is a unit of angular measure equal to $\frac{1}{6400}$ of one complete revolution. The word "mil," meaning "one-thousandth," was first suggested for an angle that subtends an arc equal to $\frac{1}{1000}$ of the radius. Such an angle subtends 1 foot at the distance of 1000 feet or 1 yard at the distance of 1000 yards. The angle subtended by a circle would be $\frac{2\,\pi}{.001}$, or $6283 +$ mils. This number is too inconvenient for practical use; so the circle is divided into 6400 equal parts, and each of these is called a mil.

The mil is used by the Army and Navy in computing firing data, mapping, sketching, and reconnaissance

The use of the mil furnishes a quick method for approximating distances. For small angles the following formula is used: $s = \frac{rm}{1000}$, where s is the chord, r is the radius (distance), and m is the angle.

Example 1. If two points, A and B, are 80 yards apart and 4000 yards away from the observer, how many mils do they subtend?

Solution.

$$s = \frac{rm}{1000}.$$

$$80 = \frac{4000\,m}{1000}.$$

$$80 = 4\,m.$$

$$m = 20 \text{ (mils)}.$$

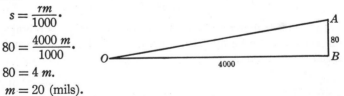

Example 2. If the angular distance between points C and D, 2000 yards away, is 40 mils, what is the distance between C and D?

Solution.

$$s = \frac{rm}{1000}.$$

$$s = \frac{2000 \times 40}{1000}, \text{ or } 80 \text{ (yards)}.$$

Example 3. If the angular distance between E and F is 30 mils and they are 60 yards apart, how far away are they?

Solution.

$$s = \frac{rm}{1000}.$$

$$60 = \frac{30\,r}{1000}.$$

$$60{,}000 = 30\,r.$$

$$r = 2000 \text{ (yards)}.$$

Example 4. Change 25° to mils.

Solution. Since 6400 mils = 360°, 1 degree = $\frac{6400}{360}$, or $\frac{160}{9}$, mils. $25 \times \frac{160}{9} = \frac{4000}{9}$, or 444 (mils).

Example 5. Change 120 mils to degrees.

Solution. $\qquad$ 1 mil = $\frac{9}{160}$ degree.
$\qquad\qquad$ $120 \times \frac{9}{160} = 6\frac{3}{4}$ (degrees).

EXERCISES

1. Change to mils:

a. 18°. $\qquad$ *b.* 20°. $\qquad$ *c.* 35°. $\qquad\qquad$ *d.* 70°.

2. Change to degrees:

a. 1600 mils. $\qquad$ *b.* 80 mils. $\qquad$ *c.* 120 mils.

3. The angular distance from A to B is 50 mils. If the points are 7500 yards away, how far apart are they?

4. A battery* 6000 yards from an observer has a 20-yard front. What angle does the battery subtend at the observer's position?

5. A target 1000 yards from an observer has a 4-yard front. What angle does the target subtend at the observer's position?

540. Direction of Fire.

The simplest form of artillery firing is sighting directly at the target (direct laying). Usually the target is not visible from the guns and a method known as *indirect laying* must be used. In the simplest case of indirect laying an observation post, O, and an "aiming point," P, are selected that are visible from both gun and target.

*A battery is a firing unit of artillery usually consisting of four guns.

In the diagram, the gun is at G, T is the target, P the aiming point, and O the observation post. GP is the plane of sight, GT is the plane of fire, and $\angle TGP$, measured clockwise from GT to GP, is the deflection. If $OA \parallel GT$, $\angle t = \angle r$ (alternate-interior $\angle$ of $\parallel$ lines are $=$). In like manner, if $OB \parallel GP$, $\angle m = \angle p$. $\angle TGP = \angle AOB$ (having their sides parallel, right side to right side and left side to left side). Then the

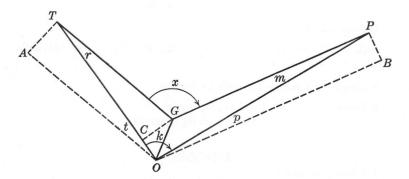

deflection is $\angle x = \angle k + \angle t + \angle p$. The *range* is the distance GT.

If a map of the locality is available, and T, G, and P can be identified on the map, the deflection and the range can be measured from the map. Otherwise the artillery officer selects an object at A such that $OA \parallel GT$. Then with an instrument the officer can measure $\angle t$, which is called the *target offset*. In like manner OB is taken parallel to GP. $\angle p$ is called the *aiming-point offset*. $\angle k$ can be measured directly. Then $\angle x = \angle t + \angle k + \angle p$.

In most battles speed is essential in taking up position and opening fire. For this reason the range GT is often estimated. The artillery officer from training and experience can do this quite accurately. If time is available, the distances OT and OG can be measured by a *range finder* (a telescope for measuring distances), and the distance GT can be computed by trigonometry by the use of the formula $\dfrac{GT}{\sin k} = \dfrac{OG}{\sin r}$.

Example 1. In the diagram on page 514, if the target offset is 400 mils, the aiming-point offset is 300 mils, $\angle k$ is 1600 mils, $\angle TOG$ is 900 mils, $OT = 5400$ yards, and OG is 1500 yards, find the deflection and range.

Solution.

$$\angle x = \angle t + \angle k + \angle p.$$
$$\angle x = 400 + 1600 + 300.$$
$$\angle x = 2300 \text{ mils.}$$
$$\text{Deflection} = 2300 \text{ mils.}$$

In $\triangle TOG$ draw $GC \perp OT$. Then, in rt. $\triangle OCG$,

$$CG = OG \sin \angle TOG.$$
$$CG = 1500 \sin 900 \text{ mils.}$$
$$CG = 1500 \sin 50.6°.$$
$$CG = 1500 \ (.7727).$$
$$CG = 1159 \text{ (yards).}$$

In rt. $\triangle TCG$,

$$GC = TG \sin 400 \text{ mils.}$$
$$1159 = TG \sin 22.5°.$$
$$1159 = TG \ (.3827).$$
$$TG = 3028 \text{ (yards).}$$
$$\text{Range} = 3000 \text{ yards.}$$

Example 2.

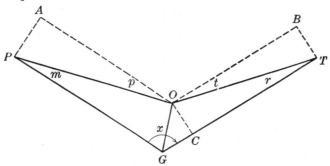

In this case the aiming-point offset is 300 mils, target offset is 250 mils, $\angle POT = 2600$ mils, $\angle GOT = 1800$ mils, OT is 3000 yards, and OG is 1000 yards. Find the deflection and range.

(The solution to this example is given on the following page.)

Solution.

$$\angle x = \angle POT - \angle p - \angle t.$$
$$\angle x = 2600 - 300 - 250.$$
$$\angle x = 2050.$$

$\angle TGP$, measured clockwise from T to P, is $6400 - 2050 = 4350$. Therefore the deflection is 4350 mils. The sum of the angles of a triangle is 180°, or 3200 mils. In rt. $\triangle OCG$, $\angle OGT = 3200 - 1800 - 250 = 1150$ (mils).

$$GC = OG \cos 1150 \text{ mils.}$$
$$GC = 1000 \cos 64.7°.$$
$$GC = 1000 \,(.4273).$$
$$GC = 427 \text{ (yards)}.$$

In rt. $\triangle OCT$,

$$CT = OT \cos 250 \text{ mils.}$$
$$CT = 3000 \cos 14.1°.$$
$$CT = 3000 \,(.9699).$$
$$CT = 2910 \text{ (yards)}.$$

$GT = GC + CT = 427 + 2910 = 3337$ yards. The range is 3400 yards. Range is taken to the nearest 200 yards.

EXERCISES

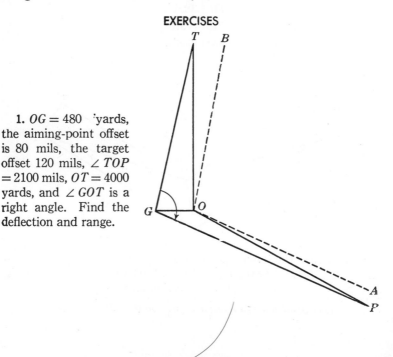

1. $OG = 480$ yards, the aiming-point offset is 80 mils, the target offset 120 mils, $\angle TOP = 2100$ mils, $OT = 4000$ yards, and $\angle GOT$ is a right angle. Find the deflection and range.

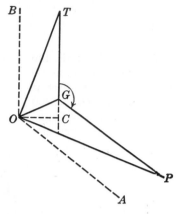

Find the deflection and range in Exs. 2–4.

2. $OG = 2000$ yards, the aiming-point offset is 300 mils, the target offset is 380 mils, $\angle TOP = 2400$ mils, and $OT = 5000$ yards.

3. $OG = 1600$ yards, the aiming-point offset is 220 mils, the target offset is 260 mils, $\angle TOP = 3150$ mils, and $OT = 6000$ yards.

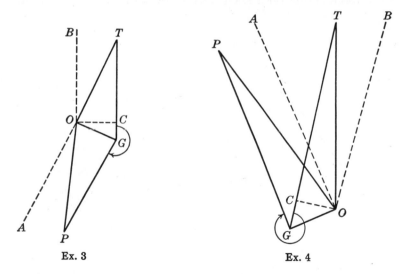

Ex. 3   Ex. 4

4. $OG = 900$ yards, the aiming-point offset is 200 mils, the target offset is 150 mils, $\angle TOP = 700$ mils, and $OT = 5000$ yards.

SUGGESTION. Acute $\angle PGT = \angle POT - \angle AOP + \angle BOT$. The deflection is $\angle TGP$ measured clockwise from GT to GP.

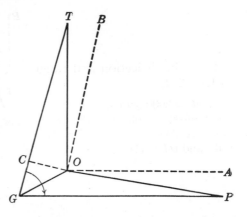

5. $OG = 600$ yards, the aiming-point offset is 60 mils, the target offset is 140 mils, $\angle TOP = 3400$ mils, and $OT = 3600$ yards. Find the deflection and range.

541. The Trajectory. When an object called a *shell* is thrown by a gun, the path of the shell is the *trajectory*. If the only force acting on a shell during its flight were gravity, its

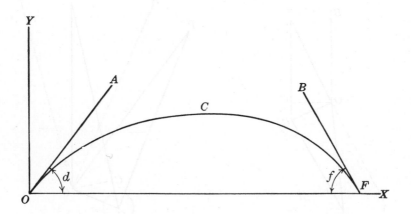

trajectory would be a parabola. The weight, form, and caliber of the projectile, the wind, the air resistance, and the bore of the gun all affect the trajectory.

In the diagram above, $\angle d$ is the angle of departure of the projectile, the curve OCF is the trajectory, $\angle f$ is the angle of fall, and OF is the range. You know from algebra that the graph of a first-degree equation like $x - 2y = 6$ is a straight line and the graph of a second-degree equation like $y = x^2 + 6$ is a parabola. The equation for the trajectory of a shell is $y = x \tan d - \dfrac{gx^2}{2\,v_0{}^2\cos^2 d}$, where v_0 is the muzzle velocity of the gun. The range is given by the formula $R = \dfrac{v_0{}^2 \sin 2\,d}{g}$. Under actual firing conditions the trajectory is not a parabola. The descending branch is steeper than the ascending branch. The point of fall is rarely level with the gun.

In the diagram below, O is the muzzle of the gun, B is the point of fall, OA is the horizontal line, OB is the line of *site*, the curve OHB is the trajectory, OG is the line of elevation, OE is the line of departure and is tangent to the trajectory at

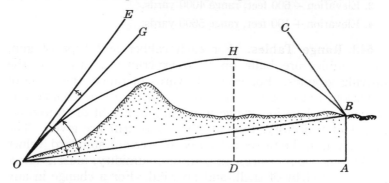

O, BC is tangent to the trajectory at B, HD is the maximum height of the trajectory, OA is the range, $\angle EOB$ is the angle of departure, $\angle EOG$ is the jump, $\angle AOB$ is the *site*, $\angle GOB$ is the angle of elevation, $\angle EOA$ is the quadrant angle of departure, and $\angle CBO$ is the angle of fall.

When the muzzle velocity is fixed and the elevation is increased from 0° to about 45°, the height, angle of fall, and time of flight increase. The range is the greatest for about 45°. It then decreases to zero for an elevation of about 90°.

542. Site. *Site* is the angle of elevation of the target above, or the angle of depression of the target below, the horizontal plane. The difference in elevation of the gun and target and their distance apart can be read from a map and site computed from the mil relation. For example, if the target is 100 yards above the guns and the range is 5000 yards, the site is given by the formula $m = \dfrac{1000\,s}{r}$, or $m = \dfrac{1000 \times 100}{5000} = 20$ (mils). The site is positive when the target is above the guns and negative when the target is below the guns.

EXERCISES

Give the site for the following elevations and ranges:

1. Elevation + 200 feet, range 2500 yards.

2. Elevation − 20 yards, range 3000 yards.

3. Elevation − 600 feet, range 4000 yards.

4. Elevation + 100 feet, range 5600 yards.

543. Range Tables. For each caliber and type of gun, range tables are built up from experimental firing at the proving grounds. For each 100 yards of range, the angle of elevation, angle of fall, terminal velocity, range change due to 1 mil of elevation, range to maximum height of trajectory, height of trajectory, time of flight, and drift are given. The data given in the tables are based on certain standard values for barometric pressure, temperature, humidity, muzzle velocity, fuse, weight of shell, and no wind. For a change in any of these factors a correction must be made.

When a gun is fired, the axis of its bore rotates in a vertical plane through a small angle called *jump*. The causes are complicated and not all of them are fully understood. Jump is determined experimentally, and allowance is made for it in the angle of elevation.

In order to keep the nose of a shell forward in its flight, most guns are rifled, usually clockwise. The resistance of the air causes the rotating shell to veer to the right. This deflection from the plane of fire is called *drift*. If the gun is rifled counterclockwise the drift is to the left. A lateral wind also causes a shell to be deflected from its path

3. Maps and Map Reading

Men have made maps since the dawn of history. Forty-five hundred years ago Sumerians drew maps of lands and estates for their kings and great landholders. Egyptian priests and

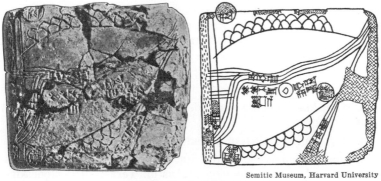

Semitic Museum, Harvard University

An Ancient Map

This clay map found in Iraq is about 4000 years old. It represents a sea, two rivers, two mountain ranges, and three cities

scribes thirty-two hundred years ago put down on maps the results of vast land surveys ordered by the Pharaohs. By 550 B.C. Anaximander of Miletus had made a map of the "whole circuit of the earth, every sea and all rivers." But Anaximander's earth was a flat disk, surrounded by the ocean. He knew only of the lands about the Mediterranean and southwestern Asia. Even this was inaccurately drawn. Two hundred years later Aristotle had proved that the earth was a sphere and men had begun to measure and to draw accurately.

By this time men had discovered the need of a grid system, whereby points on a map could be located accurately and distances between points more correctly determined. By 200 B.C. Rome had conquered Carthage and, in the formerly Carthaginian city of Cyrene, Eratosthenes had made his map of the known world, with seven parallels and seven meridians. Today we have devised a system of latitude and longitude whereby any point on the earth can be located exactly.

544. Latitude. *Latitude* is the distance north or south of the equator and is measured in degrees. The locus of all points having the same latitude is a parallel.

EXERCISES

1. How many degrees are there in a circle? Latitude is measured along a great circle of the earth passing through the poles. What part of the circle would be the distance from the equator to the North Pole? What is the latitude of the North Pole? of the South Pole?

2. A parallel may be defined as the locus of all points a given distance north or south of the equator. What kind of circle is a parallel?

3. What kind of figure is included between two parallels? between a parallel and a pole?

4. How many parallels of latitude are there?

5. From a map of the United States find the latitude of Wichita, Kansas; of Denver, Colorado; of Austin, Texas; of Boston, Massachusetts.

6. From a map of South America find the latitude of Buenos Aires, Lima, Sucre, Quito, and Rio de Janeiro.

545. Longitude. A meridian is a great semicircle of the earth extending from one pole to the other. *Longitude* is the distance east or west of one of these meridians which has been selected as the principal meridian. It was only natural to select the equator as our principal parallel, but there is no natural principal meridian. The world has agreed to accept the meridian passing through the Royal Observatory at Greenwich, England, as the principal meridian, although, during the last century, the meridians through Paris and Washington were often so used. All points west of Greenwich have west longitude and all points east of it have east longitude.

EXERCISES

1. Define the meridian of 10° W. as a locus; of 70° E.

2. Are the meridians of 60° E. and 60° W. parts of the same great circle? of 60° E. and 120° W.? of 80° E. and 100° W.? Formulate a rule.

3. Find the latitude and longitude of Washington, Ottawa, Rome, and Capetown.

4. Find the country in which the following are located: Lat. 15° N., Long. 150° E.; Lat. 35° S., Long. 85° W.; Lat. 70° N., Long. 120° W.; Lat. 75° S., Long. 4° E.

5. Find the difference in longitude between two points if one is 28° 32' E. and the other is 75° 27' W.

6. Since the earth rotates through 360° every 24 hours, any given point on its surface passes through 15° of longitude in 1 hour. It follows that if two places are 15° apart, their local time differs by 1 hour. What is the difference in local time between two places 1° apart? between two places 10° 32' 45'' apart?

546. Scales. Anaximander's map was little more than a rough sketch of the world as he conceived it. Today maps are drawn with the greatest accuracy. In order that we may measure distances on them exactly, maps have scales. Ordinarily there are three types of scales:

a. Word and Figure Scales. Scales may be expressed in words and figures, as 1 inch = a given number of miles. For example, let us suppose that on a given map 1 inch = 5 miles and the distance on the map from A to B is $1\frac{1}{2}$ inches. Then $\frac{1}{1\frac{1}{2}} = \frac{5}{x}$ or $x = 7\frac{1}{2}$ (miles). Then we know that the distance from A to B is $7\frac{1}{2}$ miles.

b. The Graphic Scale. In this type a scale for measuring in miles is drawn on the map. It consists of a primary scale to

| 100 | 10 0 | 100 | 200 | 300 | 400 |

Miles ■■■■■■ ▬▬▬▬▬ ▬▬▬▬▬ Miles

the right of the zero point and a smaller extension scale to the left. The distances given on the scale represent actual ground distances in the surface represented by the map. To measure the distance between two points A and B on a map having the above scale, take a plain strip of paper and place the edge along the line *AB*. Mark the strip of paper at *A* and *B* as shown on page 523. If the line segment *AB* is shorter than the graphic scale, place the right-hand mark at a division on the primary scale so that the left-hand mark will fall in the extension scale. The ground distance between *A* and *B* will be the sum of the distances intercepted on the primary and extension scales. This is illustrated below. *B* is placed on 200

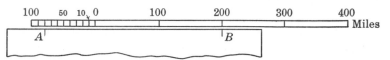

and *A* falls on a point 80 miles to the left of zero. Therefore the ground distance is 280 miles.

c. The Representative Fraction. The representative fraction, or R.F., expresses the exact ratio between distances on the map and distances on the ground. For example, if the R.F. of a map is $\frac{1}{62,500}$, then 1 inch on the map represents 62,500 inches on the ground. Since there are 63,360 inches in a mile, the R.F. of a map drawn to the scale of 1 inch = 1 mile is $\frac{1}{63,360}$. To measure the distance between any two points *A* and *B* on a map, find the distance *AB* in inches and multiply by the denominator of the representative fraction. Thus, if the R.F. of a map is $\frac{1}{125,000}$ and the distance between *A* and *B* is found to be $2\frac{1}{2}$ inches, then $2\frac{1}{2} \times 125,000$ inches = 312,500 inches. To find the distance in miles, divide 312,500 by 63,360. $312,500 \div 63,360 = 4.93$ (miles).

EXERCISES

1. If the scale on a map is 1 inch = 3 miles, what distance on the ground will be represented by a map distance of 3 inches? $2\frac{1}{2}$ inches? $\frac{3}{4}$ inch? 2.2 inches?

2. If the scale of a map is 1 inch = 2 miles, what distance on the map will represent a ground distance of 1000 yards? 2500 yards? 3 miles?

3. If the scale on a map is 1 inch = 20 miles, what distance on the ground will be represented by a map distance of $1\frac{1}{4}$ inches?

4. If the R.F. of a map is $\frac{1}{62,500}$, how many miles on the ground are represented by 3 inches on the map? by $2\frac{1}{2}$ inches? by 5 inches? by $\frac{3}{4}$ inch?

5. The R.F. of a map is $\frac{1}{125,000}$. A ground distance of 5000 yards represents how many inches on the map? 2500 yards? 500 miles?

6. From the map on page 526 find the number of yards from Big Island to Mud Lake. Express this distance in kilometers.

7. On the same map find the number of yards from Hitching Post Point to Hook Point. Find the distance in kilometers.

8. On the same map find the distance in feet from Round Island to Long Point.

9. From the same map find the width of Mattawamkeag Lake from West Cove to The Pocket. Give this distance in yards.

547. Finding the Scale of a Map. If for any reason the scale is not shown on a map, it can be found. If a second map with a scale, covering at least a part of the region, is available, measure the distance on both maps between two points shown on both the maps. Then

$$\frac{\text{R.F. of first map}}{\text{R.F. of second map}} = \frac{\text{distance on first map}}{\text{distance on second map}}.$$

If the distance between the known points on the second map, whose R.F. is $\frac{1}{250,000}$, is 2 inches, and the distance between the known points on the first map is 4 inches, then

$$\frac{x}{\frac{1}{250,000}} = \frac{4}{2}.$$
$$2\,x = \frac{4}{250,000}.$$
$$x = \frac{2}{250,000}, \quad \text{or} \quad \frac{1}{125,000},$$

the R.F. of the first map.

If no other map with known scale is available, but the distance between the two points on the ground is known or can be measured, then the R.F. of the map can be found by the formula

$$\text{R.F.} = \frac{\text{map distance}}{\text{ground distance}}.$$

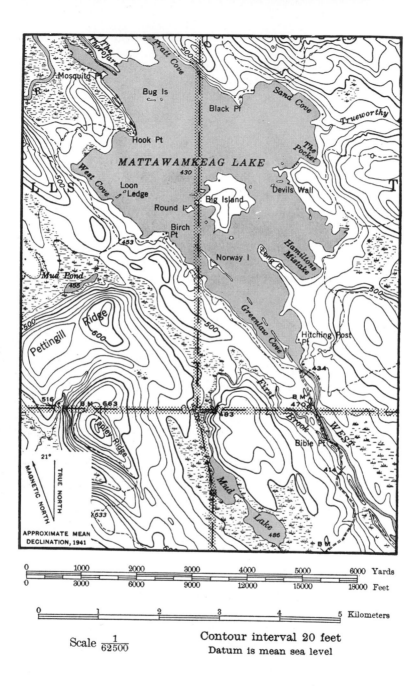

Scale $\frac{1}{62500}$

Contour interval 20 feet
Datum is mean sea level

EXERCISES

1. Find the R.F. of a map if the ground distance between two points which are 2 inches apart on the map is 4 miles.

2. The distance between two points on a map whose R.F. is $\frac{1}{125,000}$, is $1\frac{1}{2}$ inches. Find the R.F. of a second map if the distance between the same two points is $\frac{3}{4}$ inch.

548. To Construct a Graphic Scale when the R.F. Is Known. The distance on the map which represents one mile on the ground is found by the proportion $\frac{x}{63,360} = \text{R.F.}$ Thus if the R.F. of a map is $\frac{1}{20,000}$, $\frac{x}{63,360} = \frac{1}{20,000}$, or $x = 3.2$ approximately. Then construct the graphic scale with 3.2 inches $= 1$ mile.

EXERCISES

1. Construct a graphic scale for a map whose R.F. is $\frac{1}{40,000}$.

2. Construct a graphic scale for a map whose R.F. is $\frac{1}{1,000,000}$.

549. Maps of the World. Anaximander of Miletus had no difficulty in drawing a map of his flat world on a flat piece of paper. The realization that the world is almost spherical posed a new and difficult problem for which there never has been found a perfect solution. This problem is to represent the surface of a sphere upon a plane. No portion of the surface of a sphere can be spread out in a plane without either stretching or tearing it. Therefore any representation of a sphere upon a plane must be accompanied by distortion. There are some surfaces, however, that can be spread out in a plane without stretching or tearing.

550. Map Projection. Map projection consists of the systematic drawing of the meridians and parallels of the earth on a plane surface either for the whole earth or for some portion of it.

There are two main classes of map projections—the equal-area type, in which any two equal areas have equal areas on the map though their shapes may be distorted, and the conformal type, in which every region keeps its true shape but its area is distorted.

551. Lambert's Projection. One of the first men to tackle the problem of projecting a sphere upon a plane was Ptolemy (about 150 A.D.), who was the greatest of the ancient geographers. He knew that a cone could be spread out in a plane without stretching or tear-

ing. Since his time there have been many attempts at conic projection, the most common today being the Lambert projection. Although devised in 1772, it was not until the First World War that it was used extensively. In this projection the surface of the earth is projected on the surface of a right circular cone. It is a conformal projection, in which all meridians are straight lines that meet at

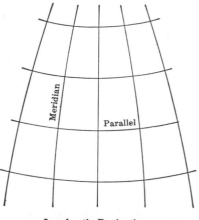

Lambert's Projection

a common point beyond the limits of the map, and the parallels are concentric circles whose common center is the point of intersection of the meridians. This projection, although unsatisfactory for mapping the entire world, is ideal for relatively small areas. In a map of the United States the maximum scale error is $2\frac{1}{2}\%$.

552. Mercator's Projection. For a thousand years after Ptolemy there were no great geographers or map-makers. Then came a revival of the map-making art under a group of Dutch scientists, the most famous of whom was Gerardus Mercator. Today we remember him chiefly as the inventor of Mercator's projection. It is the most widely used projection in making maps of the world. Moreover, it is the only projection with the property that the course of a vessel from any given point can be laid off with accuracy and ease.

The shortest distance between any two points on the surface of a sphere is the minor arc of a great circle which joins them. However, for a ship to take a great-circle course would involve constantly changing its direction. This would be impractical. A *rhumb line* is a line which crosses successive meridians at a constant angle. In Mercator's projection only, the rhumb line is a straight line. For this reason it is the most valuable projection for navigation. Although the rhumb line joining two points on the earth's surface is longer than the minor arc of a great circle joining them, it is the simplest course for the ship to follow. In actual practice points are selected at convenient distances along the great circle joining the two points and the ship is steered along the rhumb lines joining the successive points.

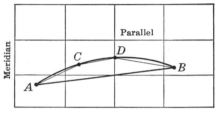

Section of a Mercator's Projection

In Mercator's projection the parallels are straight lines parallel to a straight line representing the equator, and the meridians are straight lines perpendicular to them. Hence the meridians are parallel to each other. The meridians are also equally spaced. As one progresses from the equator to either pole, the parallels become progressively farther apart.

In the above figure the curved line *ACDB* is the arc of a great circle. Lines *AB*, *AC*, *CD*, and *DB* are rhumb lines. The broken line *ACDB* is the course of a ship sailing from *A* to *B*.

Mercator's projection is a conformal projection but is not an equal-area projection. While small regions keep their true shape everywhere, they become progressively larger the farther they are from the equator.

553. Topographic Maps. Topographic maps are large-scale maps which show the roads, railroads, rivers, towns, hills, valleys, marshes, and any feature of importance. They were first devised by the military staffs of Europe during the wars of the

eighteenth century. Today topographic maps are of vital importance in both war and peace.

554. Locating Places on a Map. There are three standard
methods of locating places on a map. These are (1) geographic
co-ordinates (latitude and longitude), (2) polar co-ordinates
which give direction and distance, (3) grid co-ordinates.

555. Polar Co-ordinates. In polar co-ordinates a place is
located by giving its direction and distance from a known
point. The direction is called *azimuth* and is measured clockwise from a reference line. This reference line is a line pointing
the direction of true north, magnetic north, or grid north, being
called *true azimuth, magnetic azimuth,* or *grid azimuth* respec-

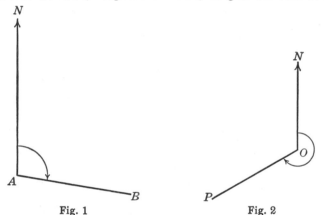

Fig. 1   Fig. 2

tively. True north is the direction to the North Pole and is
shown by the meridians on a map. Magnetic north is the
direction of the north magnetic pole and is the direction in
which the compass needle points. Magnetic north is frequently
used because it can be found directly by means of a compass.
Grid north is the direction of the vertical grid lines found on
military maps.

Azimuth is measured by a protractor graduated in mils or
degrees. The most common protractor is semicircular.

In Fig. 1, if B is 1000 yards from A and $\angle NAB$ measured
clockwise from NA to AB is 100°, the polar co-ordinates of B

from A are (1000, 100°). The distance is given first and is separated from the azimuth by a comma.

In Fig. 2, to obtain the azimuth of point P from O, measure $\angle NOP$ and subtract from 360°. If $\angle NOP = 120°$, the azimuth of P from O is 240°.

If there is no north-south line through a point from which the azimuth is to be measured, it is necessary to draw a line through the point parallel to a given north-south line.

EXERCISE

From the sketch below give the polar co-ordinates of points A, B, C, and D from point P.

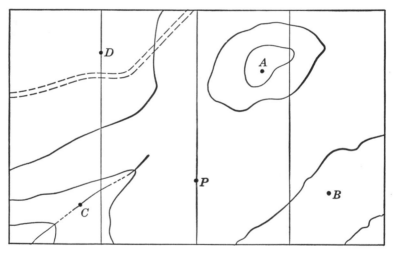

Scale: 1 inch = 1 mile

556. Declination. Magnetic declination is the difference between true north and magnetic north. The north magnetic pole is located in the northern part of Canada. East of the meridian through the magnetic pole the declination is west, while west of it the declination is east. Unlike the true North Pole, the north magnetic pole moves slightly from year to year. These movements can be forecast, and the change in magnetic declination of any point can be determined. Magnetic declination is usually the same for any point on a topographic map and is stated on the map.

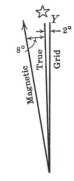

Annual Magnetic
Change 2' Increase

A figure like the one at the right is found on every topographic map, and the magnetic declination as of the year of publication can be found directly from it. To find the present magnetic declination, multiply the change indicated by the number of years since its publication. Grid declination is the difference between true north and grid north. It is always constant. Here the magnetic declination is 8° W. and the grid declination is 2° E. To change from one azimuth to another, adjustment must be made for the declination.

557. Grid Co-ordinates. A military grid is a system of evenly spaced north-and-south lines and east-and-west lines

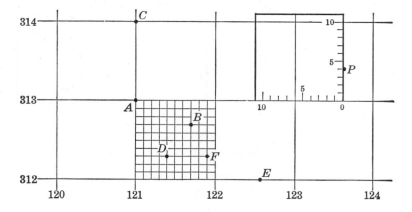

printed on a map. On a map whose R.F. is $\frac{1}{20,000}$ these lines are 1000 yards apart. For a $\frac{1}{62,500}$ map they are 5000 yards apart. The grid lines are numbered from west to east and from south to north from a common reference point called the origin.

Points are designated by co-ordinates by the intersection of the north-south (vertical) and east-west (horizontal) grid lines. Thus in the diagram at the foot of page 532, point A is (121–313). The east-west co-ordinate is given first. It is assumed that the grid squares are each subdivided into 100 small squares whose sides are each $\frac{1}{10}$ of the side of the entire square. The co-ordinates of point B are (121.7–312.7). In practice the co-ordinates of a point not at the intersection of two grid lines are read by a grid card (shown in the diagram). Thus the co-ordinates of point P are (123.6–313.4).

EXERCISE

What are the co-ordinates of C? of D? of E? of F?

558. Conventional Signs and Symbols. To represent important features of the earth's surface on maps it is necessary to use conventional signs and symbols. A good symbol is one that can be recognized without explanation. Thus, the meanings of the following symbols found on topographic maps are evident.

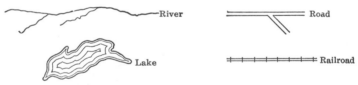

For certain other features it has been necessary to adopt symbols which, while suggestive of what they are meant to indicate, are not obvious.

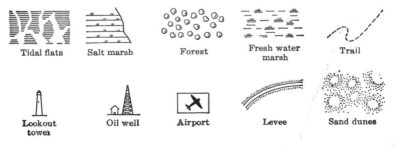

A more complete list of conventional signs and symbols is to be found on the back of most topographic maps.

559. Elevation and Relief. It is important that the commanders of the various units of an army have definite information about hills, ridges, and valleys of the area in which the troops operate.

a. Contours. One method of representing features of relief is through the use of contours. A *contour* is a line which joins points having the same elevation. On any given map the difference in elevation between any two successive contours is known as the *contour interval*. In fairly level regions the contour interval is small, perhaps 5 or 10 feet, while on relatively large-scale maps of mountainous regions the contour interval may be as great as 100 feet. Occasionally each contour is numbered, but generally every fifth contour is drawn heavier than the others and is the only one numbered. From the patterns traced by contours it is possible to obtain a surprising amount of knowledge concerning a region.

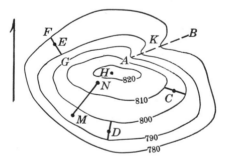

The diagram shows a hill with a ravine *AB* down one side. *H* is the top of the hill. The ravine is shown not only by the intermittent stream which flows down it, but also by the receding of the contour lines up it. Since the contour lines near the summit on the north side are nearer together than they are at the base, the hill on that side is concave. On the south side, since the contours near the summit are farther apart than nearer the base, the hill is convex.

b. Determining Elevation from Contours. If a point lies on a contour, its elevation can be read exactly from the map. Thus point *A*, in the diagram on the opposite page, has an elevation of 800 feet above sea level.

If a point is located between two contour lines, its height is between the elevations of the two contours. Although interpolation is not always accurate, it gives an approximate elevation. Thus, since point *C* is midway between the contours of 800 and 810, its approximate elevation is 805 feet. If point *D* is two thirds the distance from the 790-foot contour to the 800-foot contour, its elevation is approximately 797 feet.

We cannot interpolate to find the elevation of a point within the 820-foot contour. All we know about the elevation of point *H* is that it is greater than 820 feet but less than 830 feet.

The summits of most mountains are marked and the elevations given.

c. Determining Slopes. Slopes are usually given as per cents. To find the slope of the ground between any two contours, divide the difference in the elevation of the two contours by the horizontal ground distance between them. Thus, if the horizontal ground distance from *F* to *G* (diagram, p. 534) is 300 feet, the slope of *FG* is $10 \div 300$, or $3\frac{1}{3}\%$.

The slope up a hill is positive and down hill is negative. Thus the slope of *GF* is $-3\frac{1}{3}\%$.

Slopes are very important, since they affect selection of routes of travel and the location of military works and weapons.

EXERCISES

1. In the diagram on page 534, if the horizontal distance from *K* to *A* is 400 feet, find the slope of *KA*. What is the slope of *AK*?

2. What is the elevation of point *E*?

3. Find the elevations of *M* and *N*, and the average slope from *M* to *N* if the horizontal distance is 450 feet.

4. Using the approximate elevations of *C* and *D* given above, find the slope of *DC* if the horizontal distance is 700 feet.

4. Geometric Relations; Orthographic Projection

560. Geometric Relations. The following exercises are designed to test your powers of observation with simple geometric figures.

Example. The figure on the left below is formed from the two parts in one of the large rectangles on the right. We may think of the parts being moved about in the plane to form the figure, but it is not permissible to take the parts out of the plane. Which rectangle contains the correct parts?

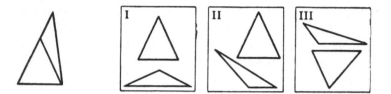

Rectangle III has the correct parts to form the given figure.

EXERCISES [A]

In each exercise decide which rectangle contains the parts that can be moved about in the plane to form the given figure.

1.

2.

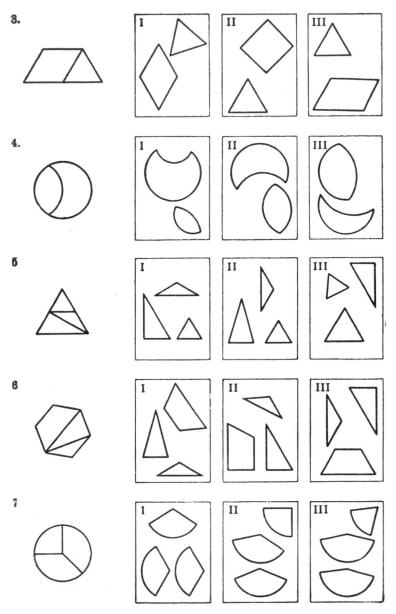

In the following exercises each figure was first constructed with cubical blocks and then the coinciding faces were glued together. In counting the cubes in each figure be sure to count all hidden cubes which are necessary to hold up the structure.

Answer the following questions for each figure:

a. How many cubes are there in the figure?

b. How many cubes have one and only one face glued?

c. How many cubes have two and only two faces glued?

d. How many cubes have three and only three faces glued?

e. How many cubes have four and only four faces glued?

f. How many cubes have five and only five faces glued?

1.

2.

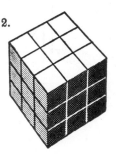

3.

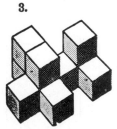

4.

5.

6.　　　　　　　　　　　　**7.**

561. Orthographic Projection. To represent material objects of three dimensions on the two-dimensional surface of a sheet of paper the system of orthographic projection is used. The drawing consists of a set of separate views made by the observer from different positions and arranged in a definite order. The usual combination is the top, front, and end views. The *top view* is the view of the object as seen by an observer directly above it. The *front view* of the object is the view observed from a position directly in front of it. The *end view* is the view of the object as seen from the right side.

In the illustrations below, the three views of the rectangular solid at the left are shown at the right. The views usually occupy the positions shown in reference to the vertical and horizontal lines. In the example and exercises that follow, you can tell from their positions what views are shown.

In the figure at the left below, the rectangular solid has a circular hole in it. The three views are shown at the right. Since the circular hole cannot be seen in the front and end views, it is represented by dotted lines.

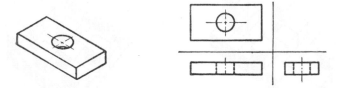

Example. In the diagram below, the top and front views of the solid are given. Draw the end view.

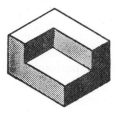 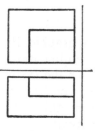

Solution. The correct end view is shown at the right.

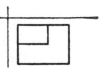

EXERCISES [A]

In each exercise two views of the solid are shown. Draw the third view.

1.

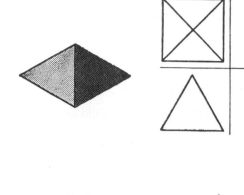

2.

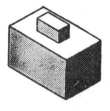

3.

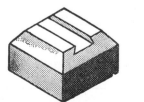

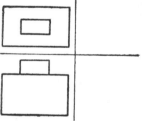

4.

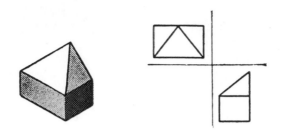

EXERCISES [B]

In each exercise the three views of a solid are given. Sketch the solid.

1.

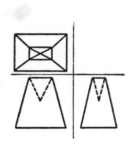

2.

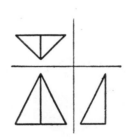

3.

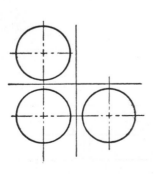

4.

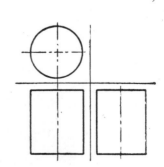

Summary of Principal Methods of Proof*

562. *Triangles congruent*

   a. If two triangles have two sides and the included angle of one equal respectively to two sides and the included angle of the other, the triangles are congruent (§ 60).

   b. If two right triangles have the two legs of one equal respectively to the two legs of the other, the triangles are congruent (§ 64).

   c. If two triangles have two angles and the included side of one equal respectively to two angles and the included side of the other, the triangles arc congruent (§ 67).

   d. If two triangles have the three sides of one equal respectively to the three sides of the other, the triangles are congruent (§ 74).

   e. If two right triangles have the hypotenuse and an acute angle of one equal respectively to the hypotenuse and an acute angle of the other, the triangles are congruent (§ 112).

   f. If two right triangles have the hypotenuse and a leg of one equal respectively to the hypotenuse and a leg of the other, the triangles are congruent (§ 119).

   g. A diagonal of a parallelogram divides it into two congruent triangles (§ 171).

563. *Line segments equal*

   a. All radii of a circle or of equal circles are equal (§ 33, Post. 16).

   b. Corresponding sides of congruent polygons are equal (§ 69).

   c. If two angles of a triangle are equal, the sides opposite these angles are equal (§ 114).

   d. An equiangular triangle is equilateral (§ 115).

   e. If one acute angle of a right triangle is 30°, the side opposite this angle is one half the hypotenuse (§ 120).

   f. The opposite sides of a parallelogram are equal (§ 172).

*The axioms are listed on pages 38–39 and 468–469.

g. Segments of parallels included between parallels are equal (§ 176).

h. The diagonals of a parallelogram bisect each other (§ 179).

i. If parallels intercept equal segments on one transversal, they intercept equal segments on any transversal (§ 185).

j. If a line bisects one side of a triangle and is parallel to a second side, it bisects the third side (§ 186).

k. The line segment joining the midpoints of two sides of a triangle is equal to one half the third side (§ 187).

l. The midpoint of the hypotenuse of a right triangle is equidistant from the vertices of the triangle (§ 188).

m. The median of a trapezoid is equal to one half the sum of the bases (§ 190).

n. In a circle or in equal circles equal arcs have equal chords (§ 268).

o. If a line through the center of a circle is perpendicular to a chord, it bisects the chord (§ 271).

p. In a circle or in equal circles equal chords are equidistant from the center (§ 274).

q. In a circle or in equal circles chords equidistant from the center are equal (§ 275).

r. The tangents to a circle from an external point are equal (§ 281).

s. The locus of points within an angle equidistant from the sides is the bisector of the angle (§ 323).

t. The locus of points equidistant from two given points is the perpendicular bisector of the line segment joining the two points (§ 325).

564. *Angles equal*

a. All right angles are equal (§ 33, Post. 9).

b. Complements of the same angle or of equal angles are equal (§§ 45, 46).

c. Supplements of the same angle or of equal angles are equal (§§ 47, 48).

d. If two lines intersect, the vertical angles are equal (§ 49).

e. Corresponding angles of congruent polygons are equal (§ 69).

f. If two sides of a triangle are equal, the angles opposite these sides are equal (§ 72).

g. An equilateral triangle is equiangular (§ 73).

h. If two parallels are cut by a transversal, the alternate interior angles are equal (§ 98).

i. If two parallels are cut by a transversal, the corresponding angles are equal (§ 99).

j. If two angles have their sides parallel, right side to right side and left side to left side, the angles are equal (§ 104).

k. If two angles of one triangle are equal respectively to two angles of another triangle, the third angles are equal (§ 108).

l. If two angles have their sides perpendicular, right side to right side and left side to left side, the angles are equal (§ 113).

m. The opposite angles of a parallelogram are equal (§ 173).

n. In a circle or in equal circles equal arcs have equal central angles (§ 265).

o. Inscribed angles which intercept the same arc are equal (§ 300).

p. Corresponding angles of similar polygons are equal (§ 394).

565. *Angles supplementary*

a. Two angles are supplementary when their sum is a straight angle (§ 19).

b. If two adjacent angles have their exterior sides in a straight line, they are supplementary (§ 33, Post. 14).

c. If two parallels are cut by a transversal, the two interior angles on the same side of the transversal are supplementary (§ 100).

d. Any two consecutive angles of a parallelogram are supplementary (§ 174).

e. If a quadrilateral is inscribed in a circle, the opposite angles are supplementary (§ 301).

566. *Angles complementary*

a. Two angles are complementary when their sum is a right angle (§ 18).

b. The acute angles of a right triangle are complementary (§ 111).

567. *Lines perpendicular; angle a right angle*

a. Two lines are perpendicular to each other if one of them forms two equal adjacent angles with the other; or if the lines form a right angle (§ 12).

b. The perpendicular is the shortest line segment that can be drawn from a given point to a given line (§ 33, Post. 11, and § 503).

c. If a line is perpendicular to one of two parallel lines, it is perpendicular to the other (§ 101).

d. A line passing through two points each equidistant from the end points of a line segment is the perpendicular bisector of the segment (§ 124).

e. All the angles of a rectangle are right angles (§ 175).

f. The diagonals of a rhombus are perpendicular (§ 180).

g. If a line through the center of a circle bisects a chord that is not a diameter, it is perpendicular to the chord (§ 272).

h. If a line is tangent to a circle, it is perpendicular to the radius drawn to the point of contact (§ 276).

i. If two circles intersect, the line joining their centers is the perpendicular bisector of the common chord (§ 282).

j. An angle inscribed in a semicircle is a right angle (§ 299).

k. The locus of points equidistant from two given points is the perpendicular bisector of the line segment joining the two points (§ 325).

568. *Lines parallel*

a. Two lines are parallel if they lie in the same plane and do not intersect even if extended (§ 88).

b. Two straight lines in the same plane are either parallel lines or intersecting lines (§ 89).

c. If two lines form equal alternate interior angles with a transversal, the lines are parallel (§ 92).

d. If two lines form equal corresponding angles with a transversal, the lines are parallel (§ 93).

e. If two lines form supplementary interior angles on the same side of a transversal, the lines are parallel (§ 94).

f. Two lines perpendicular to a third line are parallel (§ 95).

g. Two lines parallel to a third line are parallel (§ 97).

h. A parallelogram is a quadrilateral having two pairs of parallel sides (§ 169).

i. The line segment joining the midpoints of two sides of a triangle is parallel to the third side (§ 187).

j. The median of a trapezoid is parallel to the bases (§ 190).

k. If a line divides two sides of a triangle proportionally, it is parallel to the third side (§ 382).

l. If a line divides two sides of a triangle so that either side is to one of its segments as the other side is to its corresponding segment, the line is parallel to the third side (§ 383).

569. *A quadrilateral a parallelogram*

a. A parallelogram is a quadrilateral having two pairs of parallel sides (§ 169).

b. If the opposite sides of a quadrilateral are equal, the figure is a parallelogram (§ 181).

c. If two sides of a quadrilateral are equal and parallel, the figure is a parallelogram (§ 182).

d. If the diagonals of a quadrilateral bisect each other, the figure is a parallelogram (§ 183).

570. *Angles and sums of angles*

a. The sum of all the angles about a point in a plane is two straight angles (§ 33, Post. 12).

b. The sum of the angles of a triangle is a straight angle (§ 107).

c. An exterior angle of a triangle equals the sum of the two non-adjacent interior angles (§ 110).

d. The sum of the exterior angles of a polygon is two straight angles (§ 191).

e. Each exterior angle of a regular polygon of n sides contains $\dfrac{360°}{n}$ (§ 192).

f. The sum of the interior angles of a polygon having n sides is $(n - 2)$ straight angles (§ 193).

g. Each interior angle of a regular polygon of n sides contains $\dfrac{180(n - 2)°}{n}$ (§ 194).

h. The central angle of a regular polygon of n sides contains $\dfrac{360°}{n}$ (§ 443).

571. *Arcs equal*

a. In a circle or in equal circles equal central angles have equal arcs (§ 263).

b. A diameter of a circle bisects the circle (§ 264).

c. In a circle or in equal circles equal chords have equal arcs (§ 267).

d. If a line through the center of a circle is perpendicular to a chord, it bisects its arc (§ 271).

e. In a circle or in equal circles two arcs which have the same number of arc degrees are equal (§ 297).

f. Parallel lines intercept equal arcs on a circle (§ 307).

572. *Comparison of angles and their arcs*

a. A central angle is equal in degrees to its intercepted arc (§ 295).

b. An inscribed angle is equal in degrees to one half its intercepted arc (§ 298).

c. An angle formed by a tangent and a chord drawn from the point of contact is equal in degrees to one half its intercepted arc (§ 302).

d. An angle formed by two chords intersecting within a circle is equal in degrees to one half the sum of the arcs intercepted by it and its vertical angle (§ 303).

e. An angle formed by two tangents, or a tangent and a secant, or two secants, intersecting outside a circle, is equal in degrees to one half the difference of the intercepted arcs (§ 304).

573. *Lines passing through a point*

a. The perpendicular bisector of a chord passes through the center of the circle (§ 273).

b. If a line is perpendicular to a tangent at the point of contact, it passes through the center of the circle (§ 277).

c. The perpendicular bisectors of the sides of a triangle are concurrent in a point equidistant from the vertices (§ 335).

d. The bisectors of the angles of a triangle are concurrent in a point equidistant from the sides (§ 337).

e. The altitudes of a triangle are concurrent (§ 339).

f. The medians of a triangle are concurrent in a point which lies two thirds of the distance from each vertex to the midpoint of the opposite side (§ 341).

574. *Line segments in proportion*

a. A line parallel to one side of a triangle divides the other two sides proportionally (§ 376).

b. A line parallel to one side of a triangle divides the other two sides so that either side is to one of its segments as the other side is to its corresponding segment (§ 377).

c. Parallel lines intercept proportional segments on two transversals (§ 378).

d. The bisector of an interior (or exterior) angle of a triangle divides the opposite side internally (or externally) into segments which are proportional to the adjacent sides (§§ 385, 386).

e. Any two corresponding sides of two similar polygons have the same ratio as two other corresponding sides (§ 394).

f. The corresponding altitudes of two similar triangles have the same ratio as any two corresponding sides (§ 398).

g. The altitude on the hypotenuse of a right triangle is the mean proportional between the segments of the hypotenuse (§ 406).

h. Either leg of a right triangle is the mean proportional between the hypotenuse and its projection on the hypotenuse (§ 408).

i. The perpendicular from any point on a circle to a diameter of the circle is the mean proportional between the segments of the diameter (§ 409).

j. If two chords intersect within a circle, the product of the segments of one chord is equal to the product of the segments of the other (§ 412).

k. If a tangent and a secant are drawn to a circle from the same point, the tangent is the mean proportional between the secant and its external segment (§ 414).

575. *Proportions involving polygons and circles*

a. Two rectangles, parallelograms, or triangles having equal bases have the same ratio as their altitudes (§§ 221, 226, 228).

b. Two rectangles, parallelograms, or triangles having equal altitudes have the same ratio as their bases (§§ 222, 226, 229).

c. The areas of two triangles have the same ratio as the products of their bases and altitudes (§ 230).

d. The perimeters of two similar polygons have the same ratio as any two corresponding sides (§ 415).

e. The areas of two similar triangles have the same ratio as the squares of any two corresponding sides, or as the squares of any two corresponding altitudes (§§ 419, 420).

f. The areas of two similar polygons have the same ratio as the squares of any two corresponding sides (§ 421).

g. The areas of two regular polygons of the same number of sides have the same ratio as the squares of any two corresponding sides, or as the squares of their radii, or as the squares of their apothems (§§ 450, 452).

h. The circumferences of two circles have the same ratio as their radii, or as their diameters (§§ 461, 462).

i. The areas of two circles have the same ratio as the squares of their radii, or as the squares of their diameters (§ 470).

j. The area of a sector of a circle is to the area of the circle as the angle of the sector is to 360° (§ 471).

576. *Similar polygons*

a. Similar polygons are polygons whose corresponding angles are equal and whose corresponding sides are proportional (§ 393).

b. If two triangles have two angles of one equal respectively to two angles of the other, the triangles are similar (§ 396).

c. If two right triangles have an acute angle of one equal to an acute angle of the other, the triangles are similar (§ 397).

d. If two triangles are similar to a third triangle, they are similar to each other (§ 399).

e. If two triangles have an angle of one equal to an angle of the other and the including sides proportional, the triangles are similar (§ 403).

f. If two triangles have their sides respectively proportional, they are similar (§ 404).

g. The altitude on the hypotenuse of a right triangle forms two right triangles which are similar to the given triangle and to each other (§ 405).

h. If two polygons are similar, they can be separated into the same number of triangles which are similar each to each (§ 416).

i. If two polygons are composed of the same number of triangles, similar each to each and similarly placed, the polygons are similar (§ 417).

j. Two regular polygons of the same number of sides are similar (§ 449).

577. *Areas*

a. The area of a rectangle is equal to the product of its base and altitude (§ 220).

b. The area of a square is equal to the square of one of its sides (§ 223).

c. The area of a parallelogram is equal to the product of its base and altitude (§ 224).

d. The area of a triangle is equal to one half the product of its base and altitude (§ 227).

e. The area of a rhombus is equal to one half the product of its diagonals (§ 231).

f. The area of a trapezoid is equal to one half the product of its altitude and the sum of its bases (§ 233)

g. The area of an equilateral triangle having a side s is given by the formula $A = \frac{s^2}{4}\sqrt{3}$ (§ 238).

h. The area of a triangle whose sides are a, b, and c is given by the formula $A = \sqrt{s(s-a)(s-b)(s-c)}$, where $s = \frac{1}{2}(a+b+c)$ (§ 241).

i. The area of a regular polygon is equal to one half the product of its apothem and its perimeter (§ 448).

j. The area of a circle is equal to one half the product of its radius and its circumference (§ 468).

k. The area of a circle is given by the formula $S = \pi r^2$ (§ 469).

578. *Figures equal in area*

a. Parallelograms having equal bases and equal altitudes are equal (§ 225).

b. If a triangle and a parallelogram have equal bases and equal altitudes, the area of the triangle is half the area of the parallelogram (§ 232).

c. The square upon the hypotenuse of a right triangle is equal to the sum of the squares upon the legs (§ 234).

579. *Miscellaneous numerical relations*

a. The diagonal of a square is equal to one side multiplied by $\sqrt{2}$ (§ 237).

b. The square of the hypotenuse of a right triangle is equal to the sum of the squares of the legs (§ 411).

c. The circumference of a circle is expressed by the formula $c = \pi d$, or $c = 2\pi r$ (§ 464).

d. $\pi = \frac{c}{d} = 3.1416$, approximately (§ 467).

580. *Polygons regular*

a. A regular polygon is a polygon which is both equilateral and equiangular (§ 168).

b. If a circle is divided into any number of equal arcs, the chords of these arcs form a regular inscribed polygon and the tangents at the points of division form a regular circumscribed polygon (§§ 444, 447).

c. An equilateral polygon inscribed in a circle is a regular polygon (§ 445).

d. If the midpoints of the arcs of a regular inscribed polygon are joined to the extremities of the respective sides, a regular inscribed polygon of double the number of sides is formed (§ 446).

581. *Inequalities*

a. An exterior angle of a triangle is greater than either nonadjacent interior angle (§ 82).

b. The perpendicular is the shortest line segment that can be drawn from a given point to a given line (§ 33, Post. 11, and § 503).

c. Each side of a triangle is less than the sum of the other two sides (§ 500).

d. If one side of a triangle is greater than a second side, the angle opposite the first side is greater than the angle opposite the second side (§ 501).

e. If one angle of a triangle is greater than a second angle, the side opposite the first angle is greater than the side opposite the second angle (§ 502).

f. The hypotenuse of a right triangle is greater than either leg (§ 504).

g. If two triangles have two sides of one equal respectively to two sides of the other and the included angle of the first greater than the included angle of the second, the third side of the first is greater than the third side of the second (§ 505).

h. If two triangles have two sides of one equal respectively to two sides of the other and the third side of the first greater than the third side of the second, the angle opposite the third side of the first is greater than the angle opposite the third side of the second (§ 506).

i. If two oblique line segments are drawn to a line from a point in a perpendicular to that line, the one having the greater projection upon the line is the greater (§ 507); and conversely (§ 508).

j. In a circle or in equal circles the greater of two unequal central angles has the greater arc (§ 509); and conversely (§ 510).

k. In a circle or in equal circles the greater of two unequal chords has the greater arc (§ 511); and conversely (§ 512).

l. In a circle or in equal circles the greater of two unequal chords is nearer the center (§ 513); and conversely (§ 514).

m. A diameter of a circle is greater than any other chord (§ 515).

582. *Constructions*

a. To construct a triangle, given the three sides (§ 149).

b. To bisect a given angle (§ 150).

c. To construct an angle equal to a given angle (§ 151).

d. To construct a triangle, given two sides and the included angle (§ 153).

e. To construct a triangle, given two angles and the included side (§ 154).

f. To construct the perpendicular bisector of a given line segment (§ 155).

g. To construct a perpendicular to a given line from a given point without the line (§ 156).

h. To construct a perpendicular to a given line at a given point in the line (§ 157).

i. Through a given point to construct a line parallel to a given line (§ 158).

j. To divide a given line segment into any number of equal parts (§ 195).

k. To construct a triangle equal to a given polygon (§ 245).

l. To bisect a given arc of a circle (§ 308).

m. To construct the tangent to a given circle at a given point on the circle (§ 309).

n. To construct the tangents to a given circle from a given external point (§ 310).

o. To inscribe a square in a given circle (§ 311).

p. To inscribe a regular hexagon in a given circle (§ 312).

q. To circumscribe a circle about a given triangle (§ 343).

r. To inscribe a circle in a given triangle (§ 348).

s. Upon a given line segment as a chord to construct an arc of a circle in which a given angle can be inscribed (§ 351).

t. To construct the fourth proportional to three given line segments (§ 379).

u. To divide a given line segment into *n* parts which are proportional to *n* given line segments (§ 381).

v. To construct the mean proportional between two given line segments (§ 410).

w. Upon a given line segment corresponding to one side of a given polygon to construct a polygon similar to the given polygon (§ 418).

Comprehensive Tests

TEST 1

Completing Statements

On your paper write one word, and only one, for each blank to make the following statements true:

1. If two figures have the same shape, they are __?__.

2. An angle of a triangle formed by a side and the extension of an adjacent side is called an __?__ angle.

3. The perpendicular from any vertex of a triangle to the side opposite is called the __?__

4. A circle that is drawn through the three vertices of a triangle is said to be __?__

5. A parallelogram whose sides are equal is a __?__.

6. A statement of the equality of two ratios is a __?__.

7. The ratio of the circumference of a circle to its diameter is __?__.

8. Two regular polygons of the same number of sides are __?__.

9. The perpendicular from the center of a regular polygon to a side is called the __?__.

10. A line segment joining the vertex of a triangle to the midpoint of the opposite side is the __?__

11. Circles having a common center are called __?__.

12. A portion of a line having a definite length and limited by two end points is called a __?__

13. The second and third terms of a proportion are called the __?__,

14. Two triangles having the same size and shape are __?__.

15. A parallelogram whose angles are right angles is a __?__

16. Any portion of a circle is called __?__ __?__.

554

TEST 2

Supplying Reasons

Give a reason for each statement in the following proofs:

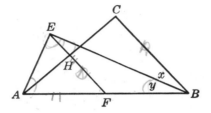

1. *Given* △ *ABC* with *EB* bisecting ∠ *ABC*, *AE* ⊥ *BE*, *EF* ∥ *CB*, and *EF* intersecting *AC* at *H*.

To prove that AH = HC.

a. *EB* bisects ∠ *ABC*.

b. ∠ *x* = ∠ *y*.

c. *EF* ∥ *CB*.

d. ∠ *FEB* = ∠ *x*.

e. ∴ ∠ *FEB* = ∠ *y*.

f. ∴ *FE* = *FB*.

g. ∠ *AEB* is a rt. ∠.

h. △ *AEB* is a rt. △.

i. ∠ *BAE* is comp. ∠ *y*.

j. ∠ *AEF* is comp. ∠ *FEB*.

k. ∴ ∠ *FAE* = ∠ *AEF*.

l. ∴ *AF* = *EF*.

m. ∴ *AF* = *FB*.

n. ∴ *AH* = *HC*.

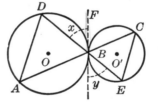

2. *Given* ⊚ *O* and *O'* tangent externally at *B* with st. lines *ABC* and *DBE* forming △ *ABD* and *BEC*.

To prove that $\dfrac{AB}{BC} = \dfrac{DB}{BE}$.

a. Draw common tangent *BF*.

b. ∠ *A* ≐ ½ $\widehat{DB}$.

c. ∠ *x* ≐ ½ $\widehat{DB}$.

d. ∴ ∠ *A* = ∠ *x*.

    Likewise ∠ *C* = ∠ *y*.

e. ∠ *x* = ∠ *y*.

f. ∴ ∠ *A* = ∠ *C*.

    Likewise ∠ *D* = ∠ *E*.

g. △ *ABD* ~ △ *CBE*.

h. ∴ $\dfrac{AB}{BC} = \dfrac{DB}{BE}$.

TEST 3

Multiple-Choice Statements

On your paper write the word or group of words printed in boldface type which makes each statement true:

1. The locus of points at a given distance from a given point is **a line   a circle   an angle   a point.**

2. The two acute angles of any right triangle are **supplementary   complementary   equal   obtuse.**

3. The locus of points one inch distant from a circle with a two-inch diameter is **a circle   a line   two circles   a circle and a point.**

4. The complement of an angle of n degrees is equal to **$90° − n$ $180° − n$ $n − 90°$ $n − 180°$.**

5. The sum of all the angles formed on one side of a line at a given point on the line is **a straight angle   an acute angle   a right angle   a 360° angle.**

6. An angle that is nine times as large as its complement is **9°   80°   162°   81°.**

7. The locus of the midpoints of parallel chords in a circle is **a circle   tangents at the end points   the perpendicular bisector of one of the chords   the center of the circle.**

8. If two lines form equal alternate interior angles with a transversal, they are **oblique   perpendicular   parallel   equal.**

9. If two lines in a plane are perpendicular to the same line, they are **parallel   equal   bisected   perpendicular.**

10. The area of a circle is **$4\pi r$ $2\pi r^2$ $\frac{1}{4}\pi d^2$ cr.**

11. The number of points at a given distance from two intersecting lines is **two   four   one   an infinite number.**

12. A central angle in a circle is formed by **two radii   two secants   two chords   a diameter and a tangent.**

13. The number of lines required in drawing the altitudes, medians, and angle bisectors in an isosceles triangle is **five   six   seven   nine.**

14. Lines are concurrent if they **are everywhere equally distant   intersect in one point   lie in the same plane   form a triangle.**

15. The acute angle formed by the hands of a clock at 2 P.M. is **30°** 45°   60°   90°.

16. The areas of two circles are to each other as **their radii   the squares of their radii   their diameters   their circumferences.**

17. The number of points on a circle equidistant from the ends of a diameter is **one   two   four   an infinite number.**

18. If the angle at the center of a regular polygon is 40°, the polygon has **nine sides   four sides   six sides   ten sides.**

19. If the distance between the centers of two circles is equal to the difference of their radii, the circles are **equal   concentric   tangent internally   tangent externally.**

20. If the hypothesis and conclusion of a theorem are interchanged, the resulting statement is called **an axiom   a corollary   a postulate   its converse.**

21. A polygon with five sides is called a **decagon   octagon   pentagon   hexagon.**

22. A circle may be inscribed in any **triangle   quadrilateral   trapezoid   octagon.**

23. If two parallels are cut by a transversal, the sum of two interior angles on the same side of the transversal is **90°   180°   270°   360°.**

24. The locus of points 4 inches from each of two given points 3 inches apart is **a circle   one point   two points   a line.**

25. An angle that is four times as large as its complement is **64°   162°   98°   72°.**

26. The sum of the interior angles of a quadrilateral is **180°   270°   360°   720°.**

27. An angle inscribed in a semicircle is a **straight angle   right angle   acute angle   obtuse angle.**

28. The locus of a point equidistant from the sides of an angle is **the vertex   a circle   one line   two lines.**

29. A circle can be circumscribed about **a rhombus   an isosceles trapezoid   an equiangular polygon   an equilateral polygon.**

30. The medians of a triangle are concurrent in a point which is called the **orthocenter   circumcenter   incenter   centroid.**

31. If one acute angle of a right triangle is 22°, the other acute angle is **90°   78°   68°   72°.**

TEST 4

Applications

1. The line segment joining the midpoints of two sides of a triangle is 6 feet. Find the length of the third side of the triangle.

2. The median on the hypotenuse of a right triangle is 3 inches. How many inches are there in the hypotenuse?

3. How many degrees are in one exterior angle of a regular pentagon?

4. How many sides does a polygon have if the sum of the interior angles is 1260°?

5. How many degrees are there in each arc of a circle circumscribed about a regular octagon?

6. The leg opposite an angle of 30° in a right triangle is 4 inches. Find the number of inches in the other leg.

7. Find the mean proportional between 4 and 49.

8. Find the fourth proportional to 2, 5, and 8.

9. The altitude on the hypotenuse of a right triangle divides it into segments of 4 and 9 inches respectively. Find the length of the altitude.

10. The sides of a triangle are 6, 11, and 13 feet respectively. Find the longest side of a similar triangle whose shortest side is 9 inches.

11. In a right triangle a leg 5 inches in length has a projection on the hypotenuse of 3 inches. Find the length of the hypotenuse.

12. Two chords intersect within a circle. The segments of one chord are 3 and 7 inches respectively. The length of the second chord is 27 inches. Find the lengths of its segments.

13. Find the length of the altitude of an equilateral triangle if a side is 6 inches.

14. Find the area of a square if a diagonal is 8 inches.

15. Find the perimeter of a rhombus whose diagonals are 6 and 8 inches respectively.

16. Find the area of a parallelogram if one angle is 30° and two adjacent sides are 10 and 16 inches respectively.

17. What is the area of a circle whose circumference is π inches?

18. Find the area of an equilateral triangle if a side is 12 feet.

19. Two sides of a triangle are 12 and 18 inches respectively. A line parallel to the third side cuts off 3 inches from the lower end of the longer side. Find the segments of the other side.

20. Find the altitude of a trapezoid if the bases are 9 and 13 inches respectively and the area is 66 square inches.

21. Find the area of a rhombus if the diagonals are 6 and 16 feet respectively.

22. The sides of a triangle are 10, 16, and 20 respectively. If a line segment 15 inches in length parallel to the longest side terminates in the other two sides, find the segments into which it divides them.

23. The sides of a quadrilateral are 3, 7, 6, and 8 respectively. The longest side of a similar quadrilateral is 20. Find its perimeter.

24. The sides of a triangle are 8, 10, and 16 feet respectively. Find the lengths of the segments into which the longest side is divided by the bisector of the opposite angle.

25. In a circle of radius 6 inches, a perpendicular from a point on the circle to a diameter is 4 inches. Find the lengths of the segments into which the perpendicular divides the diameter.

TEST 5

Constructions

Make the following constructions, without proof:

1. Divide a triangle into two equal parts.

2. Construct the tangents to a given circle from a given external point.

3. Inscribe a square in a given circle.

4. Construct the locus of points equidistant from two given points and also equidistant from two given parallel lines.

5. Construct a square equal to a given parallelogram.

6. Given the line segment a, construct the line segment $a\sqrt{3}$.

7. Circumscribe a circle about a given triangle.

8. Divide a given line segment in extreme and mean ratio.

9. Construct a line that is tangent to a given circle and makes an angle of 30° with a given line.

10. Construct a circle that has twice the area of a given circle.

TEST 6

Formulating Conclusions

In each of the following state a conclusion based upon *all* the data which are given and then give the reason for your conclusion:

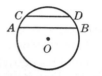

1. *Given* ⊙ *O* with parallel chords *AB* and *CD*.

2. *Given* ⊙ *O* with diameter *AB* and chords *AC* and *BC*.

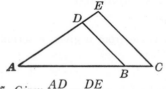

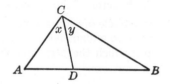

3. *Given* △ *RST* with ∠ *S* = ∠ *T*.

4. *Given* △ *ABC* with ∠ *x* = ∠ *y*.

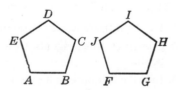

5. *Given* $\dfrac{AD}{AB} = \dfrac{DE}{BC}$.

6. *Given* regular polygons *ABCDE* and *FGHIJ*.

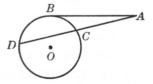

7. *Given* ⊙ *O* with tangent *AB* and secant *ACD*.

8. *Given* ⊙ *O* with diameter *AB* and *CD* ⊥ *AB*.

TEST 7

Fundamental Theorems

Write complete demonstrations of the four theorems designated by your teacher:

1. If two triangles have the three sides of one equal respectively to
the three sides of the other, the triangles are congruent.
2. If two parallels are cut by a transversal, the alternate interior
angles are equal.
3. The sum of the angles of a triangle is a straight angle.
4. If the opposite sides of a quadrilateral are equal, the figure is a
parallelogram.
5. If a line through the center of a circle is perpendicular to a chord
it bisects the chord and its arc.
6. If two triangles have an angle of one equal to an angle of the other
and the including sides proportional, the triangles are similar.
7. The area of a regular polygon is equal to one half the product of its
apothem and its perimeter.

TEST 8

Original Theorems

Prove the four theorems designated by your teacher:

1. In the quadrilateral $ABCD$, $AB = AD$ and $\angle B = \angle D$. Prove
that $BC = DC$.
2. $ABCD$ is a square. On diagonal AC point P is taken so that
$AP = AD$. At P a perpendicular is drawn to AC intersecting DC
in E. Prove that $DE = PC$.
3. If a square is inscribed in a circle, its diagonal is a diameter of the
circle.
4. Two parallelograms with equal angles are to each other as the
product of the sides including a pair of equal angles.
5. The line segments formed by joining the midpoints of the opposite
sides of a quadrilateral bisect each other.
6. The sum of the nonparallel sides of a circumscribed trapezoid
equals the sum of the bases.

Tables for Reference

LINEAR MEASURE

12 in. (12″) = 1 ft. (1′)
3 ft. = 1 yd.
16.5 ft. = 1 rd.
320 rd. = 1 mi.
5280 ft. = 1 mi.

SQUARE MEASURE

144 sq. in. = 1 sq. ft.
9 sq. ft. = 1 sq. yd.
272.25 sq. ft. = 1 sq. rd.
160 sq. rd. = 1 acre
100 sq. ft. = 1 square

FORMULAS OF PLANE GEOMETRY

Notation

a, apothem of a regular polygon
a, *b*, *c*, sides of $\triangle ABC$
A, area
b, base
c, circumference
c, the hypotenuse of rt. $\triangle ABC$

d, diagonal of a square
d, *d*′, diagonals of a rhombus
h, altitude
p, perimeter
r, radius
s, semiperimeter, side

Formulas

Circle: $A = \pi r^2, \quad c = 2\pi r$

Equilateral triangle: $A = \frac{1}{4} s^2 \sqrt{3}, \quad h = \frac{1}{2} s \sqrt{3}$

Parallelogram: $A = bh$

Regular polygon: $A = \frac{1}{2} ap$

Rhombus: $A = \frac{1}{2} dd'$

Right triangle: $A = \frac{1}{2} ab, \quad c^2 = a^2 + b^2$

Sector of a circle: $A = \dfrac{\text{central } \angle}{360°} \pi r^2$

Segment of a circle: $A = \text{sector} - \triangle$

Square: $A = \frac{1}{2} d^2, \quad A = s^2$

Trapezoid: $A = \frac{1}{2} h(b + b')$

Triangle: $A = \frac{1}{2} bh, \quad A = \sqrt{s(s-a)(s-b)(s-c)}$

562

TABLE I. SQUARE ROOTS

N	$\sqrt{N}$	N	$\sqrt{N}$	N	$\sqrt{N}$	N	$\sqrt{N}$	N	$\sqrt{N}$	N	$\sqrt{N}$
1	1.000	51	7.141	101	10.050	151	12.288	201	14.177	251	15.843
2	1.414	52	7.211	102	10.100	152	12.329	202	14.213	252	15.875
3	1.732	53	7.280	103	10.149	153	12.369	203	14.248	253	15.906
4	2.000	54	7.348	104	10.198	154	12.410	204	14.283	254	15.937
5	2.236	55	7.416	105	10.247	155	12.450	205	14.318	255	15.969
6	2.449	56	7.483	106	10.296	156	12.490	206	14.353	256	16.000
7	2.646	57	7.550	107	10.344	157	12.530	207	14.388	257	16.031
8	2.828	58	7.616	108	10.392	158	12.570	208	14.422	258	16.062
9	3.000	59	7.681	109	10.440	159	12.610	209	14.457	259	16.093
10	3.162	60	7.746	110	10.488	160	12.649	210	14.491	260	16.124
11	3.317	61	7.810	111	10.536	161	12.689	211	14.526	261	16.155
12	3.464	62	7.874	112	10.583	162	12.728	212	14.560	262	16.186
13	3.606	63	7.937	113	10.630	163	12.767	213	14.594	263	16.217
14	3.742	64	8.000	114	10.677	164	12.806	214	14.629	264	16.248
15	3.873	65	8.062	115	10.724	165	12.845	215	14.663	265	16.279
16	4.000	66	8.124	116	10.770	166	12.884	216	14.697	266	16.310
17	4.123	67	8.185	117	10.817	167	12.923	217	14.731	267	16.340
18	4.243	68	8.246	118	10.863	168	12.962	218	14.765	268	16.371
19	4.359	69	8.307	119	10.909	169	13.000	219	14.799	269	16.401
20	4.472	70	8.367	120	10.955	170	13.038	220	14.832	270	16.432
21	4.583	71	8.426	121	11.000	171	13.077	221	14.866	271	16.462
22	4.690	72	8.485	122	11.045	172	13.115	222	14.890	272	16.492
23	4.796	73	8.544	123	11.091	173	13.153	223	14.933	273	16.523
24	4.899	74	8.602	124	11.136	174	13.191	224	14.967	274	16.553
25	5.000	75	8.660	125	11.180	175	13.229	225	15.000	275	16.583
26	5.099	76	8.718	126	11.225	176	13.267	226	15.033	276	16.613
27	5.196	77	8.775	127	11.269	177	13.304	227	15.067	277	16.643
28	5.292	78	8.832	128	11.314	178	13.342	228	15.100	278	16.673
29	5.385	79	8.888	129	11.358	179	13.379	229	15.133	279	16.703
30	5.477	80	8.944	130	11.402	180	13.416	230	15.166	280	16.733
31	5.568	81	9.000	131	11.446	181	13.454	231	15.199	281	16.763
32	5.657	82	9.055	132	11.489	182	13.491	232	15.232	282	16.793
33	5.745	83	9.110	133	11.533	183	13.528	233	15.264	283	16.823
34	5.831	84	9.165	134	11.576	184	13.565	234	15.297	284	16.852
35	5.916	85	9.220	135	11.619	185	13.602	235	15.330	285	16.882
36	6.000	86	9.274	136	11.662	186	13.638	236	15.362	286	16.912
37	6.083	87	9.327	137	11.705	187	13.675	237	15.395	287	16.941
38	6.164	88	9.381	138	11.747	188	13.711	238	15.427	288	16.971
39	6.245	89	9.434	139	11.790	189	13.748	239	15.460	289	17.000
40	6.325	90	9.487	140	11.832	190	13.784	240	15.492	290	17.029
41	6.403	91	9.539	141	11.874	191	13.820	241	15.524	291	17.059
42	6.481	92	9.592	142	11.916	192	13.856	242	15.556	292	17.088
43	6.557	93	9.644	143	11.958	193	13.892	243	15.588	293	17.117
44	6.633	94	9.695	144	12.000	194	13.928	244	15.620	294	17.146
45	6.708	95	9.741	145	12.042	195	13.964	245	15.652	295	17.176
46	6.782	96	9.798	146	12.083	196	14.000	246	15.684	296	17.205
47	6.856	97	9.849	147	12.124	197	14.036	247	15.716	297	17.234
48	6.928	98	9.899	148	12.166	198	14.071	248	15.748	298	17.263
49	7.000	99	9.950	149	12.207	199	14.107	249	15.780	299	17.292
50	7.071	100	10.000	150	12.247	200	14.142	250	15.811	300	17.321

TABLE II. TRIGONOMETRIC RATIOS

Angle	sin	cos	tan	Angle	sin	cos	tan
0°	.0000	1.0000	.0000	45°	.7071	.7071	1.0000
1°	.0175	.9998	.0175	46°	.7193	.6947	1.0355
2°	.0349	.9994	.0349	47°	.7314	.6820	1.0724
3°	.0523	.9986	.0524	48°	.7431	.6691	1.1106
4°	.0698	.9976	.0699	49°	.7547	.6561	1.1504
5°	.0872	.9962	.0875	50°	.7660	.6428	1.1918
6°	.1045	.9945	.1051	51°	.7771	.6293	1.2349
7°	.1219	.9925	.1228	52°	.7880	.6157	1.2799
8°	.1392	.9903	.1405	53°	.7986	.6018	1.3270
9°	.1564	.9877	.1584	54°	.8090	.5878	1.3764
10°	.1736	.9848	.1763	55°	.8192	.5736	1.4281
11°	.1908	.9816	.1944	56°	.8290	.5592	1.4826
12°	.2079	.9781	.2126	57°	.8387	.5446	1.5399
13°	.2250	.9744	.2309	58°	.8480	.5299	1.6003
14°	.2419	.9703	.2493	59°	.8572	.5150	1.6643
15°	.2588	.9659	.2679	60°	.8660	.5000	1.7321
16°	.2756	.9613	.2867	61°	.8746	.4848	1.8040
17°	.2924	.9563	.3057	62°	.8829	.4695	1.8807
18°	.3090	.9511	.3249	63°	.8910	.4540	1.9626
19°	.3256	.9455	.3443	64°	.8988	.4384	2.0503
20°	.3420	.9397	.3640	65°	.9063	.4226	2.1445
21°	.3584	.9336	.3839	66°	.9135	.4067	2.2460
22°	.3746	.9272	.4040	67°	.9205	.3907	2.3559
23°	.3907	.9205	.4245	68°	.9272	.3746	2.4751
24°	.4067	.9135	.4452	69°	.9336	.3584	2.6051
25°	.4226	.9063	.4663	70°	.9397	.3420	2.7475
26°	.4384	.8988	.4877	71°	.9455	.3256	2.9042
27°	.4540	.8910	.5095	72°	.9511	.3090	3.0777
28°	.4695	.8829	.5317	73°	.9563	.2924	3.2709
29°	.4848	.8746	.5543	74°	.9613	.2756	3.4874
30°	.5000	.8660	.5774	75°	.9659	.2588	3.7321
31°	.5150	.8572	.6009	76°	.9703	.2419	4.0108
32°	.5299	.8480	.6249	77°	.9744	.2250	4.3315
33°	.5446	.8387	.6494	78°	.9781	.2079	4.7046
34°	.5592	.8290	.6745	79°	.9816	.1908	5.1446
35°	.5736	.8192	.7002	80°	.9848	.1736	5.6713
36°	.5878	.8090	.7265	81°	.9877	.1564	6.3138
37°	.6018	.7986	.7536	82°	.9903	.1392	7.1154
38°	.6157	.7880	.7813	83°	.9925	.1219	8.1443
39°	.6293	.7771	.8098	84°	.9945	.1045	9.5144
40°	.6428	.7660	.8391	85°	.9962	.0872	11.4301
41°	.6561	.7547	.8693	86°	.9976	.0698	14.3007
42°	.6691	.7431	.9004	87°	.9986	.0523	19.0811
43°	.6820	.7314	.9325	88°	.9994	.0349	28.6363
44°	.6947	.7193	.9657	89°	.9998	.0175	57.2900
45°	.7071	.7071	1.0000	90°	1.0000	.0000	∞

Index

Abbreviations, 7

Abscissa, 319

Algebra, solutions by, 40–42, 188, 214, 224, 225, 291, 294, 320, 344, 377, 441

Alternation, 346

Altitude, of an equilateral triangle, 227; of a parallelogram, 170; of a trapezoid, 183; of a triangle, 95

Analysis of a problem, 330

Analytic geometry, 482

Analytic method of proof, 128, 360

Angles, acute, 17; adjacent, 16; alternate, 105; bisectors of, 22, 96; central, 250, 419; complementary, 20; corresponding, 105, 365; of depression, 464; dihedral, 196; of elevation, 464; equal, 14; exterior, 96, 105; formed by a transversal, 105; generating, 15; inscribed, 250; interior, 105; measurement of, 18, 283; naming, 14; oblique, 17; obtuse, 17; opposite sides of a triangle, 78; right, 16, 17; sides of, 14, 112; size of, 14; straight, 17; supplementary, 20; trisection of, 164; vertex, 63; vertex of, 14; vertical, 20; wind-correction, 507

Apothem, 418

Applications of geometry relating to: architecture, 2, 249, 256, 275; artillery fire, 316, 465, 512; aviation, 337, 402, 495; carpentry, 92, 134, 135; designs, 4, 190, 286, 300; engineering, 63, 140, 207, 274, 301, 407, 457; everyday reasoning, 33, 34, 57, 94, 115, 198, 243, 277, 302, 338; finding distances, 91, 92, 133, 134, 140, 195, 375, 406, 407; maps and scale drawings, 388, 400–402, 521; mechanical drawing, 111, 128,

406, 444; miscellaneous situations, 89, 91, 134–135, 140, 166, 180, 195, 214, 215, 217, 225, 226, 230, 231, 234, 235, 238, 274, 301, 407, 426, 438; nature, 2, 136–137, 439, 441, 445; painting and sculpture, 255, 439, 447; science, 114, 139, 140, 165, 166, 269–271, 407, 409, 451

Arc, 23, 250; major, 250; measurement of an, 283; minor, 250

Arcs, comparison of, 285

Area, of a circle, 431, 436; of a circular cylinder, 449; of any figure, 208; figures equal in, 213; of an irregular polygon, 230; of a parallelogram, 216; of a prism, 240; of a rectangle, 214; of a right circular cone, 450; of a segment of a circle, 437; of a sphere, 450; of a triangle, 218, 227, 229; unit of, 208

Axioms, fundamental, 38; of inequalities, 468; use of, 40

Base, of a parallelogram, 170; of a triangle, 63

Bases of a trapezoid, 183

Bearing, 500

Bisector, 22, 24, 25, 96

Center, of a circle, 23, 249; of a regular polygon, 418

Centroid, 327

Chord, 249

Circle, 23, 249; arc of a, 23, 250; area of a, 431, 436; center of a, 23, 249; central angle of a, 250; circumference of a, 250; circumscribed, 254; diameter of a, 249; division of a, into equal arcs, 443; equation of a, 492; inscribed, 293; inscribed angle of a, 250; lines related to the, 249; measurement of

565

PRINTED IN THE UNITED STATES OF AMERICA

JKLMNOPQRST—06987654321